Growth and Structure of Human Population in the Presence of Migration

This is a volume in

STUDIES IN POPULATION

A complete list of titles in this series appears at the end of this volume

Growth and Structure
of Human Population
in the Presence of Migration

M. Sivamurthy
Department of Statistics,
Karnatak University, Dharwad, India

1982

ACADEMIC PRESS

A Subsidiary of Harcourt Brace Jovanovich, Publishers

London   New York
Paris   San Diego   San Francisco   São Paulo
Sydney   Tokyo   Toronto

ACADEMIC PRESS INC. (LONDON) LTD
24/28 Oval Road,
London NW1

United States Edition published by
ACADEMIC PRESS INC.
111 Fifth Avenue,
New York, New York 10003

British Library Cataloguing in Publication Data
Sivamurthy, M.
　Growth and structure of human population in the
　presence of migration.
　1. Population geography
　I. Title　　II. Series
　304.6'2　　HB1951
　ISBN 0-12-647250-5
　LCCCN 82-071578

Printed in Great Britain by
Page Bros (Norwich) Ltd

Foreword

It was with the work of Alfred J. Lotka that the theoretical investigations of human population change started around 1920. Later Bernardelli, Lewis and Leslie introduced the matrix representation for the population projection model. This work has been furthered in recent years by Coale, Goodman, Keyfitz and Lopez. These writers mainly concentrated on growth and changes in the age-sex structure of populations which are not affected by migration. Hence theoretical investigations involving the migration component have been rather rare. The present book by Dr. Sivamurthy fills this gap to some extent.

In this book he presents a comprehensive study of a particular mathematical model of population growth in which migration is specified by an over-all migration rate and an associated age-sex structure of migrants. The model appears to be the most appropriate for studying the effects, firstly of migration on population growth and structure, secondly of changes in the magnitudes of over-all migration rate when the age-sex structure of migrants is of a particular type, and also of the changes in the age-sex structure of migrants at certain levels of over-all migration rate. Such investigations are useful for understanding the implications of proposed migration policies for a given population. To my knowledge, this is perhaps the first book which explores a model of this particular type which may be used either for understanding or for examining potential implications of migration policies.

From the demographic point of view the investigation is thorough and of a high standard. By an extension of stable population theory, it is shown in the book that the operation of a constant and continuous stream of migration having an unchanging age-sex structure of migrants along with constant vital rates leads to an equilibrium state population (defined as the population having a constant growth rate and an unchanging age-sex structure), and that the time required to attain this state is dependent on migration. Similar results are also proved for the case where the fertility, mortality and migration schedules are changing over time for both one- and two-sex models. Proofs are presented informally so that rigorous mathematics will not distract the reader from practical implications. The mathematical results have been supported by extensive numerical evidence or illustrations, and the conclusions generally hold true in demographic contexts.

Following the procedures adopted by other researchers in the case of closed populations, Dr. Sivamurthy has derived mathematical formulae which demonstrate explicitly the relationship of the growth rate and age-sex composition to the operating schedules of fertility, mortality and migration. Although these formulae appear to be quite complicated for practical applications, a systematic arrangement of the computations seems to make them feasible for application.

In order to analyse the effects of varying conditions of fertility, mortality and migration on population change during a given period of time Dr. Sivamurthy has suggested an elegant method of decomposition which utilizes the factorial design from the field of statistics. Here, he has wisely chosen to define interaction effects in a manner which is appropriate for the application, and which is quite different from the definition commonly used in statistical design of experiments.

The extensive numerical illustration of mathematical results presented in the book is a very useful and an attractive feature for both students and teachers alike. It is sincerely hoped that the academic community will welcome this book as a useful contribution to Demographic Knowledge.

Ottawa   K.G. Basavarajappa
February 1982

To

the JAGADGURU

the Universal Teacher
who is the source of all knowledge

Preface

This book is concerned with the investigation of the effects of introducing migration into the process of population growth using an overall net migration rate and an age-sex composition of net migrants (i.e. the net number of migrants) as compared with the case in which there is no migration.

Although the effects of fertility and mortality on the growth and age-sex composition of human populations have been examined extensively in the earlier studies through theoretical and empirical investigations, it appears that the study of the effects of introducing migration into the process of population change has not received the same attention. When migration is included, two procedures have been followed: one in which a set of age-sex-specific net migration rates is assumed, and another in which an overall net migration rate and an age-sex composition of net migrants are assumed.

In many theoretical investigations, age-sex-specific net migration rates have been used. This has reduced the mathematical difficulties because these migration rates, suitably defined, could be incorporated into the survival rates. However, in this model an age-cohort which is zero (for example), due to some calamity will continue to be zero at successive ages in succeeding years, even when immigration is assumed to occur. Thus, the procedure is not suited to examine the effects of either the intensity of migration (i.e. a given overall net migration rate) or a specified age-sex pattern of migrants (i.e. a specified age-sex composition of net migrants) on the growth and the changes in the age-sex distribution of a population. These can be studied only when the second procedure is adopted.

Hence, an attempt is made in this study to examine analytically the effects of migration on the growth and the changes in the age-sex structure of a population when migration is specified by an overall net migration rate and an age-sex composition of the net migrants at the time of migration.

The results in the absence of migration are used as the standard of reference to compare the effects of migration. Also, the effects of using age-sex-specific net migration rates are examined for comparison.

The investigations are carried through the use of deterministic models of one- and two-sex cases. The one-sex case is used only for analytical convenience, and the results are always extended to the two-sex case. The outcomes of numerical illustrations using the two-sex model are presented.

The book consists of three parts, each part containing two chapters. Part I includes (in Chapter 1) a discussion of the models used in demography to study population change and (in Chapter 2) an analysis of the characteristics of the different data sets used in the numerical illustrations throughout the book. This is followed by Part II which is devoted to the investigation of the changes in the growth rate and in the age-sex distribution of a population under constant conditions of fertility, mortality and migration. It is shown in Chapter 3 that a unique equilibrium state population which has a constant growth rate and an unchanging age-sex structure, is ultimately evolved. The time required for this evolution is also examined.

In Chapter 4, formulae are presented which bring out explicitly the relationship between the characteristics of the equilibrium state population on the one hand and the operating schedules of fertility, mortality and migration on the other.

The study of the population change under changing conditions of fertility, mortality and migration, is the subject of Part III. It is proved in Chapter 5 that the 'initial' shape of the age-sex distribution of a population is 'forgotten' in the course of time, and the resulting age-sex distribution depends entirely on the history of the fertility, mortality and migration conditions. Again the time required for the 'forgetting' is discussed. Finally a method, called the factorial projections method, is presented in Chapter 6 for analysing the changes in the characteristics of a population during a given time period. This is then used to analyse the changes in the characteristics of the population of Australia during the three time periods 1911–66, 1933–66 and 1947–66.

The work done at the Department of Demography, The Australian National University (A.N.U.), Canberra (Australia), during 1967–70 forms the main basis for this book. Later research has enabled me to modify some of the results and to reorganise the material into the form presented here. I have drawn heavily from three of my articles published in the *Australian Journal of Statistics* (Vol. 13, 1971), *Australian Immigration* (No. 3, 1975) and *Theoretical Population Biology* (Vol. 16, No. 3, 1979). I would like to thank the respective referees from whose comments I have benefitted greatly.

I gratefully acknowledge the financial help from the A.N.U., through the award of a Research Scholarship, and the leave of absence from the Karnatak University, Dharwad (India), which enabled me to undertake this work at the Department of Demography.

I am greatly indebted to Dr. K. G. Basavarajappa, Associate Director, Demography Division, Statistics, Canada, Ottawa (who was a staff member of the Department of Demography, A.N.U. when this work was undertaken) for his constant encouragement and guidance during the course of this work.

Professor W. D. Borrie who was then the Head of the Department of Demography, A.N.U. and other members of the Staff contributed to this work through their comments at the Departmental Seminars and to them I am also grateful. I would like to pay homage to my dear friend, the late Dr. Jaipal P. Ambannavar, an accredited Indian Demographer, who was a source of inspiration to me when I was working on the problems discussed in this book.

My sincere thanks are due to the late Mr. H. P. Brown, Department of Economics, A.N.U., for allowing me to utilize the data on the arrivals and departures from his Demographic Data Bank for Australia; to Mr. I. Simpson, Computer Centre, A.N.U. for his friendly assistance in solving some problems of computer programming; to Mrs. E. M. Cameron for preparing graphs; and to the Bureau of Census and Statistics, Canberra, for providing me with some of the unpublished data needed for the study.

I would also like to record my deep appreciation to my wife, Smt. M. Shambhavi Sivamurthy, for her patience and understanding during the period of this work.

It is hoped that the book will serve as a reference volume for students of Demography as well as researchers involved in Demographic analyses. I would greatly appreciate any constructive criticism and suggestions for further improvements.

Dharwad, India   M. SIVAMURTHY
January 1982

Contents

Part I Introduction

1 Use of models in studying population change

2 Some characteristics of the data used in the numerical illustrations

Main Symbols Used in the Book

Symbol	Definition
x	Age (in completed years).
w	The highest age to which persons can live.
$P(x,t)$, $V(x,t)$, $W(x,t)$	Population at age x years.
$p(x)$	Proportion of the population at age x years.
(P_t), (V_t), (W_t)	Population vector: a column vector giving population by age.
$S(b,t)$	Survival rate from birth to age 0 years.
$S(x,t)$	Survival rate from age x years to $(x + 1)$ years.
$f(x,t)$	Age-specific fertility rate at age x years.
α and β	The youngest and the oldest ages at which reproduction occurs among the females. (α' and β' are used when fertility rates for both males and females are used.)
$n(t)$	Net migration rate taking the population at the beginning of the year as base.
$n(x,t)$	Proportion of net number of migrants at age x years at the time of migration. $$[\sum_{x=0}^{w} n(x,t) = 1.0].$$
$u(t)$	Net migration coefficient for the cohort born during the year [derived from $n(t)$, $n(0,t)$, $f(x,t)$, $S(b,t)$, and $a(x,t)$].
$a(x,t)$	Net migration coefficient at age x years [derived from $S(x,t)$, $n(t)$, and $n(x,t)$].
$u'(t)$	Age-specific net migration rate for the cohort born during the year.
$a'(x,t)$	Age-specific net migration rate at age x years.
GI (x,t)	Growth index at age x years.

Symbol	Definition
MaxGI, MinGI	Maximum and minimum of the growth indexes at individual ages.
$GI(t)$	Growth index for the total population.
s_t and s'_t	Sex ratio at birth and among net migrants, respectively.
$SR(x,t)$ and $SR(t)$	Sex ratio at age x years and in the total population.
$L(t)$, $L'(t)$, $L''(t)$ and $M(t)$	Population projection matrices in the absence of migration.
$L_M(t)$, $L'_M(t)$	Population projection matrices when migration is included using a net migration rate and an age-sex composition of net migrants.
$P(T,i,x)$	Population at age x years at the end of the i-th period in the T-th cycles.
$\phi(T,i,x)$	Ratio of the population at age x years to the population aged 0 years at the end of the i-th period in the T-th cycle.
$R(i)$	Growth index at age 0 years in the i-th period. [$R(i)$, $i = 1, 2, \ldots , k$ are the parameters of the cyclical model of population change.]

Note: The presence of t in the symbols denotes that the value refers to the year t. The absence of t indicates that the values are constant over time. Suffixes f and m are used with these symbols to distinguish the corresponding values for females and males.

Part I
INTRODUCTION

1

USE OF MODELS IN STUDYING POPULATION CHANGE

1.1 Introduction

To analyse the mechanisms that produce an observed real situation in any field of research in social or natural sciences is not an easy task because of the multiplicity of variables involved in it, their interdependence, and the difficulties of measuring the effects of some of them. Further, in social sciences, no controlled experiments can be used to study the real situations. Demography is no exception in this regard. The use of models helps to delimit the number of variables and to produce a replica of a real situation under the operation of precisely known values of these variables. Thus models deliberately simplify the given situations for the convenience of analysis.

Although hypothetical and to an extent limited in scope, the value of models lies in the fact that they enable a clearer understanding of the mechanisms at work in producing a real situation. Using this knowledge, they may also be employed to estimate the missing values of some of the variables involved in producing an observed situation. Models can be made more sophisticated depending on the demands made by real situations and on the mathematical and/or numerical manoeuvrability. With the increasing availability of computer facilities, models are gaining greater importance and are finding wider applications in demography.

1.2 What is a model?

A model is a "design, style of structure". Wilhelm Winkler (1961, p. 358) specifies the characteristics of a model as follows:

3

> There must be an *a priori* assumption about the necessary building stones of the population in its whole or its parts or facts happening on it, which then, worked out in an appropriate way, lead to the model. In most cases the necessary assumptions will be taken from observed populations, but that is not a constitutive character of a model but enhances its practical value.

According to this definition, the projections of a population under assumed conditions are population models. Such models have been used in many demographic studies.

Models can be constructed either by defining the processes in mathematical terms or by using certain empirical assumptions. The models of the first kind are called mathematical models, while those of the second the numerical models. There is now a vast amount of literature on mathematical models and active research is still in progress. The works by Joshi (1965), Tabah (1965), Keyfitz (1968a, 1969), Sheps *et al.* (1969), among others provide an adequate account of the developments in the field, and only a brief summary is presented in Section 1.3.

On the numerical models too there exists quite an extensive literature. But it appears that very little attention has been given to collate the same. Some relevant material is referred to in Section 1.4.

1.3 Mathematical models

Fitting of simple mathematical functions such as the linear, the geometric or the exponential were perhaps the earliest of the mathematical models used in the analysis of population growth. The study of the long-term trends in population growth then led to the use of the logistic model. However, the limitations of such methods of curve fitting were soon realized and more elaborate models based on the principle of the component method of population projections were built and the results analysed.

A study of the mathematical models currently in use may be divided under two main headings: (1) the deterministic, and (2) the stochastic. These can be further classified as one-sex or two-sex models, depending on whether they consider only the female (or the male) population or whether they consider the male and the female populations together.

Among the deterministic models of one-sex, we may consider the life table as the first. But it takes into account only the deaths. Also, its interpretation as a stationary population model gained wider recognition with the work of Lotka (1922) who, in a way, extended it to formulate the stable population model of one sex using an integral equation which related births of one generation to the births of the preceding one. Feller (1941) continued the work of Lotka and employed the Laplace transform to solve the integral equation. Later, Coale (1957c) gave a convenient method for finding the numerical solution of the dominant root of the integral equation.

The treatment of age and time as discrete variables instead of continuous as considered by Lotka, was examined by Bernardelli (1941), Lewis (1942) and Leslie (1945) using matrix representation of the population projection model. Lopez (1961) and Keyfitz (1967, 1968a) made extensive use of matrix algebra in this direction. Rogers (1968) employed it to analyse the population growth over spatial units. Keyfitz (1967) and Goodman (1967a) studied both the continuous and the discrete approaches and showed that they can be reconciled. Goodman (1967b) also gave an elementary approach to the population projection model which avoided the use of the matrix algebra and brought out clearly the relationships between the population growth and the demographic variables—fertility and survival rates. Murphy (1965) generalized the stable population model by taking into account age and parity.

The inconsistencies that arose when the one-sex model was used separately for males and females gave rise to the development of models which considered both the sexes simultaneously, viz. the two-sex models. Early work which could be classified under the two-sex model was done by Karmel (1947) and A. H. Pollard (1948) and this was followed by Kendall (1949), Yntema (1952) and Goodman (1953). In studying the two-sex model, we are faced with the problem as to which sex the births should be related. If the births are related to the female population only, it is called female dominance; while if they are related to the male population only, it is called male dominance. On the other hand, if the births are related to both sexes in some way—for example, by taking a linear or a geometric or a harmonic average of the male and the female populations—it is called intermediate dominance. Although both the one-sex dominant methods and the intermediate dominance methods have been used by different authors, there appears to be no definite answer as yet to this problem. Here also, as in the one-sex models, age and time have been studied as continuous and discrete variables.

The models are called deterministic if no allowance is made for the chance variations in the components which are inherently dependent on chance. Kendall (1949), perhaps inspired by Bartlett, constructed stochastic versions of the one-sex and two-sex population models with time as a continuous variable. Goodman (1953) and Leslie (1958) followed him up. However, it was J. H. Pollard (1969) who studied general stochastic models with age and time as discrete variables. He employed the technique of matrix multiplications for this purpose. Recently, Thomas (1969) has used probability generating functions to study these models; while Sykes (1969) has examined, among others, a model which treats the projection matrix itself as a matrix random variable. These models, except some by Kendall, are one-sex models.

The study of the two-sex stochastic models appears to present serious difficulties. So far, only simple models which did not take age into account have been investigated. J. H. Pollard (1969, p. 186) has now constructed a two-sex age-specific stochastic population programme incorporating marriage, and claims that it enables the demographer to investigate.

> . . . the effect on a population of a change in marriage rates, or divorce rates, or due to changes in economic conditions, or due to changes in government immigration policy, etc. It is possible with this model to carry out objective numerical investigations of such problems on digital computers.

The account of the deterministic and the stochastic models employed to study population change, given in this section, is admittedly brief. The literature has become vast and the subject has been well documented in the references cited earlier.

Both the deterministic and the stochastic models of varying complexity have also been used in the study of the variations in fertility, mortality and migration themselves. Since the present study is concerned with the models representing population change, the discussion here is limited to these models only.

1.4 Numerical models

Numerical model building is similar in nature to conducting scientific experiments. It enables us to evaluate the mathematical models and also allows for the introduction of considerable complexity into the models to make them more realistic. The numerical models are, generally, more restricted in nature and are applicable only to the situations represented in the set of data used in their construction. But, as Tabah (1965, p. 62) puts it:

> Since calculations are strictly arithmetical, the results are necessarily dictated by the hypotheses adopted, and it is thus possible to reproduce a given situation or even, by comparing two models which differ in only one variable, to estimate the "weight" of that variable.

It is this that has made the numerical models popular in demographic analyses. In fact, every population projection is a numerical model though it has not been the practice to name it so.

The technique of population projection has been employed by different researchers to investigate several problems in demography. In this section we shall give a brief account of some of these attempts.

As in Section 1.3 we may distinguish the one-sex and the two-sex models; the deterministic and the stochastic ones. The elementary form of the one-sex model is the stationary population model, or the life table. This shows the resulting population structure if the survival probabilities observed in a certain period of time, or for a generation, remain unchanged and a constant number of births—equal to the radix of the life table, l_0—occurs every year. Although unrealistic, the model has proved very useful in comparing the mortality conditions in different populations or at different time points and also in constructing more realistic models. These models are now constructed for all populations for which the basic data needed for their construction are available. Also, attempts have been made to produce hypothetical sets of these models by utilizing the relations observed in the populations for which reliable data were available (United Nations, 1955; Tabah, 1960; Coale and Demeny, 1966). Such models have become extremely handy in the analysis of the characteristics of the populations with deficient vital statistics.

The highly unrealistic nature of the stationary model was partly relaxed by the one-sex stable population model developed by Lotka. This model represents the population structure which results from the continuous operation of a constant set of survival and fertility rates over a long period of time. Hence the demographers turned their attention to the construction of the stable population models (United Nations, 1958; Tabah, 1960; Coale and Demeny, 1966), and utilized them in analysing certain consequences of population growth (United Nations, 1956; Spengler, 1962), in estimating the characteristics of the populations for which data were either lacking or defective (El-Badry, 1955; Coale and Hoover, 1958; United Nations, 1967). Keyfitz and Murphy (1964) and Keyfitz and Flieger (1968) have constructed stationary and stable population models and have analysed the projection matrices from simple data on births and deaths for several countries.

Although many of the studies which used the stable population models considered only one sex, there were some studies which used the female dominant method to construct the two-sex stable population models (Coale and Demeny, 1966; Glass, 1967).

Other one-sex and two-sex numerical models have been employed by research workers to examine the consequences of the changes in mortality (Stolnitz, 1956; Basavarajappa, 1963) or fertility, or both (Lorimer, 1951; United Nations, 1953; Schwarz, 1968), and also to study the effects of the change in the age pattern of mortality (Basavarajappa, 1968a) and fertility (Coale and Tye, 1961).

Stochastic versions of the numerical models require the use of giant computers. Hence there do not appear to be many studies which explored population change through empirical stochastic models. J. H. Pollard (1966) conducted such an experiment using the data for the Australian female population of 1960, and obtained the expected size and its variance for the year 2210 and 2211. He has also performed such experiments including both males and females (J. H. Pollard, 1969).

Apart from these experiments, the numerical stochastic models have been applied to study the variations in fertility (Sheps and Perrin, 1963) and mortality (Keyfitz, 1968c) themselves.

1.5 Population models including migration

When considering mathematical models, migration has often been dispensed with by saying that emigration is similar to death and could be incorporated into the survival rates and immigration could well be dealt with by constructing "presence ratios" (Hyrenius, 1966; Tabah, 1965). Following the application of matrix algebra to study population growth, it has become possible to incorporate migration into the growth process without much difficulty (Lopez, 1961; J. H. Pollard, 1966; Rogers, 1968). However, the field is still relatively underexplored. While commenting on this aspect, Tabah (1965, p. 63) remarked that:

> Many other models remain to be developed, introducing new variables and new hypotheses such as migration differentials according to sex, differences in fertility and mortality between the migrants and the receiving populations, migrant age-structure curves of different shapes, various possible fertility and mortality trends, etc.

The effect of migration on the population growth, and on the age–sex structure in particular populations, has been studied. These could be counted as studies in numerical models. For example, Notestein (1960) analysed the growth of the female population in the United States during 1930–55 with the help of numerical models, and tried to estimate the effect of migration on the growth and age structure of the female population, while Stone (1967) examined "in what respects and to what extent would its age distribution have differed from that actually observed" if Canada had been closed to migration from 1951 to 1961. In Australia, where migration has played an important role in the population growth, there appears to have been no detailed investigation of the long-term effects of migration, though several studies examined the contribution of migration to population growth during certain periods (Borrie, 1948, 1949, 1959; Zubrzycki, 1960; Price, 1959, 1962; Geyl, 1963).

Among the hypothetical experiments conducted using numerical models for investigating the effects of migration, two may be mentioned here. The first of these was a United Nations study (1951) in which a stationary population, constructed on the basis of the French life table for 1933–38, was projected to study the effects of a continuous stream of emigration and immigration on the population characteristics. It was assumed that migration occurred for a period of thirty years and then suddenly discontinued. In the case of emigration, the "age-specific propensities to emigrate" (age-specific emigration rates) were computed on the assumption that emigration took place at an initial rate of 1 per cent of the total population per annum and the age distribution of the initial emigrants was that of the emigrants from Norway in the year 1900. These age-specific emigration rates were then combined with the life table survival rates. Using these modified survival rates, the populations alive at the end of the five year periods were obtained. On the other hand, when immigration was assumed, the annual number of immigrants amounting to 1 per cent of the total population was distributed by age according to the age distribution of emigrants from Norway in 1900, and was added to the surviving population every year. The immigrants were then projected on the assumption of the same constant mortality and fertility rates as in the receiving population. It was observed that, in the case of emigration, the old-age dependency ratio increased greatly, and it took another thirty years after the emigration stopped for the ratio to return to its initial level. In the case of immigration, the child dependency started increasing after ten years and continued to increase until immigration came to an end. But the old-age dependency decreased during the period of immigration. A peak of ageing was observed some thirty to forty years after the cessation of immigration. The study also showed that, if a country had no population and was built up over a period of thirty years by immigration, the child dependency rises as the young immigrants start reproducing, and the old-age dependency remains small during the period of immigration. As immigration discontinues, the child dependency falls off and the old-age dependency rises very rapidly.

The second study was conducted by Tabah and Cataldi (1963). They projected, over a period of 150 years, a female stable population corresponding to the mortality level approximately equal to that in the United Nations model life table with a life expectation at birth, $°e_0$, of 30 years,[‡] and a gross reproduction rate of 3. For one set of projections they assumed no migration. For another set, they assumed that immigration occurred every year according to the age-specific immigration rates calculated on the basis of the results of the Santiago Fertility Survey. The immigrants

---

‡ They have reported that the model life tables actually used were taken from L. Tabah, *Poblaciones Modelos Estables . . . ,* 1960.

were incorporated into the population at the middle of each five year period and were then subjected to the same fertility and mortality rates as in the receiving population. This accounted for an average rate of immigration of 1 per cent per annum over the period. The whole period of 150 years was divided into three fifty year periods. In the first of these subperiods, the fertility and survival rates were kept constant, while in the second only mortality was assumed to decline, and in the third both fertility and mortality were assumed to decline. Their study indicated that though the part played by immigration in increasing the size of the population was significant, it did not produce marked changes in the age structure.

It may be noticed that in the two hypothetical examples presented here, two different procedures have been used to incorporate migration into the population. In the first procedure, the total number of migrants is obtained by multiplying the total population by an assumed overall migration rate. Then distribution of the migrants by age is obtained on the basis of an assumed proportionate age distribution. Finally, the migrants are added to the survivors of the population in the respective age groups and are treated as members of the population. This is how the immigrants were added into the population in the United Nations study.

In the second procedure, the numbers of migrants in the age groups are calculated by multiplying the populations in the corresponding age groups at the beginning of a year, by assumed age-specific migration rates. The migrants are then added to the survivors of the population in the relevant age groups. If the age-specific migration rates are computed using the numbers of migrants alive in the respective age groups at the end of the year, they can be incorporated into the survival rates, as the emigration rates were incorporated in the United Nations study. Whereas, if the age-specific migration rates are obtained by using the migrants during the year, the migrants in the respective age groups calculated as above, must then be survived to the end of year on the assumption that they all came into the population at the mid-year, as was done by Tabah and Cataldi (1963). We may also survive the migrants on the assumption that they are evenly distributed over the year in which they migrate, and over the year of their age.

1.6 The present study: its objectives and scope

From the brief survey of literature given in Section 1.5, it appears that research on streams of migration has not received the same attention as that on the other components of population change. This may partly be due to the fact that often migration may not be a continuing force. But for theoretical completeness, it is necessary that this component be given the same attention as the others. Such theoretical expositions may reveal interesting information such as the implications of intended policy measures on migration, etc., which may be of considerable practical value.

When migration is included into the process of population growth, it is the age-specific net migration rates, calculated from the net numbers of migrants alive at the end of the year, that have been utilized in most theoretical investigations. Accordingly, they have been incorporated as additions to, or subtractions from, the survival rates. No new mathematical procedures have therefore been found necessary. This appears to be another reason why migration has not been given adequate attention in theoretical investigations.

But it may be noted that, if we use the age–sex-specific migration rates, the numbers of migrants in the respective age–sex groups are determined by the sizes of the populations in the corresponding age–sex groups. Hence the total number of migrants as well as the proportionate age-sex distribution of migrants are determined not only by the age–sex specific migration rates but also by the age–sex structure of the particular population.

For example, consider a female population which has the following sizes at specified ages at the beginning of a year: Age 1, P_1; Age 2, 0; and Age 3, P_3. Suppose the net immigration rates at these ages are a_1', a_2' and a_3', and are strictly positive. Then the number of immigrants alive at the end of the first year in which these rates operate, are: Age 2, $a_1'P_1$; Age 3, 0; and Age 4, $a_3'P_3$. The corresponding population figures are: Age 2, $(S_1 + a_1')P_1$; Age 3, $(S_2 + a_2')0 = 0$; and Age 4, $(S_3 + a_3')P_3$, where S_x denotes the survival rates. Now, if we continue the process for one more year using the same mortality and migration rates, we obtain the immigrants as: Age 3, $a_2'(S_1 + a_1')P_1$; Age 4, 0; and Age 5, $a_4'(S_3 + a_3')P_3$. The values in the population can be written down as before. It is easy now to see that the age composition of the surviving migrants is not the same for the first year and the second year. This is not because we have assumed a different migration situation for the two years, but simply because the age distribution of the population has changed over the years. Thus, in this case, the overall net migration rate and the age composition of the net migrants are affected by the characteristics of the population and hence cannot be maintained as desired.

Therefore, by using the age–sex-specific net migration rates in the process of population growth, we cannot investigate questions such as: What would be the effect of a given rate of net migration on the growth and the age–sex distribution of the population?; or: How would a given age–sex composition of net migrants affect the population growth and its age–sex structure?, etc. From a practical point of view such questions are important.

For instance, government policies are often aimed at obtaining a specified number of migrants and/or to maintain a certain age–sex composition of net migrants, and it would be of interest to know their effects on the population characteristics.

As against this, if we use an overall migration rate and an age–sex composition of migrants to introduce migration into the process of population change, the numbers of migrants in the age–sex groups are determined not by the sizes of the populations in the corresponding age–sex groups, but by the total size of the population and the assumed age–sex composition of migrants. Hence it is possible, in this case, to investigate the consequences of a migration stream occurring at a given overall rate and having a certain age–sex composition of migrants. Thus this procedure would be quite suitable for investigating the type of questions raised above.

The present study, therefore, attempts a theoretical investigation into the effects of migration when it is specified by an overall net migration rate and an age–sex composition of net migrants at the time of migration. For convenience, throughout this study, the term "net migrants" is used for the net number of migrants. The case with no migration is used as the standard of reference to examine the effects of migration on the population characteristics. Though the results obtained by using the age–sex-specific net migration rates are used for comparison, no detailed discussion of this case is presented because the procedures that are applicable to the case with no migration are directly applicable in this case also. Hence, unless it is specifically mentioned otherwise, the effect of migration in this study means the effect of migration when it is specified by an overall net migration rate and an age–sex composition of net migrants at the time of migration. But in the analysis of the population change in Australia, the actual net numbers of migrants by age and sex are utilized, since they are known from the observed statistics and need not be estimated.

It must be mentioned, at this stage, that a practical difficulty may arise when a net migration rate and an age–sex composition of net migrants are used to represent a migration situation, if one sex shows net emigration and the other net immigration. Similar difficulties may arise in interpreting the percentage age distributions of net migrants when there is net emigration at some ages and net immigration at others. However, these do not affect the theoretical considerations or the numerical analyses but call for care in the interpretation of the age–sex composition of net migrants. If the net migration rate is zero, the sex composition and the age structures of net migrants have no meaning. However, there may be situations where a zero net migration is the result of a net immigration for one sex and a net emigration for another. This kind of situation may also arise in the case where the net immigration at some ages exactly balances the net emigration at others. Such situations are of a special nature and are rarely found in the actual populations. For instance, except in periods of war or economic stringency, or such other disturbances, it is observed that an immigration or emigration of males is accompanied by a similar movement of females. However, these difficulties could easily be overcome by considering immigration and emigration separately instead of taking net migration. This would not alter the procedures developed in this study, except for the fact that the number of variables would be increased because, wherever net migration rates and the age–sex compositions of net migrants are used, we must substitute the gross immigration rates and the age–sex compositions of the immigrants along with the corresponding details regarding the emigrants. Moreover, the effect of migration would, in any case, depend on the net effect of immigration and emigration on the population characteristics. Hence we have retained the use of the net migration rate and the age–sex composition of net migrants.

Specifically, an attempt is made here to examine the growth and the changes in the age–sex structure of human populations both when the operating schedules of fertility, mortality and migration remain constant over time (Part II) and when these are changing over time (Part III). It is shown in Chapter 3 that, under the operation of constant schedules, an equilibrium-state age–sex distribution (defined later) is evolved; as a stable age–sex distribution is evolved in the absence of migration. The time required for this process is also discussed. Further, the resulting equilibrium-state age–sex distribution and the corresponding growth rate are derived as functions of the operating schedules (Chapter 4). The case where a constant sequence of k schedules operates repeatedly is also examined.

When the operating schedules are changing over time, no fixed growth rate or age–sex distribution is obtained. But both are changed over time due to the operation of the components of change. However, the initial form of the age–sex distribution of the population is "forgotten" (i.e. the age–sex distribution becomes, after some time, only the function of the operating schedules). This result, which was proved in the absence of migration, is shown to hold good even in the presence of migration (Chapter 5). Again the time required for this process is examined. Finally, in Chapter 6, an attempt is made to assess the contribution of the changes in the components during a certain period of time towards the changes in the growth rate and in the age–sex composition of a population during that period. A method, called the factorial projections method, is suggested for the purpose and is applied to study the changes in the population of Australia during 1911–66.

An equilibrium-state population is defined here as a population which has an unchanging age–sex structure and grows at a constant rate under the operation of a specified set of fertility, mortality and migration schedules that remain constant over time. It has constant birth, death and net migration rates. Thus a stable population which is well known in the literature is an equilibrium-state population under the operation of a given set of fertility and mortality schedules but with zero net migration. Therefore, all stable populations are equilibrium-state populations, whereas all equilibrium-state populations are not stable populations. The unchanging age–sex distribution of the equilibrium-state population is called the equilibrium-state age–sex distribution, and the constant growth rate the intrinsic growth rate.

The analysis, in this study, is carried through the use of the deterministic models of population change, of one sex and two sexes. In the case of the two-sex model, though both the female dominance case and the equal dominance case are considered, the former is given greater emphasis because it is the one often used in practice. Hence, unless specifically mentioned, it is assumed that the female dominance method is used.

In order to make the analysis more realistic, we keep the study of the two-sex model as our ultimate objective, although we use the one-sex model for the sake of clarity and convenience of argument. Thus the exposition begins with a one-sex model with no migration, and then migration is introduced by assuming an overall net migration rate and an age–sex composition of net migrants at the time of migration. Finally, the results are extended to the two-sex case with female dominance and with equal dominance and some numerical analyses using the two-sex model are presented.

For the numerical illustrations, the demographic data used are those observed in Australia during the period 1911–66 and are some hypothetical data prepared on the basis of certain assumptions. The population of Australia is used because Australia is one of the few countries where migration is an important factor of population growth and for which the required data on the components, including those on migration, are readily available and are reliable for all practical purposes. The period 1911–66 had witnessed two wars—the First and the Second World Wars; an epidemic—the influenza epidemic of 1919; and a severe economic depression—that of the early 1930s. Consequently, large variations in the components had occurred during this period, except in mortality which was already comparatively low by 1911. Further, except for the first decade, i.e. 1911–20, the data required are available in fair detail for almost the whole of the period.

1.7 Numerical data used in the study

The data required for the construction of the numerical examples in the study, are: (a) some populations having significantly different initial age–sex distributions—for testing the convergence of age–sex distributions; (b) survival rates by single years of age for males and females; (c) fertility rates by single years of age of females (and of males for some models); (d) net numbers of migrants by age and sex, the overall net migration rates and the age–sex compositions of net migrants at the time of migration, and the age–sex-specific net migration rates; and (e) the sex ratio at birth. We shall present in this section a brief description of the data mentioned above. Their main characteristics will be discussed in the next chapter.

The initial populations

Three populations have been used in the numerical illustrations. These could be identified as the 1911 obs. population, the 1911 stb. population and the 1966 obs. population. The sizes of these populations were assumed to be the same at the initial point of time and were taken to be equal to the size of the population of Australia as at 30 June 1911. Their age–sex distributions were assumed to be different. The age–sex distribution of the 1911 obs. population was taken as the graduated age–sex distribution observed in the 1911 census of Australia, while the age–sex distribution of the 1911 stb. population was the stable population age–sex distribution computed by the female dominance method using the fertility and survival rates by single years of age for the year 1911, with a sex ratio at birth of 105.22 which was the average value for the three years 1910–12. On the other hand, the age–sex distribution obtained by projecting the 1911 obs. population to 1966 with the fertility, mortality and migration schedules as observed during 1911–66 and with a sex ratio at birth of 105, was taken as the 1966 obs. population age–sex distribution. It may be seen from Appendix C that the age–sex distribution of the projected population in 1966 was not significantly different from that of the population enumerated in the 1966 census.

The size of the Australian population was used for convenience and in order to facilitate the analysis of the population change in Australia during 1911–66. The results of the study, except those presented in Chapter 6, would not have been different if we had used a different size of the initial population.

The survival rates

In this study, the mortality situation was taken to be represented by the survival rates by single years of age of males and females. In Australia, these were available for the census years 1921–66 from the official life tables of 1920–22, 1932–34, 1946–48, 1953–55, 1960–62, and from the life table of 1965–67 constructed for the present study. The details of the procedures used for the construction of the 1965–67 life table are given in Appendix B. For the census year 1911, the survival rates were obtained using the L_x values linearly interpolated from the official life tables of 1901–10 and 1920–22. The survival rates for each of the intercensal years were also computed using the L_x values linearly interpolated from the life tables at the census years. Thus the complete set of survival rates for the years 1911–66 was obtained and used in the study. No hypothetical survival rates were prepared.

The fertility rates

Age-specific birth rates by single years of age of females and for some models by single years of age of males, were used in the study. For the period 1921–66, the rates for females were provided by the Commonwealth Bureau of Census and Statistics, while for the decade 1911–20, they were obtained from the published data on births and the estimated population by single years of age. The procedure adopted is discussed in Appendix A. Some hypothetical fertility rates were also used along with these observed ones. The fertility rates by single years of age of males were computed only for the years 1911 and 1966.

The migration data

In Australia, the basic data on migration, viz. the numbers of arrivals and departures by sex and age, are recorded in fair detail in recent years. But, for the earlier years, only total numbers of arrivals and departures by sex were published. Hence, for the period 1911–20, the age distributions of the male and female arrivals and departures had to be estimated. Also, for the years 1921–23, the first half of 1924 and for some of the years during the Second World War, these details were not available. For many of the years, the age distributions were published in five year age groups. However, a complete series of arrivals and departures by single years of age and sex for all the years from 1921 to 1966 was prepared by Brown‡ using the published and unpublished information given by the Bureau of Census and Statistics. This series was utilized in the study, and a separate estimation

---

‡ H. P. Brown, Department of Economics, Australian National University, Canberra, has prepared a Demographic Data Bank for Australia for the years 1921 onwards.

was done only for the period 1911–20. The estimation procedure is given in Appendix A.

These data on arrivals and departures were used to compute: the net migration rates for each of the financial years with the population at the beginning of the year as the base; the sex ratio among net migrants; the age distributions for male and female net migrants; and the age–sex-specific net migration rates. These, along with certain hypothetical data on the net migration rates and on the age–sex compositions of net migrants, were used in the numerical illustrations. However, for estimating the effects of the changes in the components—fertility, mortality and migration—on the growth and the changes in the age–sex structure of the population of Australia during 1911–66 (see Chapter 6), the actual net numbers of migrants by age and sex were used.

The sex ratio at birth

This was assumed to be 105 males per 100 females in all the numerical illustrations and in the analysis of population change in Australia.

1.8 Assumptions and limitations

The general assumptions on which the investigations rest, are as follows:

(1) Age x and time t are discrete variables taking values $0, 1, 2, \ldots$.
(2) w is the maximum age beyond which no person, male or female, ever lives. We assume that w does not change with time.
(3) $f(x, t)$ is the age-specific fertility rate at age x years defined as the ratio of the number of births occurring to women aged x years during a year to the mid-year female population aged x years. These are assumed to be positive in the range α to β years, and are zero at other ages. For theoretical purposes, it is enough if this age range consists of two fixed consecutive ages.
(4) $S(b, t)$ and $S(x, t)$, $(x = 0, 1, 2, \ldots, (w - 1))$ are, respectively, the proportion of births during a year t surviving to the end of the year and the survival rate for persons aged x years at time t to become aged $(x + 1)$ years at time $(t + 1)$. These are assumed to be positive and bounded above.
(5) $n(t)$ is the net migration rate defined as the ratio of the net number of migrants during a year t, to the total population at the beginning of the year. It is less than 1 and is not equal to zero; but may be positive or negative. If it is equal to zero, the situation is assumed to be identical with the case where there is no migration. It should, however, be noted that

zero net migration need not necessarily mean in real life that there is no migration. When it is positive, we call it immigration and if negative, emigration. Whenever $n(t)$ is not equal to zero, it is associated with an age composition of net migrants at the time of arrival or departure. $n(x, t)$ denotes the proportion at age x years in the age composition of net migrants at the time of migration. It is finite and may be positive, negative or zero; but the sum of $n(x, t)$ over all values of x, is equal to 1, for all t.

When age–sex-specific net migration rates are used to specify the migration conditions, we define $u'(t)$, the net migration rate for the cohort born during a year t, as the ratio of the net number of migrants aged 0 years at the end of a year to the number of births during that year;‡ and $a'(x, t)$, the net migration rate at age x years, as the ratio of the net number of migrants surviving at age $(x + 1)$ years at the end of a year t to the population aged x years at the beginning of that year. These are assumed to be less than 1 and could be positive, negative or zero.

(6) Once they are in the population, the fertility and survival rates in the general population apply to the migrants as well. Further, the fertility and survival rates are not changed by the occurrence of migration.

(7) The flow of migration, namely the arrival and departure, is even throughout the year and the migrants are uniformly distributed over the years of their age at arrival or departure. Thus the migrants entering or leaving the population are assumed to experience the fertility and mortality of the population only for half of the year in which they migrate, and one half of the survivors remains at the same age while the other half joins the next higher age.

(8) Whenever there is emigration, the net migration rate and the age–sex composition of the net migrants are such that no age cohort becomes negative at the end of any year. This restriction applies to the age–sex-specific net migration rates also. In practice, this is not really a restriction because there cannot be more emigrants than there are people in any age group.

(9) The changes in the components—fertility, mortality and migration—occur independently. For example, even when net immigration as large as 5 per cent occurs every year, it will not alter the prevailing conditions of fertility and mortality; or even when fertility declines significantly, mortality and migration remain unchanged; etc.

(10) The sex ratio at birth is independent of t, the time, and x, the age of the person.

‡ Rogers (1968) had not explicitly taken account of this direct effect of migration. Stone (1968) introduced a correction by assuming that the migrant females would give birth for the full year during which they migrate. The definition adopted here seems to be more satisfactory in the sense that it explicitly takes account of the direct effect of net migration on the age cohort born during the year.

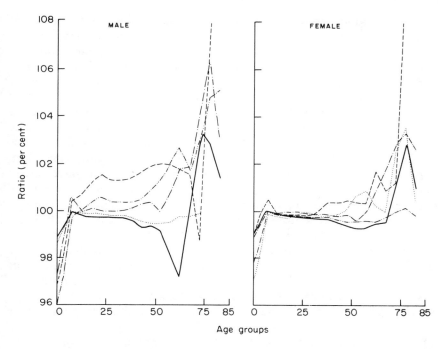

FIG. 1.1. Ratio of the survival rates for Australian born to those for overseas born in five year age groups from abridged life tables: census years. Key: ------ 1911; —··—··—·· 1921; —·—·—·- 1933; ············· 1961; ———— 1966. Note: Relevant data were not available for 1947 and 1954.

Among the assumptions made above, (6) and (9) need some justification. Assumption (6) implies that the fertility and mortality rates do not differ significantly between migrant and non-migrant populations. Investigations in this direction have shown that, though differences do exist between these two groups, they are not significant (Bernard, 1950; United Nations, 1953; Tabah and Cataldi, 1963; Basavarajappa, 1964; Borrie, 1969). It has also been observed that, generally, migrants tend to acquire the rates of the populations to which they migrate (Lorimer and Osborn, 1934; United Nations, 1953) and the rates pertaining to migrants actually remain inter-mediate between those of the sending and the receiving populations (Lee, 1966). Some numerical data required to examine this assumption were available for Australia. These have been analysed, and the results will be discussed briefly here.

Figure 1.1 presents the ratios of the survival rates of those born in

Australia to the survival rates of those born outside Australia at the respective census dates. The relevant data were not available for the census years 1947 and 1954. For computing the life tables for those born in Australia and born outside, we have used the average number of deaths in five year age groups during the three calendar years around the census dates and the respective population data from the census publications. Since the 1911 and 1921 censuses were taken in April, the respective populations had to be estimated as at 30 June. The total numbers of males and females as at 30 June were taken from the estimates published by the Commonwealth Bureau of Census and Statistics. By multiplying these numbers by the proportions of the Australian born observed in the censuses, the numbers of the Australian born were obtained. Then the distributions of the total numbers and the numbers of Australian born into five year age groups, were computed using the respective age structures observed in the censuses. Finally, the populations born outside Australia were obtained by subtracting the Australian-born groups from the total populations age group by age group. Thus the outside-born group included the population of unknown birthplace. Similarly, among the deaths to outside born also, this group was included. This is justifiable, to some extent, because there is more likelihood of birthplaces of persons born outside being not known than that of persons born in Australia. In constructing the abridged life tables with 5 year age groups, the following approximate formulae were used:

$$\text{Probability of survival} = 1 - q(x) = \frac{2 - n\,_nm_x}{2 + n\,_nm_x} \tag{1.1}$$

where $_nm_x$ is the death rate for the age group $[x, (x + n)]$,

$$L(0 - 4) = 2l_0 + 3l_5$$

$$L(x, x + 4) = 2.5[l_x + l_{x+5}], \text{ for } x = 5, 10, \ldots, 80$$

and

$$L(85+) = l_{85} \log l_{85} \tag{1.2}$$

The survival rates were then computed in the usual manner. The l_x and the survival rates thus computed are given in Appendix D.

The abridged life tables were also constructed for the total population using the same approximate formulas and the $°e_x$ values from the abridged life tables were compared with those given in the official complete life tables. The differences were found to be negligible. The comparison of the survival rates, instead of the death rates as is often done in such studies,

Table 1.1 Age–sex structure of the population born in Australia and born overseas: census years

Census year		0–14	15–64	65+	Total	0–14	15–64	65+	Total	Proportion born in Australia
		Born in Australia				Born overseas				
1911	Male	37.90	61.24	0.86	100.00	3.17	78.86	17.97	100.00	79.67
	Female	37.33	61.75	0.92	100.00	4.24	72.27	23.49	100.00	85.44
	Sex ratio	102.48	100.12	95.09	100.95	113.21	164.92	115.63	151.14	—
1921	Male	37.30	60.88	1.82	100.00	5.83	77.31	16.86	100.00	82.14
	Female	35.73	62.31	1.96	100.00	7.43	72.88	19.69	100.00	86.16
	Sex ratio	102.82	96.22	91.25	98.48	104.51	141.45	114.18	133.34	—
1933	Male	31.88	63.65	4.47	100.00	3.62	79.55	16.83	100.00	84.59
	Female	30.46	64.50	5.04	100.00	4.67	77.12	18.21	100.00	88.22
	Sex ratio	103.59	97.66	87.93	98.96	104.63	139.21	124.69	134.96	—
1947	Male	28.60	65.47	5.93	100.00	0.22	80.14	19.64	100.00	89.02
	Female	26.94	65.78	7.28	100.00	0.20	76.42	23.38	100.00	91.35
	Sex ratio	103.89	97.38	79.72	97.84	137.20	133.69	107.08	127.48	—
1954	Male	32.31	61.24	6.45	100.00	10.63	77.17	12.20	100.00	83.86
	Female	30.41	61.28	8.31	100.00	12.95	71.22	15.83	100.00	87.55
	Sex ratio	104.20	98.01	76.04	98.07	108.87	143.82	102.25	132.72	—
1961	Male	34.89	58.38	6.73	100.00	11.87	78.69	9.44	100.00	81.42
	Female	32.74	57.97	9.29	100.00	13.73	73.51	12.76	100.00	84.77
	Sex ratio	104.64	98.89	71.12	98.20	107.84	133.52	92.27	124.73	—
1966	Male	34.64	58.68	6.68	100.00	10.62	80.61	8.77	100.00	80.17
	Female	32.39	58.01	9.60	100.00	11.65	76.34	12.01	100.00	82.95
	Sex ratio	104.83	99.17	48.24	98.04	107.52	124.54	76.08	117.94	—

[Source: Computed from the population data in the respective censuses of the Commonwealth of Australia.]

was resorted to because it is the differences in the former that are important for the purpose of this study.

Figure 1.1 reveals that the differences for males were slightly larger than for females. In the case of females, the differences were almost negligible while in the case of males they were fairly small, except in the youngest age group (0–4) and in the old age groups (65–69), etc. The differences in these age groups might have arisen partly due to the fact that the proportion of the outside-born population in the younger age groups was small while that in the older age groups was high when compared with the respective proportions of the Australian-born population (see Table 1.1).

A similar procedure to the above could not be used for the comparison of the fertility rates because, although the total number of confinements occurring to overseas-born and Australian-born females were available, they were not classified by the age of females. Hence an indirect method was used. The age-specific confinement rates in five year age groups for the females in the total population were computed using the average number of confinements during the three years around the census dates and the female populations in the respective censuses—the census data being adjusted as described earlier where necessary. By applying these rates to the female populations born in Australia and born outside, the expected numbers of confinements were calculated. These were compared with the observed numbers of confinements among the Australian-born

Table 1.2 Ratio (per cent) of observed to expected confinements for females born in Australia and born overseas: around census years

Years	All women		Married women	
	Aust. born	Overseas	Aust. born	Overseas
1910–12	101.44	89.59	NA	NA
1920–22	99.28	105.34	101.44	91.81
1932–34	99.97	100.30	NA	NA
1946–48	100.40	94.19	NT	NT
1953–55	100.83	94.12	101.47	90.21
1960–62	101.40	94.04	NT	NT
1965–67	98.93	103.73	100.12	99.64

Note: NA—The distribution by age of the married females was not available. NT—The distribution by marital status and birthplace was not available.

[Source: Commonwealth Bureau of Census and Statistics: Demography Bulletin and respective Census volumes. For 1965–67 unpublished but made available by the Bureau.]

and outside-born females. A similar procedure was applied in the case of married females when the required data were available. The results are presented in Table 1.2.

Table 1.2 shows that the females born outside Australia had lower fertility than those born in Australia, except during 1920–22 and 1965–66. A similar observation was made by Borrie (1948). Since the population in the reproductive ages was dominated by the females born in Australia in all the censuses, the expected numbers of confinements among those born in Australia were very close to the observed numbers of confinements. Even in the case of those born outside Australia, the differences did not exceed 6 per cent except for the period 1910–12. The large difference for 1910–12 might have arisen due to the fact that there was heavy immigration during the period and there is likely to be some time-lag between the time of arrival of immigrants and the time they start reproducing. The comparison of the nuptial confinements, given in the Table 1.2, reveals that, when the age–sex composition of the outside-born population was not dominated very much by males, as for instance in 1965–67, the differences became negligible. However, the available series was insufficient to draw any firm conclusions. On the other hand, the comparison of the average number of issues per existing marriage, given in Table 1.3, suggests that, though the outside born had a slightly smaller completed family size, the

Table 1.3 Average issue of existing marriage of wives aged (45–49) years at the census date: Australia, 1911–66

Census year	Born in Australia	Total population	Post-world War II migrants
1911	5.33[a]	5.25	—
1921	4.13	4.02	—
1933	NA	NA	—
1947	NA	2.77	—
1954	2.47	2.43	2.18
1961	2.52	2.50	2.44
1966	NA	2.66	NA

Note: NA—Not available.
[a] Based on all marriages.
[Source: Commonwealth Bureau of Census and Statistics, Census of the Commonwealth of Australia: 1911 Census Vol. III p. 1160; 1921 Census Vol. II pp. 1966–67; 1947 Census Vol. III—Statistician's Report p. 322; 1954 Census Vol. VIII—Statistician's Report pp. 327, 331; 1961 Census Vol. VIII—Statistician's Report p. 396; 1966 Unpublished—made available by the Bureau.]

difference was not very significant. On the whole, assumption (6) does not seem to be as unsatisfactory as it appears at first glance.

Now, we examine the validity of assumption (9). There is no doubt that the components of population change vary concomitantly to some extent. But, speaking less rigorously, declines in mortality are generally associated with the efforts of the institutions—for instance, public health and sanitation improvements, new discoveries in the field of medicine, etc.; while changes in fertility are dependent more on the individual behaviour—such as the use or non-use of family planning or family limitation methods, etc. Migration, on the other hand, is very much conditioned by the political and economic conditions in the country and by the policies of the ruling government.

In Australia, for example, mortality declined continuously during the period 1911–66 (see Section 2.3.1); whereas fertility declined, increased and again showed a downward trend (see Section 2.3.2); and net migration was highly sensitive to the measures adopted by the Government such as the granting of assistance to migrants, and the political and economic situation in the country (see Section 2.3.3). We should not, however, conclude that the factors effecting changes in one component will not cause any change in others. For instance, an economic depression such as the one during the early 1930s would cause not only a reduction in migration but also a decline in fertility rates due to the postponement of marriages and births (Whelpton, 1954; Basavarajappa, 1964). But the degree of dependence seems to vary.

Further, when the population is affected by migration, the fertility and survival rates may change due not only to the differences in these rates between the migrant population and the rest of the population, but also to the indirect effects such as the increase (or decrease) in the number of eligible brides or grooms, or the reunion or separation of spouses, or the changes in the living conditions, or the changes in the social values, etc.

It is difficult to assess the impact of these indirect effects on the fertility and mortality rates because of the lack of relevant data and also because such an assessment would probably involve a very detailed examination of several related aspects. However, it can be inferred that some of these effects will act in opposite directions, and hence the resulting net changes in the fertility and mortality rates are not likely to be significant (United Nations, 1953; International Labour Organization (ILO), 1959).

1.9 Plan of the book

Following the introductory discussion about population models presented in this Chapter, the results of an analysis of the fertility, mortality and migration data sets used in the numerical illustrations in the study are presented in Chapter 2, in order to aid the understanding of the outcomes of the illustrations. These data sets consist of the data for Australia for the period 1911–66 and of some hypothetical data derived on the basis of certain assumptions.

Part II consists of Chapters 3 and 4 and is devoted to the investigation of the changes in growth rate and in the age–sex distribution under constant conditions of fertility, mortality and migration. From the stable population theory, it is well known that, when an arbitrary age–sex distribution of a closed population is subjected to unchanging schedules of fertility and mortality rates for a sufficiently long period of time, it converges to a stable age–sex structure which is determined entirely by the known schedules of fertility and mortality rates. An examination of whether such a convergence occurs if a constant stream of migration is introduced into the process of population growth and how the time required for the convergence, which is called the duration of convergence, is affected due to the inclusion of migration, is the chief concern of Chapter 3. Using matrix multiplication technique, it is shown in Chapter 3 that a unique equilibrium state population is ultimately established. Though the intrinsic growth rate and the age–sex distribution of this equilibrium state population could be computed from matrix methods, the relationship between these characteristics of the equilibrium state population on the one hand and the operating schedules of fertility, mortality and migration on the other will not, in that case, be shown explicitly. In Chapter 4, explicit relations are derived through elementary methods using purely demographic considerations. The chapter also examines the age–sex distributions and the growth rates resulting from the repeated operation of a set of k schedules of fertility, mortality and migration conditions, which Namboodiri (1969) called the cyclical models of population change in the case of the closed populations.

Part III includes Chapters 5 and 6, and is devoted to the study of population change under changing conditions of fertility, mortality and migration. When the schedules of fertility, mortality and migration are changing over time, no fixed age–sex structure nor constant growth rate is evolved. But it is known from the weak ergodicity theorem that, in an arbitrary closed population, the initial shape of the age–sex distribution is "forgotten", in course of time, and the resulting age–sex distribution depends completely on the history of the fertility and mortality rates. In Chapter 5, it is proved that this theorem holds good even when migration is included in the process of population growth. The changes in the duration of convergence due to the presence of migration are also analysed.

Next, an examination of the effect of the variations in the fertility, mortality and migration rates during a given period, on the growth rate and the age–sex distribution of a real population, is taken up in Chapter 6. For this purpose, a method of analysis, called the factorial projections method, is presented to decompose the observed changes in the population characteristics into the effects of the changes in the components and the effects of the interactions of these changes. The proposed method is used to analyse the changes in the characteristics of the population of Australia during three time periods 1911–66, 1933–66 and 1947–66.

Throughout the study, the terms age–sex distribution, age–sex composition and age–sex structure are used as synonyms to denote the proportionate age–sex distribution.

1.10 Concluding remarks

Before closing this chapter, we should mention that it may be possible to define demographic processes with a given growth rate and given fertility and mortality schedules assuming some age pattern for migrants; or with a given crude birth rate and given mortality and migration schedules as specified in this study; etc., which would lead to equilibrium-state populations, in analogy with the processes studied by the United Nations (1968) to obtain Malthusian populations. In each case, however, we must examine whether the defined process is determinate or not in the sense that, given the assumptions and an arbitrary initial population, it is always possible to compute a projection of the population for any time (United Nations, 1968, p. 45). This study however, is confined to the cases where fertility and mortality schedules are known and migration is specified either by a known net migration rate and an age–sex composition of net migrants, or by a known set of age–sex-specific net migration rates. These give rise to equilibrium state populations which are similar in nature to the well-known stable populations. The processes as defined in the present study are always determinate under the conditions assumed here.

2

SOME CHARACTERISTICS OF THE DATA
USED IN THE NUMERICAL ILLUSTRATIONS

2.1 Introduction

Before embarking on the theoretical investigations, it is worthwhile to
analyse the characteristics of the basic data used in the numerical illustrations because the results that are obtained from the numerical models
depend on the nature of the changes in the basic data used in their
construction. As stated in Section 1.7, the data used for the illustrations
include three initial populations with different age–sex distributions, and
a series of fertility, mortality and migration schedules. In this chapter are
presented a comparison of the age–sex distributions of the initial populations and an examination of the changes in the survival rates, fertility rates
and migration data observed in Australia during 1911–66 and also the
nature of the other hypothetical data derived for the study.

2.2 Age–sex distributions of the initial populations

Comparison of the age–sex distributions of any two populations could be
done in two ways: (1) by computing the percentages of the populations in
the age–sex groups to the total population and then comparing these
percentages for the two populations; or (2) by computing the percentage
age distributions for males and females separately and then comparing
these age distributions in the two populations along with a comparison of
the sex ratios in the same age groups in the two populations. The first
procedure may be called the joint analysis and the second the two-sex
analysis. The latter is used in this study since it gives a separate picture of

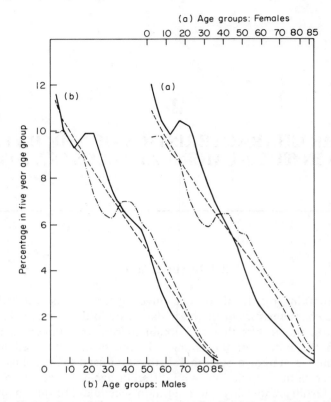

FIG. 2.1. Comparison of the percentage age distributions of the initial populations in five year age groups. Key: ———— Population with 1911 obs. age–sex distribution; – – – – – Population with 1911 stb. age–sex distribution; —·—·—· Population with 1966 obs. age–sex distribution.

the sex composition and the male–female age distributions in the populations.

Figure 2.1 presents the age distributions in five year age groups separately for males and females, and Fig. 2.2 the sex ratios in those age groups. Although single year age distributions were used in the study, the percentages in five year age groups, are presented for convenience. In fact, in all the numerical illustrations the age distributions in five year age groups were used for comparison.

The curves of the age distributions for males and females in the 1911 obs. and 1966 obs. populations compared with the smooth curves of those in the 1911 stb. population, reveal the impact of the demographic history

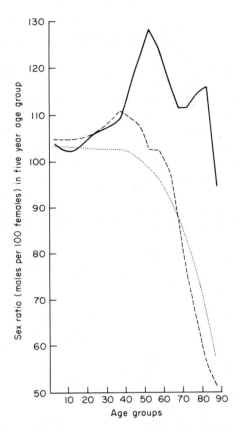

FIG. 2.2. Sex ratios in five year age groups in the initial populations. Key: ——— Population with 1911 obs. age–sex distribution; – – – – –Population with 1911 stb. age–sex distribution; ·············· Population with 1911 obs. age–sex distribution.

of Australia on the age distributions. Immigration into Australia, which had virtually ceased since 1891, started gaining force from 1909 and there was comparatively heavy immigration during 1910–11. The birth rate, which was declining during that period, also showed an increasing trend during a few years prior to the census of 1911.‡ The effect of these events on the male and female age distributions was to make the proportions in the younger and the middle age groups higher; and consequently, those in the older ages lower than in the 1911 stb. population. The high sex ratios

‡ Commonwealth Bureau of Census and Statistics, *Demography*, Bulletin No. 83, 1965, pp. 132, 137.

in the 1911 obs. population in the age groups above 40 years, seen in Fig. 2.2, show the effect of the large preponderance of males among the migrants prior to 1890 (Borrie, 1948, Chap. 3).

Similarly, the smaller population in the younger age groups and a trough in the middle age range seen in the curves for the 1966 obs. population as compared with those for the 1911 stb. population were, respectively, the results of the recent decline in fertility since 1961, and its decline to a very low level during and following the economic depression of the early 1930s, which was also accompanied by a decrease in immigration around the same years. These variations in fertility and migration during 1911–66 are discussed in greater detail in Section 2.3.

The dissimilarity in the age distributions can be quantified by computing an age distribution dissimilarity index (ADI), which is defined as the sum of the absolute differences in the percentages in the respective age groups in the two populations being compared (Keyfitz and Murphy, 1964, p. 8; Keyfitz, 1968, p. 47). The value of this index was 9.85 between the age distributions of the 1911 obs. and 1911 stb. populations; 10.93 between those of the 1911 stb. and 1966 obs. populations; and 17.34 between those of the 1911 obs. and 1966 obs. populations, in the case of males. The corresponding values in the case of females were 15.36, 10.73 and 25.75. A zero value of this index would indicate that the two age distributions are identical. But this index does not show whether the differences are in the younger age groups or in the older age groups. For this purpose we have to examine other indexes such as the mean age, proportion in the old age group, etc. The mean ages in the three populations—1911 obs., 1911 stb. and 1966 obs.—were, respectively, 27.67, 29.13 and 31.08 years for males and 26.64, 30.20 and 32.43 years for females. The same order was observed when the populations were classified according to the increasing magnitudes of the proportion of the population in the old age group (65+). Thus the 1911 obs. population was young compared to both the 1911 stb. and 1966 obs. populations, whereas the 1966 obs. was the oldest of all.

The overall sex ratios (number of males per 100 females) in the three populations were 108.26, 100.18 and 102.49 respectively. The dissimilarity in the sex ratios by age between any two populations may be measured by the sex ratio dissimilarity index (SRDI), which is defined as the sum of the absolute differences of the sex ratios in five year age groups between the populations being compared. As in the case of the ADI, the value of SRDI would be zero if the sex ratios are the same for the two populations. The value of SRDI was 315.42 between the sex ratios in the 1911 obs. and 1911 stb. populations; 94.54 between those in the 1911 stb. and 1966 obs. populations; and 307.86 between those in the 1966 obs. and 1911 obs. populations.

From these numerical values and the graphs presented, it can be seen that the age–sex distributions of the initial populations were considerably different from one another.

2.3 Australian data on the components of population change: 1911–66

2.3.1 Survival rates

Since the survival rates used in the study were interpolated for each calendar year from the official life tables for Australia and from the life table constructed on the basis of the 1966 census (see Appendix B), it would be sufficient as well as convenient to examine the variations in the survival rates observed at these points of time during the period 1911–66. The values for the year 1911 were also interpolated from the life tables for 1901–10 and 1920–22. However, it was found that the survival rates for five year age groups obtained from the interpolated life table for 1911, did not differ much from those obtained from an abridged life table constructed on the basis of the deaths during 1910–12 and the estimated population as at 30 June 1911.

The expectation of life at birth, $°e_0$, which was 56.59 years for males and 60.39 for females in 1911, increased, respectively, to 67.71 and 74.11 years in 1966. The increasing trend in the $°e_0$ which continued up to 1961, experienced a slight setback during 1961–66 in the case of males and a negligible increase in the case of females. However, in this study we are not interested in the changes in the expectation of life at birth but in the variations in the survival rates by single years of age. The importance of examining the survival rates in studies of population change is not often stressed. Some authors, though, have made it clear that it is the variations in the survival rates that are important in studying population change (Stolnitz, 1956; Daw, 1961, pp. 20–43). Hence we shall examine how the survival rates by single years of age for males and females have changed in Australia during the period 1911–66.

Apart from $°e_0$, there seems to be no single composite index to represent the survival rates. But the variations in $°e_0$ may not be a good guide to the variations in the survival rates. For instance, $°e_0$ increased from 1911 to 1966 by about 20 per cent in the case of males and by about 23 per cent in the case of females, while even the survival rate from birth to age 0 years, which showed the maximum improvement, increased by only 4 to 5 per cent in either case. The survival rates at most of the other ages, especially in the age range 15–64 years, did not change by more than 0.5

Table 2.1 Changes in the area covered by the survival rates curve in broad age groups and in other measures: Australia, 1911–66

Census year	S(b)	Age groups							TLS	Mean age $\bar{S}$	Median age $\bar{S}_{md}$	Expectation of life at birth $\overset{\circ}{e}_0$
		0	1–5	6–14	15–34	35–44	45–64	65+				
MALE												
1911	0.93588	0.96766	4.97355	8.98301	19.91856	9.92418	19.60053	17.97930	83.29167 (100.00)	41.15 (100.00)	40.91 (100.00)	56.59 (100.00)
1921	0.94556	0.97558	4.97576	8.98490	19.93267	9.93713	19.63895	18.07026	83.46081 (100.20)	41.18 (100.07)	40.95 (100.10)	59.26 (104.72)
1933	0.96203	0.98840	4.98468	8.98820	19.95080	9.95248	19.67142	18.15667	83.65468 (100.44)	41.20 (100.12)	40.98 (100.17)	63.49 (112.19)
1947	0.97238	0.99387	4.99217	8.99238	19.96546	9.96440	19.66910	18.17320	83.72296 (100.52)	41.20 (100.12)	40.96 (100.12)	66.09 (116.79)
1954	0.97816	0.99518	4.99337	8.99386	19.96560	9.96881	19.68560	18.18618	83.76676 (100.57)	41.20 (100.12)	40.97 (100.15)	67.13 (118.63)
1961	0.98031	0.99634	4.99548	8.99541	19.96906	9.96870	19.69055	18.22830	83.82415 (100.64)	41.22 (100.17)	40.99 (100.20)	67.91 (120.00)
1966	0.98195	0.99667	4.99597	8.99582	19.96879	9.96742	19.67896	18.16673	83.75231 (100.55)	41.22 (100.17)	40.95 (100.10)	67.71 (119.65)
FEMALE												
1911	0.94827	0.97204	4.97579	8.98505	19.92280	9.93543	19.72195	18.32471	83.78604 (100.00)	41.31 (100.00)	41.13 (100.00)	60.39 (100.00)
1921	0.95816	0.97985	4.97860	8.98751	19.93728	9.94781	19.75478	18.38475	83.92874 (100.17)	41.33 (100.05)	41.15 (100.05)	63.39 (104.97)
1933	0.97024	0.98993	4.98673	8.99108	19.95354	9.95865	19.77032	18.51076	84.13125 (100.41)	41.36 (100.12)	41.20 (100.17)	67.13 (111.16)
1947	0.97828	0.99498	4.99386	8.99508	19.97380	9.97055	19.79409	18.54650	84.24714 (100.55)	41.37 (100.15)	41.20 (100.17)	70.62 (116.94)
1954	0.98312	0.99572	4.99475	8.99630	19.98370	9.97745	19.81995	18.64153	84.39252 (100.72)	41.41 (100.24)	41.25 (100.29)	72.70 (120.38)
1961	0.98466	0.99687	4.99618	8.99716	19.98571	9.98042	19.83961	18.74534	84.52595 (100.88)	41.45 (100.34)	41.31 (100.44)	74.07 (122.65)
1966	0.98603	0.99711	4.99680	8.99737	19.98525	9.98001	19.83290	18.75141	84.52688 (100.88)	41.45 (100.34)	41.31 (100.44)	74.11 (122.72)

Note: Figures in brackets show the ratio to the corresponding value in 1911.
[Source: 1911 values from the interpolated L_x values; 1921–61 values from the official life tables for Australia; and 1966 values from the life table given in Appendix B.]

per cent. The best way to examine the variations in the survival rates would, therefore, be to draw and compare the histograms of the survival rates, with age as the abscissa and the value of the survival rate as the ordinate at the mid-year of age. Then the changes in the area under the survival rates curve would show the changes in the survival rates, if we keep the age range the same.

For obtaining a quantitative measure, we may assume that $S(b)$ and the survival rate for the last open-end age group have the same width for their age intervals as the survival rates at other ages. The age interval in the present study is one year. Then the sum of the product of the respective survival rates and the width of the age interval, gives the area under the survival rates curve. We shall call this quantity the total lifetime survived (TLS). If we now obtain a measure of location for this survival rates curve, say the mean age $(\overline{S})$ or the median age $(\overline{S}_{md})$, then that would indicate whether the weight of the improvements in the survival rates was more on the younger ages than on the older ages, or vice versa.

The changes in these measures, viz. TLS and $\overline{S}$ or TLS and $\overline{S}_{md}$, could be used for examining the changes in the survival rates. These would not only show the absolute changes in the survival rates, but would also indicate the age pattern of the change to some extent. However, owing to the averaging effect, the variations in these measures conceal the relatively large variations in the survival rates at the very young and at old ages. This may be seen from Table 2.1, which presents the areas under the survival rates curves in the infant ages and in broad age groups along with $°e_0$, TLS, $\overline{S}$ and $\overline{S}_{md}$.

It is clear from Table 2.1 that the improvements in the survival rates for both males and females were considerable only in the infant ages and in the old ages—65 years and over. Since 1961 there was a retardation in the improvements in the survival rates for males in the middle and in the old-age range and for females in the old-age range. This appears to have happened due to the fact that, in recent years, there were significant increases in the death rates from motor vehicle and other accidents and from suicide which affected the age range 15–34 years; from the diseases of the heart and lungs which accounted for the maximum tolls in the age range 45 years and over (for example, these accounted for more than 50 per cent of deaths in this age range during 1967 both for males and females); and from malignant and lymphatic neoplasms which, along with the two mentioned earlier, were the major causes of deaths in the age range 35–44 years (McDonald, 1969). Further, the survival rates for females, which were already at a higher level than those for males in 1911, recorded a faster improvement since 1933. Much of this improvement occurred in the survival rates at the older ages, as can be observed from Fig. 2.3. The

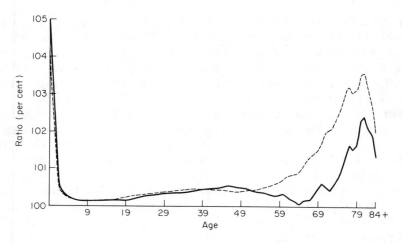

FIG. 2.3. Ratios of survival rates in 1966 to those in 1911 at single years age, Australia. Key: ———— Males; ------ Females.

slower improvement in the survival rates for males was probably due to the greater impact on males of the deaths from the causes mentioned above. Similar trends in mortality have been observed in the populations of England and Wales, and the United States (Martin, 1967; Spiegelman, 1968).

Before closing this discussion, it must be mentioned that no allowance was made for the effect of the epidemic on the survival rates for 1919. Therefore, the deaths during the years 1918–20, especially for 1919, were underestimated and consequently the survived populations at the younger ages were slightly overestimated when compared with the populations enumerated at the 1921 census. However, the differences between the projected and the enumerated populations in the different age groups were not so large as to invalidate the use of the interpolated survival rates (see Appendix A).

2.3.2 Fertility rates

The age-specific fertility rates could change in two ways—(a) in their total intensity which is called the level, and (b) in their age pattern. The variation in the level of fertility is measured by the variation in the total fertility rate (TFR), which is the sum of all the fertility rates at single years of age. This is the area under the fertility rates curve, as explained in the case of the survival rates curve. The variation in the age pattern is measured by the variation in the mean age of the fertility schedule $(\overline{m})$, which is a measure of location for the fertility rates curve. It has also become customary to compute the variance of the fertility rates curve, which indicates the concentration of births around the mean age.

Using these measures, the age-specific fertility rates observed in Australia during 1911–66 were analysed and the results are presented here. The analysis concentrated more on the changes in the fertility rates by age of females than on those by age of males because the female dominance method was used in most of the numerical illustrations. The fertility rates by age of males which were required in a few cases where equal dominance was used, were analysed only for the two years 1911 and 1966.

(i) Fertility rates by age of females

TFR and $\overline{m}$ for Australia during 1911–66 are displayed in Fig. 2.4. The graph shows that the TFR declined from a relatively high value of 3.51 in 1911 till 1920 when it registered a temporary recovery, only to decline again. After reaching a minimum of 2.10 in 1935, it started increasing and recorded a rapid growth from about 1947—the period described as the period of the "baby boom". But from 1951 onwards the rate of increase in TFR slowed down and since 1961 a downward trend has set in.

During all these years, from 1911 to 1966, $\overline{m}$ declined from 30.49 years in 1911 to 27.34 years in 1966 except at brief intervals during or immediately following the two World Wars, viz. during 1916–19 and 1944–47.

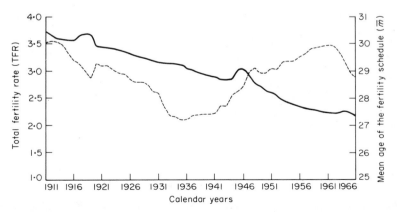

FIG. 2.4. Trend in the level and pattern of fertility rates at single years of age of females: Australia, 1911–66. Key: ------ TFR; ———— $\overline{m}$.

Figure 2.5 brings out some of the features of how these changes were brought about. In general, the observed variations in TFR and $\overline{m}$ were caused by the increase in the fertility rates at the younger ages and by the decrease in those at the older ages. If we divide the female reproductive life of 35 years from age 15 to 49 years into three broad age groups—(15–19), (20–34) and (35–49)—we can obtain the percentage contribution by women in these age groups to the total fertility in each calendar year by calculating the ratio of the sum of the fertility rates at these ages to the TFR. Such percentages for some selected years are presented in Table 2.2

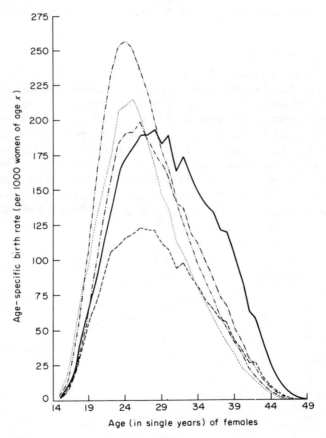

FIG. 2.5. Age-specific fertility rates at single years of age of females: selected calendar years, Australia. Key: ——— 1911; –––––– 1935; –·–·–·– 1947; –··–··–··– 1961; ············ 1966.

Table 2.2   Percentage contribution to TFR by females in broad age groups: selected calendar years: Australia, 1911–66

Calendar year	Age group				TFR (per 1000 women)	Mean age	Variance
	15–19	20–34	35–49	Total			
1911	3.83	69.67	26.50	100.00	3512.47	30.49	42.71
1916	3.96	71.17	24.88	100.00	3203.95	30.13	41.84
1921	4.45	71.79	23.77	100.00	3105.11	29.90	42.14
1926	5.10	72.39	22.51	100.00	2843.22	29.62	42.27
1931	5.81	73.18	21.01	100.00	2576.09	29.33	41.70
1934	5.81	73.85	20.34	100.00	2161.34	29.28	41.18
1935	5.70	74.10	20.21	100.00	2101.44	29.25	40.92
1936	5.75	75.14	19.11	100.00	2107.66	29.09	39.83
1941	5.19	77.66	17.15	100.00	2244.92	28.80	36.79
1946	4.29	77.59	18.11	100.00	2733.12	29.07	36.15
1951	5.80	79.30	14.90	100.00	3048.90	28.22	35.45
1956	6.54	80.38	13.08	100.00	3275.95	27.70	34.39
1960	6.88	81.06	12.06	100.00	3466.30	27.50	33.34
1961	6.76	81.46	11.78	100.00	3473.74	27.48	32.86
1962	7.05	81.30	11.65	100.00	3456.71	27.48	32.85
1966	8.34	80.25	11.41	100.00	2887.82	27.34	32.13

[Source: Computed from the age-specific fertility rates by single years of age of females.]

along with TFR, mean and variance of the respective fertility schedules. It is clear from the table that the contribution of women aged 20–34 years consistently increased while that of women aged 35–49 years consistently decreased over the years. The trend in the case of women aged 15–19 years also was one of increase with minor fluctuations. These trends and the changes in the values of the mean age and the variance, depict clearly the increasing concentration of births in the early years of the reproductive life in recent years as compared to the situation in 1911. Borrie (1969) and McArthur (1967) came to the same conclusion through the analysis of the data on the completed family size and on the confinements by duration of the existing marriage.

These observed trends were caused by the decrease in the marital fertility rates, the decrease in the age at marriage, the increase in the proportion of women marrying and the increase in the births within the early years of marriage (Basavarajappa, 1964; McArthur, 1967).

From 1911 till about the late 1930s there appears to have been only small changes in the age pattern and in the concentration of births in the younger ages of reproduction (see Table 2.2). Therefore, the decline in the total fertility rate during this period was contributed by the declines in the rates at almost all ages. It was found that, during this period, there were only small changes in the age at marriage, in the proportion of the currently married among the females in the reproductive ages and hence the decline in TFR was largely the result of the declines in the marital fertility rates (Basavarajappa, 1964).

During the period of the Second World War, 1939–45, the increasing trend in the TFR was the effect of the rise in the proportions currently married in the younger age group (15–24), and perhaps the effect of the "making up" tendency of the females in the older age groups who had postponed their childbearing due to the economic depression of the early 1930s (Basavarajappa, 1964). A similar trend was observed by Whelpton (1954) in respect of the fertility performance of the American women.

At the close of the Second World War, there was the "marriage boom". The expected mean age at first marriage decreased sharply and there was a tremendous drop in the expected proportion of females remaining unmarried by the end of their reproductive age (Sivamurthy, 1970). These factors, coupled with the increase in the fertility of married females, caused the fertility rates at the younger and middle ages to rise. But the fertility rates for females in the older reproductive age range, 35 years and over, showed very little change or even declined further at some ages, indicating clearly the widespread practice of family limitation in Australia.

The reversal of the trend in fertility since 1961 was brought about by a general decline in the rates at almost all ages except at a few of the youngest ages. The increase at these youngest ages was governed by the increase in the ex-nuptial birthrate at these ages and in the proportion of pre-marital pregnancies (Basavarajappa, 1968b). The declines at other younger ages were probably caused by a caution in the early years of married life in response to the economic recession of 1961 (Borrie, 1969), and at the older ages were due to the effective use of contraceptives to plan the families and to limit the family size. The "pill" is mentioned as responsible for this effective control of the family size. But it has been observed that the desire for small family size came much earlier than the pill (Borrie, 1967). Perhaps the pill has become a convenient instrument to fulfil that desire. With the increased knowledge of contraception it seems that "for many, childbearing within marriage has become an episode of life, not an end in itself, and exactly when children are born is increasingly a rational decision likely to be determined by immediate economic and social circumstances" (Borrie, 1969, p. 67). Thus early marriage, early childbearing, restriction of effective reproductivity to a short period and rearing of small families appear to have become a widespread reproductive norms in Australia as in other economically developed countries.

(ii) *Fertility rates by age of males*

We shall now briefly look at the fertility rates by age of males during the two years 1911 and 1966. These two years were selected to see the possible changes that have occurred in these rates over the period 1911–66. But only the values for 1911 were used in the illustrations. In calculating the fertility rates by age of males, a particular difficulty arose due to the lack of information regarding the age of fathers of ex-nuptial children. It was not possible to use any of the known relationships between the ages of fathers and those of mothers because the fathers of ex-nuptial children may have an entirely different age pattern. Hence it was assumed arbitrarily that the ages of fathers of ex-nuptial children would be two years higher

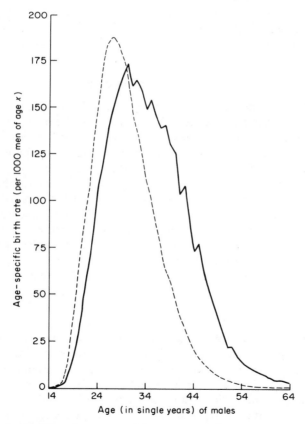

FIG. 2.6. Age-specific fertility rates at single years of age of males: selected calendar years, Australia. Key: ——— 1911; – – – –1966.

than those of mothers though, in some cases, it is possible that the fathers might be younger than mothers. The effect of this assumption would be to introduce only a small error in the average age of the fertility schedules since the ex-nuptial births constitute a small proportion (3 to 8 per cent) of all births, and occur at relatively young ages of females which reduces to some extent the possibility of fathers being younger than mothers. Nearly 58 to 66 per cent of mothers of ex-nuptial births were less than 25 years of age and hardly 3 per cent of them were above 40 years of age.

Figure 2.6 presents the fertility rates by age of males. It exhibits the same phenomenon of concentration of births into the younger age groups in recent years as was observed in the case of females. In fact, the variance of the fertility schedule for males was nearly 35 per cent less in 1966 than in 1911 (44.23 as against 68.68), while that of the fertility schedule for females was about 25 per cent less (32.13 as against 42.71). The mean age decreased from 35.15 years in 1911 to 30.44 years in 1966, and the TFR from 3.54 to 2.85.

2.3.3 Migration data

The variations in the basic data on migration—the numbers of arrivals and departures—and in those derived from them, viz. the overall net migration rates, the age–sex compositions of net migrants and the age–sex-specific net migration rates, observed in Australia during 1911–66 are discussed in this section. In obtaining the derived data, the financial years were used because, in Australia, the census was taken as at 30 June of the respective census years except in 1911 and 1921 when it was taken in April. Moreover, for this study the population as at 30 June 1911 was taken as the initial population and therefore, the projections always referred to the financial years June to June. The numbers of arrivals and departures for the financial years were obtained from those for the calendar years on the assumption that the movements were evenly distributed over the calendar years.

(i) *Net numbers of migrants*

The observed numbers of arrivals and departures during the calendar years 1911–66 are presented in Fig. 2.7. It is clear from the graph that there were significant variations in the net numbers of migrants during this period. These variations were correlated with the economic conditions in the country and the policies pursued by the Government.

Immigration into Australia which had virtually ceased as a result of the stringent economic conditions of the 1890s, began to recover by about 1909 and a big inflow occurred during 1910–12. This was mainly due to the

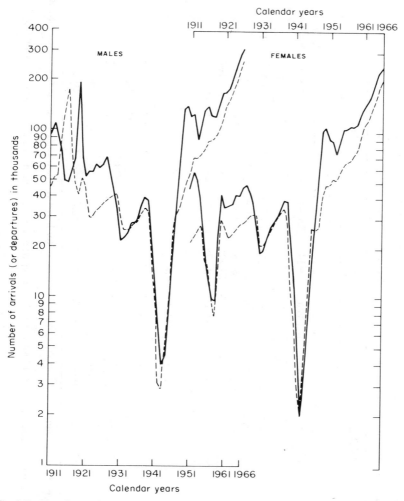

FIG. 2.7. Total number of arrivals and departures during each calendar year: Australia, 1911–66. Key: ——— Arrivals; – – – – – Departures. Note: For 1914–19 the troop movements were included, for 1939–45 they were not included.

efforts of the state governments to bring in migrants. But the outbreak of the First World War in 1914 cut the immigration down and even caused emigration during some of the war years. However, the large emigration and immigration observed respectively during 1914–17 and 1918–19, especially 1919, were the result of the inclusion of troop movements in the migration statistics.

Table 2.3 Net numbers of migrants in broad age groups: Australia, 1911–66

	MALE						FEMALE					
	Age groups						Age groups					
Years	0–14	15–44	45–64	65+	Total	Average per year	0–14	15–44	45–64	65+	Total	Average per year
							Absolute Numbers					
1911–21	23 822	47 047	−3 215	−230	67 424	6 742	39 279	69 315	2 931	62	111 587	11 159
1921–33	32 929	131 955	7 766	−1517	171 133	14 261	28 871	70 044	9 836	1195	109 946	9 162
1933–47	6 403	17 162	2 478	−725	25 318	1 808	5 167	7 652	3 626	1208	17 653	1 261
1947–54	86 943	269 676	24 838	2341	383 798	54 828	79 236	152 372	25 209	4777	261 594	37 371
1954–61	86 661	199 464	15 680	2355	304 160	43 451	78 278	158 754	21 092	4858	262 982	37 569
1961–66	68 794	121 999	13 490	4106	208 389	41 678	63 535	115 737	18 857	6072	204 201	40 840
					Percentage Distribution							
						Sex Ratio						
1911–21	35.33	69.78	−4.77	−0.34	100.00	60.42	35.20	62.12	2.63	0.05	100.00	
1921–33	19.24	77.11	4.54	−0.89	100.00	155.65	26.26	63.71	8.95	1.09	100.00	
1933–47	25.29	67.78	9.79	−2.86	100.00	143.42	29.27	43.35	20.54	6.84	100.00	
1947–54	22.65	70.27	6.47	0.61	100.00	146.71	30.29	58.24	9.64	1.83	100.00	
1954–61	28.49	65.58	5.16	0.77	100.00	115.66	29.77	60.36	8.02	1.85	100.00	
1961–66	33.01	58.55	6.47	1.97	100.00	102.05	31.11	56.69	9.23	2.97	100.00	

Note: The data refer to the period June to June of the respective years. The number for half a year is taken as equal to half of that for the whole year.

[Source: Computed from the single year age distributions of total arrivals and departures in Australia during the calendar years 1911–66.]

At the close of the war, concerted efforts were made to bring more people into the country. The idea that migration and colonization should be planned in a way which would mutually benefit both the mother country and the colonies gained force after the war and was supported by the Empire Settlement (Tennyson) Committee of 1917 and by the Overseas Settlement Committee of 1918. In 1920 the Federal Government of Australia, which had only advisory status, gained full control over migration matters and it negotiated with the Government of the United Kingdom "an enduring policy of overseas settlement". Accordingly, the Empire Settlement Act was passed in 1922 and the £34 million loan agreement was signed in 1925, both aiming to assist migrants to come and settle in Australia. The plans did not work satisfactorily, and in fact proved uneconomical.‡ However, due to such aids and the economic stability in the country, net gain from migration did improve. But soon came the economic depression of 1929–32 and set the migration back to an unfavourable position. No new state aid schemes were forthcoming during that period. By the time this situation changed and migration began to recover, the Second World War broke out and again migration showed a negative balance. Thus the net number of immigrants was smallest during the intercensal period 1933–47, as can be seen from Table 2.3.

With the end of the Second World War, it was realized that a large population was not only of economic significance but also of strategic importance. Even the Labour Government, which had looked upon immigration with grave suspicion, changed its policy towards "an immigration programme to fill the gaps in the younger ages of the workforce without threatening employment opportunities of native Australians" (Price, 1962, p. 162). Thus optimistic targets were set and strenuous efforts were made to obtain migrants. As a result, net immigration was spectacular during the intercensal period 1947–54 and since then, has remained more or less steady and considerable except during the economic recession of 1953 when it was purposely cut down by the Government. But during the economic recession of 1961, the Government took care not to cut down the number of immigrants. Hence immigration continued to occur but, as a result of the recession, its growth decreased (see Figs 2.7 and 2.8) to a small extent.

It is clear from this brief analysis that migration in Australia has been sensitive to the economic situation in the country and the measures taken by the Government to promote migration. In fact, "large flows of immigration have always been associated with extensive passage and other state assistance to the immigrants" (Borrie and Spencer, 1965, p. 14).

‡ K. M. Jupp, in her MA Thesis (pp. 60–88), has analysed the causes for the failure.

A rough idea of the changes in the age and sex compositions of net migrants may be obtained by examining the percentage distributions and the sex ratios given in Table 2.3. Until about 1954 there was a heavy concentration in the younger and middle age groups, especially in the age group (15–44); and there was heavy predominance of males among the net migrants. The position during 1911–21 was blurred by the inclusion of the troop movements in the migration statistics. When the numbers of troops were deducted from the numbers of arrivals and departures, the sex ratio during that period became 135.54, which was in line with the above contention though comparatively low. To an extent this lower value was caused by the coming in of war brides. The high proportion of males and the concentration in the adult and middle ages were mainly the result of the government policy to recruit workers rather than to bring in families.

After the recession of 1953, it was realized that it would be better to alter the composition of the intake at the time of difficult economic situations instead of cutting down the numbers—as was done during 1953—and then trying to resume the immigration programme later. Accordingly, during the recession of 1961 it was decided to increase the proportion of females and to encourage the migration of families (Downer, 1962, p. 12–14). Thus during the period 1961–66, not only did the sex ratio among net migrants decrease but also the former concentration in the age distribution disappeared to a considerable extent.

(ii) *The overall net migration rates and the age–sex compositions of net migrants*

A net migration rate may be defined in many different ways depending upon the practical and other considerations (Hamilton, 1965). The definition given in Section 1.8 was adopted mainly because this definition makes it convenient to include the migration component into the process of population growth.

Figure 2.8 depicts the trend in the net migration rate in Australia during 1911–66. The graph describes the same features of fluctuations in migration in relation to the economic situation in the country and the policy adopted by the Government, as revealed by the trend in the net numbers of migrants.

There were also large variations in the age–sex compositions of net migrants during this period. A rough idea of these changes has already been given. Table 2.3 provides only an average picture for each of the intercensal periods and thus the year to year variations are suppressed. Figure 2.9 presents the proportionate age distributions for four somewhat typical years and the corresponding sex distributions are given in Table

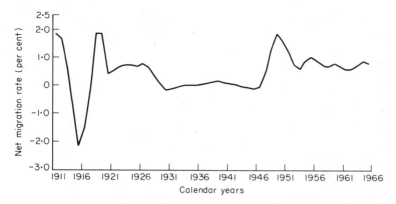

FIG. 2.8. Rate of net migration during each of the financial years in terms of the population at the beginning of the year: Australia, 1911–12 to 1965–66. Note: For 1914–19 the troop movements were included, for 1939–45 they were not included.

2.4. The years 1911–12 and 1965–66 were chosen to show the changes in these distributions over normal years. For both years, the age composition of net migrants contained positive values at all ages for males and females. The year 1915–16 was selected because during that year there was a large net emigration of males but a small net immigration of females which was mainly at ages below 28 years with net emigration at other ages; and 1945–46 was taken up because during that year there was net emigration at almost all ages for both males and females.

Table 2.4 brings out the practical difficulty inherent in using the net migration rate and the age–sex composition of net migrants for representing the migration situation such as the one during 1915–16. As far as the years 1911–12 and 1965–66 are concerned, there is little difficulty in interpreting the figures because both sexes showed net immigration during these years. Similarly, during 1945–46 both the sexes showed net emigration and the interpretation is quite clear. But the situation in 1915–16 needs a little care in interpreting the proportions.

(iii) *Age–sex-specific net migration rates*

The age-specific net migration rates can also be defined in many alternative ways. The definition adopted in this study makes it particularly easy to include the migration component into the process of population growth. The same definition has been used by other authors (Rogers, 1968; Stone, 1968). Figure 2.10 presents the age-specific net migration rates for males and females for the four selected years, viz. 1911–12, 1915–16, 1945–46

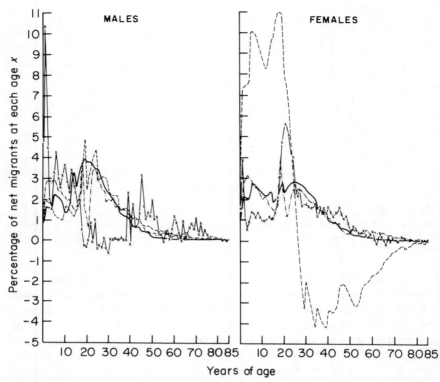

FIG. 2.9. Percentage age distributions of net migrants by single years of age: selected years, Australia. Key: ——— For the year 1911–12 with net migration rate +0.01852; ------ For the year 1915–16 with net migration rate −0.02147; ·········· For the year 1945–46 with net migration rate −0.00119; ·—·—·—·— For the year 1965–66 with net migration rate +0.00841.

Table 2.4 Net migration rate and sex proportion among net migrants in Australia during selected years

Year	Net rate	Male proportion	Female proportion
1911–12	+0.01852	0.65723	0.34277
1915–16	−0.02147	1.00921	−0.00921
1945–46	−0.00119	0.29150	0.70850
1965–66	+0.00841	0.51838	0.48162

[Source: Computed from the statistics of arrivals and departures for Australia.]

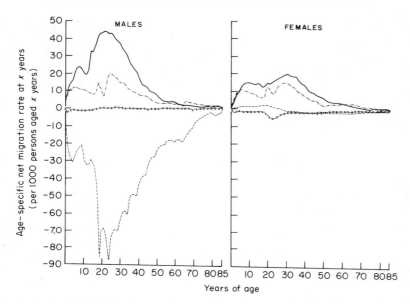

FIG. 2.10. Age-specific net migration rates at single years of age: selected years, Australia. Key: ———— For the year 1911–12; -------- For the year 1915–16; ·-·-·-·-·-· For the year 1945–46; –·–·–·– For the year 1965–66.

and 1965–66. It indicates that the effect of migration was more on the male population than on the female population. During 1915–16, owing to the troop movements, the net migration rates for males were very high between the ages 15–40 years and were negative at all ages. The lessening of the concentration of migrants in the middle ages from 1911–12 to 1965–66 can be seen in this graph also.

2.3.4 The sex ratio at birth

The other numerical data that was necessary for the construction of empirical models was the sex ratio at birth. This would not be required if, instead of one set of age-specific fertility rates computed from all births, two sets of age-specific fertility rates—one using the male births and the other using the female births—are used. However, if the sex ratio at birth does not change with the age of the females or males, the two approaches would give the same results. In this study the sex ratio at birth was assumed to be constant over time and to be independent of the ages of females and males. Its value was taken as 105 males per 100 females.

A detailed study of the sex ratio at birth in Australia during 1902–65 (Pollard, G. N. 1969) demonstrated that it fluctuated around a mean value of 105.38 and did not show any apparent trend over the period. Though a decreasing linear relationship with increasing age of females was observed, the relationship was not strong, while no significant variation with the age of males was detected. In fact, the constancy of the sex ratio at birth has become a well-recognized demographic phenomenon.

2.4 Hypothetical data used in the study

To examine the "forgetting" of the initial form of the age–sex distribution (i.e. the convergence of the different initial age–sex distributions) under changing conditions of fertility, mortality and migration it was necessary to have a fairly long series of numerical data. The sex ratio at birth was assumed to be constant in these examples also and, therefore, there was no need for any other assumptions. In the case of mortality, the survival rates observed in Australia during 1911–66, were taken for the first 56 years and those of 1966 were assumed to continue indefinitely with the presumption that significant changes in mortality are unlikely to occur in the absence of unforeseen natural or other calamities.

Hence, hypothetical data were derived only in the case of fertility and migration. The procedures adopted in obtaining the hypothetical data and a brief description of the characteristics of these data are given in this section.

(i) *Fertility rates*

In the case of fertility also, the age-specific fertility rates by age of females observed in Australia during 1911–66 were used for the first fifty-six years. For the next two years, viz. fifty-seventh and fifty-eighth years, these were taken as observed in Australia during 1967–68, while for the later years these were derived by adopting the age pattern observed in 1968 to the values of TFR assumed as follows: for the fifty-ninth year, average of the TFR for the years 1918 and 1920; and for the sixtieth and the next forty-six years, the values of TFR for the years 1920–66. The TFR for 1919 was not assumed for the fifty-ninth year because it was too low compared with the adjacent values. Finally, it was assumed that the sequence of fertility rates for the last fifty years, viz. from fifty-seventh to 106th years, would operate repeatedly so that the parabolic trend in TFR observed during 1911–61 would continue to occur over every fifty year period, but the age pattern would remain the same. This kind of estimation of fertility rates was used because it is very difficult to visualize the possible changes in fertility over such a long period of time. Also, the assumption of this kind of repetition enabled us to study the population change under a cyclical model. However, it must be mentioned that the sequence of fertility rates obtained is completely hypothetical and should not be construed as a projection of fertility rates in Australia.

Now the question to be considered is whether the above assumptions regarding the annual fertility rates, lead to any impossible results in terms of the fertility of cohorts? In order to examine this question, cohort fertility schedules were prepared by using the annual age-specific fertility rates as obtained above. For the sake of comparison, an alternative sequence of annual fertility rates was also considered. In this sequence, it was assumed that the fertility rates for the first fifty-six years were as observed in Australia during 1911–66 and for all the later years as in 1966. Figure 2.11 depicts the trend in CTFR and the mean age of the cohort fertility schedules $(\overline{m}_c)$ when the two assumptions were adopted. In analogy with TFR, the CTFR is defined as the total number of births a cohort would bear during its fertile lifetime if it is not affected by mortality during that interval, and is equal to the sum of the single year age-specific birth rates of the cohort fertility schedule.

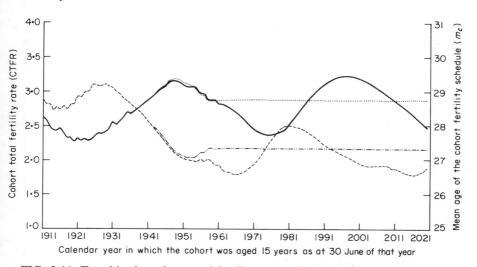

FIG. 2.11. Trend in the cohort total fertility rate and the mean age of the cohort fertility schedules resulting from the assumptions on the trend in the annual fertility rates based on the Australian data. Key: ———— CTFR, ------ $\overline{m}_c$ When the trend in the annual fertility rates during 1911–61 is assumed to be repeated; ·········· CTFR, —··—··—·· $\overline{m}_c$ When the annual fertility rates of 1966 are assumed to remain constant after the first 56 years.

It may be observed that both CTFR and $\overline{m}_c$ would have a parabolic trend when the annual TFR followed a parabolic trend and the age pattern of the annual fertility rates was assumed constant, as in the first assumption. On the other hand, when the annual fertility rates were assumed to become constant the CTFR and $\overline{m}_c$ also became constant after a comparatively short period of time. However, for the cohorts which commenced their fertility performance in 1961 or earlier years both the assumptions indicated almost identical CTFR, though the first assumption suggested a lowering of the mean age of the cohort fertility schedule. Ryder (1967) found a similar trend in CTFR from the data of the United States in respect of the cohorts born during 1891–95 to 1941–45. It may be noted that he used the year of birth to identify the cohorts whereas we have used the year in which the cohort was aged 15 years.

When the parabolic trend in the annual TFR was assumed, the CTFR fluctuated between 2.37 and 3.25 and the mean age between 26.59 to 28.01 years while, when the annual fertility rates become constant, these also became constant at 2.89 and 27.34, respectively. These fluctuations in CTFR and $\overline{m}_c$ do not appear to be abnormal as to invalidate the assumption.

(ii) *Migration data*

In the case of migration, two alternative assumptions were considered. In the first one, the net migration rates and the age–sex compositions observed

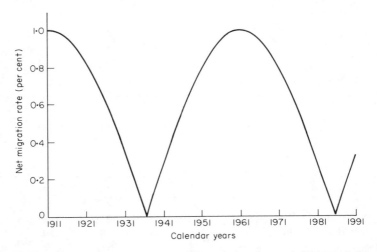

FIG. 2.12. Trend in the net migration rate under the assumption of the cosine curve (absolute values). The cosine function used: $f(t) = [0.01 \text{ ABS} (\cos 0.0628318 (t - 1))] 100$.

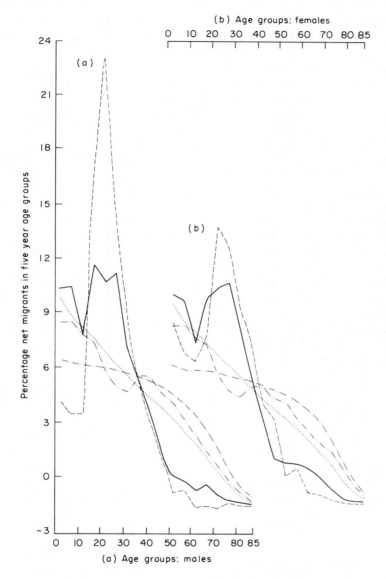

FIG. 2.13. Comparison of certain age compositions of net migrants, used in the hypothetical experiments. Key: ———— Same as in 1962–66; ------- Same as in 1925; —·—·—· Same as the 1911 life table population age distribution; —··—··—·· Same as the 1966 population age distribution (see Fig. 2.1); ·············· Same as the 1911 stable population age distribution (see Fig. 2.1).

during 1911–12 to 1965–66 were assumed during the first fifty-five years and then the values for the year 1965–66 were taken to remain the same for all the later years. In the second one, it was assumed that the trend in the net migration rate would follow a cosine curve with a maximum absolute value of 1 per cent. It was further assumed that the period from peak to peak was fifty years so that the trend would resemble, very roughly, the trend observed in Australia during 1911–61, and would correspond to the trend in the fertility rates. Since migration is influenced by the economic conditions in the country and by the policies of the Government, it is again very difficult to visualize the long-term changes. Hence we have resorted to the use of mathematical curves. Further, the use of a mathematical curve such as the cosine curve was advantageous because it became easy to manipulate the changes in the migration situation needed to test the analytical conclusions. For instance, we could easily increase the magnitude of migration by changing the absolute maximum value to 5 per cent. Similarly, we could change the trend in the net migration rate by assuming a sine curve. The assumption of the cosine curve also provided an example for the cyclical model of population change (see Section 5.3.3).

Figure 2.12 gives an idea of the trend in the net migration rate under the assumption of the cosine curve. The trend when a sine curve is assumed would be exactly the opposite to that shown in the graph.

Along with these net migration rates, the age–sex composition of net migrants observed in Australia during 1962–66 was used. This was assumed to remain constant over all the years.

Several other age–sex distributions were also used as the age–sex compositions of net migrants in the different numerical experiments conducted under assumptions of unchanging conditions. Figure 2.13 and Table 2.5 compare these special age–sex compositions of net migrants.

It may be observed that the age–sex structures of net migrants during 1962–66 and in 1925 represented two distinct features of the age–sex

Table 2.5   Proportion of net migrants by sex associated with the special age distributions of net migrants

Proportionate age distribution	Male proportion	Female proportion
Same as in 1962–66	0.50863	0.49137
Same as in 1925	0.68577	0.31423
Same as 1966 obs. population	0.50615	0.49385
Same as 1911 stb. population	0.50033	0.49967
Same as 1911 life table population	0.49608	0.50392

[Source: Computed from the relevant data for Australia.]

Table 2.6 Numerical data used in the study

			Migration		
	Mortality	Fertility	Net migration rate	Age-sex composition of net migrants	Age-sex-specific net migration rates
Constant conditions	1911 1966	1911 1966	(i) 1911–12 1915–16 1945–46 1965–66 (ii) −1.0% 0.5% 1.0% 5.0%	(i) 1911–12 1915–16 1945–46 1865–66 (ii) Same as in 1962–66 Same as in 1925 Same as 1911 stb. population Same as 1966 obs. population Same as 1911 life Table population	1911–12 1915–16 1945–46 1965–66
Changing conditions	First 56 years: 1911–66 57th year and later: 1966	First 56 years: 1911–66 57th and 58th years: 1967–68 59th to 106th years: average TFR for 1918 and 1920, and TFRs for 1920–66 with age pattern as in 1968 107th year and later: 57th to 106th years repeat	(i) First 55 years: 1911–12 to 1965–66 56th year and later: 1965–66 (ii) Cosine and sine curves	(i) First 55 years: 1911–12 to 1965–66 56th year and later: 1965–66 (ii) Same as in 1962–66	First 55 years: 1911–12 to 1965–66 56th year and later: 1965–66

Note: The calendar years in this table indicate that the data observed in Australia for those years were used in the study. The net numbers of migrants by age and sex for the period 1911–66 were also used.

compositions of net migrants. During 1962–66, there was only a small concentration in the age group (15–44) and a slight excess of males, whereas in 1925 there was a heavy concentration in that age group and a very high proportion of males. The other age–sex distributions were purely hypothetical, and were adopted for theoretical interest.

Since immigrants to one area are the emigrants from another, the age–sex composition of net migrants during 1962–66 was used both when net immigration and net emigration were assumed.

When the age–sex-specific net migration rates were used in the process of population growth, it was assumed that the age–sex-specific net migration rates observed in Australia during 1911–12 to 1965–66 would operate during the first fifty-five years and the values for 1965–66 would remain the same for all the later years. No hypothetical data were derived in this case.

2.5 Summary

The results of the analysis of the basic numerical data given in this chapter, show that the age–sex distributions of the initial populations considered for the study were quite diverse, the changes in the survival rates observed in Australia during 1911–66 were not very significant except at the very young ages and at the old ages, and there were large variations in the fertility rates and the net migration. The sex ratio at birth did not show any trend over time or any significant relationship with the increase in the age of females or males.

The hypothetical fertility rates were derived such that the trend in TFR observed in Australia during 1911–61 repeated over every fifty year period, but the age pattern observed in 1968 remained unchanged after the first fifty-six years. On the other hand, the hypothetical net migration rates were obtained by using cosine and sine curves and the age–sex composition of net migrants was kept the same as observed in Australia during 1962–66.

The different data on the components used in the numerical examples are displayed in Table 2.6 for the convenience of reference.

Part II

POPULATION CHANGE UNDER CONSTANT CONDITIONS

3

EMERGENCE OF AN EQUILIBRIUM-STATE AGE–SEX DISTRIBUTION

3.1 Introduction

The classical theory of stable populations has shown that, starting from an arbitrary state, any human age–sex structure reaches, in the absence of migration, a stable form which is independent of the initial structure if the fertility and mortality rates operating on it remain constant for a sufficiently long period of time. Lopez (1961, p. 64) indicated that the same would hold good when migration was included into the process by incorporating a set of age-specific net migration rates into the survival rates. But it is not known whether such a convergence would occur when an overall net migration rate and an age–sex composition of net migrants are utilized in the process of population growth.

Among the studies connected with the stable population theory, Coale's (1968) study drew attention to an aspect which had not been properly treated so far, that is the study of the duration of the process of convergence (i.e. the time required for the convergence) of an age distribution to the stable form. McFarland (1969) examined this problem in the general case in which the fertility and mortality rates were assumed to be changing over time, and obtained a formula to compute the duration of convergence in terms of the youngest and the oldest ages at which child bearing takes place. Again, though, what effect the introduction of migration into the process of population change has on the duration of convergence, has not been investigated.

In this chapter, the main concern will be to discuss these two questions. First, we consider the one-sex case with no migration and derive, under certain approximation, a formula which would give the duration of convergence in terms of the characteristics of the net maternity function.

For the purpose of the current discussion, the duration of convergence may be defined as the number of years needed for the difference between an arbitrary age–sex distribution and the equilibrium state age–sex distribution, to become less than a preassigned small quantity, from the time the specified schedules of fertility, mortality and migration start operating.

First, we show that the convergence to the equilibrium-state age–sex distribution occurs when migration is included into the process of population growth using an overall net migration rate and an age–sex distribution of net migrants at the time of migration (i.e. the equilibrium state age–sex distribution emerges ultimately). Then we discuss the changes in the duration of convergence due to the inclusion of migration. Although, some comments on the changes in the intrinsic growth rate are included here, the relationship between this rate and the equilibrium-state age–sex distribution on the one hand, and the given schedules of fertility, mortality and migration on the other, are examined in Chapter 4.

Finally, we extend the results to the two-sex model and present some numerical illustrations using the two-sex model.

The question as to whether the "forgetting" of the initial shape of the age–sex distribution which happens under constant conditions would occur when these conditions are changing over time, will be taken up in Chapter 5.

3.2 Equilibrium state in the absence of migration (i.e. stable state)

The process through time which leads to the stable state could be studied by successively projecting the population over time and comparing the percentage age distribution at time t with that at time $(t - 1)$, or with the one obtained by applying the stable population equation:

$$p(x) = be^{-rx}s(x) \tag{3.1}$$

where $p(x)$ is the proportion of the population at age x years, b and r are the constant birth and growth rates, and $s(x)$ is the proportion surviving to age x years. The stable population is established when the difference between the two age distributions being compared becomes smaller than a preassigned small quantity. The value of t, then, is the duration of the process of convergence.

Alternatively, we may decompose the sequence of births as the sum of a real exponential term and a series of relatively diminishing oscillatory terms and claim that:

The stable population is established no more than w years after the number of births last deviates by an arbitrarily small proportionate amount from (the) pure exponential sequence, where w is the highest age attained under the given mortality regime (Coale, 1968, p. 396).

We shall follow the procedure of population projections since it facilitates the inclusion of the migration component.

Let $P(x, t)$ be the female (or male) population aged x years at time t. Then the population at time t can be obtained from that at time $(t - 1)$ by using the following equations:

$$P(0, t) = S(b) \sum_{\alpha}^{\beta} \tfrac{1}{2}[P(x, t - 1) + P(x, t)]f(x) \tag{3.2}$$

and

$$P(x, t) = S(x - 1)P(x - 1, t - 1), \text{ for } x = 1, 2, \ldots, w \tag{3.3}$$

where the absence of t in the symbols for fertility and survival rates indicates that these are constant over time. These equations follow from the definitions of $f(x)$, $S(b)$ and $S(x)$.

Making use of the matrix notation the above equations can be written as:

$$(P_t) = L(P_{t-1}) \tag{3.4}$$

where (P_t) denotes a column vector giving the population by age which we shall call the population vector; and L is the matrix given below:

$$
L = \begin{bmatrix}
0 & 0 & . & 0 & m(\alpha) & m(\alpha+1) & . & m(\beta) & 0 & . & 0 & 0 \\
S(0) & 0 & . & 0 & 0 & 0 & . & 0 & 0 & . & 0 & 0 \\
0 & S(1) & . & 0 & 0 & 0 & . & 0 & 0 & . & 0 & 0 \\
. & . & . & . & & . & . & . & . & . & . & . \\
0 & 0 & . & 0 & 0 & 0 & . & 0 & 0 & . & S(w-1) & 0
\end{bmatrix}
$$

in which

$$m(x) = \tfrac{1}{2}[f(x) + S(x)f(x + 1)]S(b). \tag{3.5}$$

The matrix representation has an advantage in studying the process of population growth since some of the aspects of population growth could be studied conveniently by the properties of the matrix L.

The repeated application of eqn (3.4) gives:

$$(P_t) = L^t(P_0) \tag{3.6}$$

where (P_0) is the initial population vector.

The matrix L can be partitioned at the $(\beta + 1)$th row and column, and be written as follows:

$$L = \begin{bmatrix} M & 0 \\ A & B \end{bmatrix}.$$

Then it can be shown that, in any power of L, the elements of the first row will not be affected by the elements in the second row and the resultant matrix will have the same form as L. Hence, the growth of the population at ages below β years (age β years is the oldest age at which reproduction occurs) at any time, is independent of the population at ages beyond β years (Keyfitz, 1968a, p. 37). But, in course of time, the populations at ages beyond β years become linear functions of the populations at ages below β years. The coefficients of the functions are determined entirely by the known fertility and mortality schedules. Therefore, the intrinsic growth rate obtained using the populations at ages below β years must apply to the whole of the age range. In fact, it can be shown that the non-zero characteristic roots of the matrix L are the same as those of its submatrix M:

$$M = \begin{bmatrix} 0 & 0 & . & 0 & m(\alpha) & m(\alpha+1) & . & m(\beta-1) & m(\beta) \\ S(0) & 0 & . & 0 & 0 & 0 & . & 0 & 0 \\ 0 & S(1) & . & 0 & 0 & 0 & . & 0 & 0 \\ . & . & . & . & . & . & . & . & . \\ 0 & 0 & . & 0 & 0 & 0 & . & S(\beta-1) & 0 \end{bmatrix}.$$

Hence it suffices, in this case, to study the submatrix M. This matrix is an irreducible non-negative square matrix which is primitive, i.e. when it is raised to some powers it becomes a matrix with all elements positive. It has therefore a real positive characteristic root, λ_1, which is unique and whose value is greater than the absolute value of any other root, and corresponding to λ_1, there exists a characteristic vector whose elements are positive. The matrix M will be primitive whenever there are at least two consecutive ages at which the fertility rates are strictly positive (Pollard, 1966). As far as human populations are concerned, this requirement appears to be always satisfied.

Let λ_2 be another characteristic root of M, whose absolute value is greater than that of any other characteristic root except λ_1. We assume that λ_2 is also distinct. In fact, in demographic applications, it is observed that all the characteristic roots are distinct (Keyfitz, 1968a, p. 51).

Now, denoting the population vector below the age β years as K, we have:

$$(K_t) = M^t(K_0). \tag{3.7}$$

When t is sufficiently large, we assert that:

$$(K_t) \simeq \lambda_1^t C_1(V_1) \tag{3.8}$$

which implies that the other terms become relatively negligible. Here C_1 is called the stable equivalent and (V_1) the stable age distribution (Keyfitz, 1968a, p. 57). Since λ_2 is the root highest in absolute value next to λ_1 and is distinct, the ratio $[|\lambda_2|/|\lambda_1|]$ determines the value of t, the duration of convergence. If λ_2 is a complex root, then $|\lambda_2| = |\lambda_3|$ because λ_3 will be complex conjugate of λ_2 and we can use any one of them to determine t. In fact, t can be calculated as follows:

$$[|\lambda_2|/|\lambda_1|]^t = \varepsilon \tag{3.9}$$

where ε is a small quantity chosen arbitrarily to ensure the required approximation. Hence

$$t = [(\log \varepsilon)/\{\log |\lambda_2| - \log |\lambda_1|\}] \tag{3.10}$$

and we may take the highest integer contained in the expression plus one as the value of t. It can easily be seen that the value of t is always positive as it should be. Thus the examination of the duration of convergence reduces to the study of λ_1 and λ_2 of the characteristic roots of the projection matrix. λ_1 also gives the intrinsic growth rate.

For the convenience of interpretation, it is better to transform the λs into rs by the transformation $\lambda = e^r$. Then r_1 corresponding to the real positive root λ_1 is the intrinsic rate of natural increase of the stable population and $r_2 = y + iz$ (or $r_2 = y - iz$), where y and z are real quantities, corresponding to the complex root λ_2 (or λ_3) determines the rate of dampening of the waves of the oscillatory terms and their wavelength which is given by $(2\pi/z)$ (Keyfitz, 1968a, p. 73). In terms of r_1, and r_2, eqn (3.10) becomes:

$$t = [(\log_e \varepsilon)/(y - r_1)] \tag{3.11}$$

in which y will be negative in practice, or if positive it must be less than r_1, because the dampening will not occur otherwise. Again, it will have to be greater than r_1 whenever r_1 is negative because λ_1 will not be greater than the absolute value of λ_2 otherwise. Hence t is always positive as it should be. It may also be inferred that as $(y - r_1)$ increases in magnitude the value of t decreases and vice versa.

In demographic studies r_1 and r_2 can be approximated in terms of the moments or the cumulants of the net maternity function:

$$F(x) = [S(b)S(0)S(1) \ldots S(x - 1)]f(x). \tag{3.12}$$

To achieve this, different authors have used different curve fitting methods of which we shall choose here the Pearson Type III curve used by Wicksell (Keyfitz, 1968a, pp. 147–157), since it provides more flexible curves.

Let $R_i = \sum_{\alpha}^{\beta} x^i F(x)$. Then $\mu = [R_1/R_0]$ and $\sigma^2 = [R_2/R_0] - \mu^2$ are the mean and variance of the net maternity curve. Let $v = [\sigma/\mu]$ be the coefficient of variation. Adopting the Pearson Type III curve to $F(x)$, we can write the values of r_1 and r_2 as follows:

$$r_1 = C[R_0^{1/k} - 1] \tag{3.13}$$

and

$$r_2 = C[R_0^{1/k}e^{2\pi i/k} - 1]$$
$$= C[R_0^{1/k} \cos(2\pi/k) - 1] + iCR_0^{1/k} \sin(2\pi/k) \tag{3.14}$$

where

$$C = [1/(\mu v^2)] \quad \text{and} \quad k = [1/v^2].$$

Hence under this approximation, we have:

$$t = \frac{\log_e \varepsilon}{CR_0^{1/k}[\cos(2\pi/k) - 1]} = \frac{(\log_e \varepsilon)\mu v^2}{R_0^{v^2}[\cos(2\pi v^2) - 1]} \tag{3.15}$$

which is always positive for small ε.

When v is small (which is generally the case in human populations) we can write the eqn (3.15) as:

$$t = - \frac{(\log_e \varepsilon)\mu}{R_0^{v^2} 2\pi^2 v^2} \tag{3.15a}$$

If $R_0 = 1.0$, this equation becomes the same as that which would be obtained by fitting the Hadwiger curve to the net maternity function. From eqn (3.15a) we can see that the duration of convergence is directly proportional to the mean and inversely proportional to the total density and the square of the coefficient of variation of the net maternity function. For a given R_0, if $v = 0$, t becomes infinity. In this case, the density of the net maternity function is concentrated at one age and the oscillations never die out. When v is large the above approximation may not be satisfactory.

On the other hand, for given μ and σ, which implies that the age pattern of the net maternity rates is unchanged, t decreases from ∞ to 0 as R_0 increases from 0 to ∞, for theoretical considerations. The value of R_0, in practice, is rarely very near to 0 or greater than 4 for the human populations (United Nations, 1968, p. 22).

In any actual situation, however, we can calculate the intrinsic growth rate (r_1), and the duration of convergence (t), from the given schedules of fertility and mortality by computing the total density R_0 (i.e. the net reproduction rate), the mean and the coefficient of variation of the net maternity function.

But it must be noted that the formula (3.15) does not take account of the nature of the initial age structure. Therefore, the number of years needed for the convergence of any particular age distribution, under the operation of the given fertility and mortality conditions, may be far less than the number obtained from this formula, depending on how near the initial age structure is to the stable one resulting from those fertility and mortality conditions. In fact, if the initial age distribution is the stable one itself, then the required t is zero. Further, the value of t, computed here, refers to the number of years required for the convergence of the age distributions below the age β years. Hence, unless this value of t is greater than ($w + 1$) years which is the time required for the cohorts at all ages in the initial population to die out, it must be increased to make it greater than ($w + 1$) years, when we consider the convergence of the age distributions over the whole age range ($0 - w$) years.

In order to examine the nature of the process of convergence we may construct the population series using the values of r_1 and r_2 calculated from the formulas (3.13) and (3.14); or in any particular case, we may draw the graph of the maximum (MaxGI) and minimum (MinGI) of the growth indexes at individual ages (see, for example, Fig. 3.1). A growth index at age x years is defined as the ratio of the population at that age at time t to the population at the same age at time ($t - 1$). Lotka (1922) used the stable populations corresponding to the MaxGI and MinGI at each point of time, to show that the resultant age distribution is stable. However, it is well known now that, for a stable population, the growth rates at all ages are constant and are equal to the growth rate of the total population. Therefore, when MaxGI and MinGI differ negligibly we may conclude that the age distribution under consideration has reached the stable state. In fact, this criterion was used to test the convergence of the age–sex distributions in the numerical examples.

3.3 Equilibrium state in the presence of migration

If $N(x)$ denotes the net number of migrants of age x years arriving (or departing) into (or out of) the population, respectively, during a year, then the overall net migration rate n, is computed as:

$$n = \left\{ \sum_0^w N(x) \right\} / P \tag{3.16}$$

where P is the size of the total population at the beginning of that year, and their age distribution at the time of migration as:

$$n(x) = N(x) / \left(\sum_0^w N(x) \right). \tag{3.17}$$

The absence of t in n and $n(x)$ denotes that they are constant over time. Now the set of equations which enable us to calculate the population at time t in terms of the one at $(t-1)$, can be derived by modifying eqns (3.2) and (3.3) to include the survivors of migrants in the period $(t-1, t)$ at different ages.

Under assumption (7), the migrants entering or leaving the population experience the fertility and mortality of the population only for half of the year in which they migrate. Hence the probability of surviving to the end of the year (i.e. for six months) for migrants during the interval $(t-1, t)$ can be taken as the arithmetic mean of the probabilities of surviving for zero month and twelve months. Further, by the same assumption, half of the migrants aged x, who survive to time t remain at age x and the other half become aged $(x+1)$. Thus the population aged x at time t which consists of the survivors of the migrants in the interval $(t-1, t)$ is obtained as:

$$n \left[\frac{n(x-1)}{2} \left(\frac{1+S(x-1)}{2} \right) + \frac{n(x)}{2} \left(\frac{1+S(x)}{2} \right) \right] \sum_0^w P(x, t-1)$$

$$= a(x-1) \sum_0^w P(x, t-1) \tag{3.18}$$

where

$$a(x) = \frac{n}{4} [n(x)(1+S(x)) + n(x+1)(1+S(x+1))]. \tag{3.19}$$

Thus

$$P(x, t) = S(x-1)P(x-1, t-1) + a(x-1) \sum_0^w P(x, t-1)$$

$$\text{for } x = 1, 2, \ldots w. \tag{3.20}$$

For $x = 0$, we have:

$P(0, t) = $ [Population aged 0 at time t who are
survivors of the births (including to
those who are migrants during the
interval) in the interval $(t - 1, t)$]

$+$ [Population aged 0 at time t which
consists of half the number of
survivors of the migrants aged 0
in the interval $(t - 1, t)$].   (3.21)

The first component in the above equation is:

$$S(b) \sum_{\alpha}^{\beta} \tfrac{1}{2}[P(x, t - 1) + P(x, t)]f(x)$$

$$= \frac{S(b)}{2} \sum_{\alpha}^{\beta} [P(x, t - 1) + S(x - 1) P(x - 1, t - 1)$$

$$+ a(x - 1) \sum_{0}^{w} P(x, t - 1)]f(x) \qquad (3.22)$$

from eqn (3.20).
The second component is:

$$\left[n \frac{n(0)}{2} \left(\frac{1 + S(0)}{2} \right) \right] \sum_{0}^{w} P(x, t - 1) \qquad (3.23)$$

from eqn (3.18).
Therefore

$$P(0, t) = \frac{S(b)}{2} \sum_{\alpha}^{\beta} [P(x, t - 1) + S(x - 1) P(x - 1, t - 1)]f(x)$$

$$+ u \sum_{0}^{w} P(x, t - 1) \qquad (3.24)$$

where

$$u = \frac{S(b)}{2} \sum_{\alpha}^{\beta} [a(x - 1)f(x)] + \frac{n}{4}(1 + S(0))n(0). \qquad (3.25)$$

Equation (3.24) may be rewritten as:

$$P(0, t) = \sum_{\alpha}^{\beta} [m(x)P(x, t - 1)] + u \sum_{0}^{w} P(x, t - 1) \qquad (3.26)$$

where $m(x)$ is same as given by eqn (3.5).

In the case of the last age group, if it is an open-end age group a small adjustment may be made in the value of $a(x)$ as for $S(x)$. However, that will not affect the discussion here.

If we use separate schedules of immigrants and emigrants, we need to change only the values of $[n(x)n]$ in the expressions for u and $a(x)$, which will then be

$$[n(x)n] = [I(x)I] - [0(x)0], \text{ for } x = 0, 1, 2, \ldots w$$

where I and 0 denote the gross immigration and emigration rates in terms of the total population at the beginning of the year, and $I(x)$ and $0(x)$ the corresponding proportions at age x years.

Now, the growth eqns (3.20) and (3.26) can be written as the matrix equation:

$$(P_t) = L_M(P_{t-1}) \qquad (3.27)$$

where L_M is the matrix:

$$
\begin{bmatrix}
u & . & u & [m(\alpha)+u] & . & [m(\beta)+u] & u & . & u & u \\
[S(0)+a(0)] & . & a(0) & a(0) & . & a(0) & a(0) & . & a(0) & a(0) \\
a(1) & . & a(1) & a(1) & . & a(1) & a(1) & . & a(1) & a(1) \\
. & . & . & . & . & . & . & . & . & . \\
a(w-1) & . & a(w-1) & a(w-1) & . & a(w-1) & a(w-1) & . & \begin{array}{c}[S(w-1)\\+a(w-1)]\end{array} & a(w-1)
\end{bmatrix}
$$

with $m(x)$ same as in L.

Thus, as before, the characteristic roots λ_1 and λ_2 of this matrix L_M determine the ultimate growth rate and the time required to attain the equilibrium state. We cannot partition the matrix L_M as the matrix L. But, it can be shown (see Section 5.2.2) that, in course of time, the populations at ages beyond β years, become linear functions of the populations at ages below β years. The coefficients of these functions are determined entirely by the known fertility, mortality and migration schedules. This means that the elements in the first $(\beta + 1)$ rows in the matrix L_M play an important role in the population growth. We shall make use of this fact at a later stage in our argument.

3.3.1 Existence of equilibrium-state population

Now, we shall first prove that in general an equilibrium-state population exists. For this purpose, it is enough if it is proved that the matrix L_M has a unique positive dominant characteristic root and a corresponding characteristic vector of positive elements. Then, as argued in the case with no migration (see eqn (3.8)), the existence of an equilibrium state population follows. However, it is not possible, in this case, to make one general statement as in the case with no migration, because the effect of migration is not always in one direction. There may be immigration at all ages, emigration at all ages, or immigration at some ages and emigration at some others, etc. Migration may also be zero at some of the ages. Hence we shall discuss certain important possibilities so as to indicate the effect of introducing migration.

(a) Suppose $n(x)$ are all positive. If n is also positive, then we have the case where there is net immigration at all ages. In this case, u and all $a(x)$ are strictly positive so that the matrix L_M is a positive square matrix. Hence, from the properties of positive square matrices, it may be inferred that L_M has a unique real positive dominant characteristic root λ_1 and a corresponding characteristic vector of positive elements exists (Gantmacher, 1959, p. 53). Thus an equilibrium state population exists. The real dominant root gives the intrinsic growth rate and the characteristic vector yields the age distribution of the equilibrium state population.

If n is negative, then we have the case where there is net emigration at all ages, so that u and all $a(x)$ are strictly negative. It may be mentioned here that the case in which $n(x)$ are all negative and n is positive is not admissible. The matrix L_M, in this case, is not a non-negative square matrix. Hence, the conclusion regarding the existence of an equilibrium-state population in this case is not as straightforward as in the above case.

Now, each age cohort alive at the initial point of time ($t = 0$) vanishes, as a result of ageing, when it completes the age of w years and is replaced by an age cohort which is a linear function of the populations alive at different ages at $t = 0$. Thus all the age cohorts will in the course of time be linear functions of the initial age cohorts. The coefficients in these linear functions, as has already been stated, are determined by the operating schedules of fertility, mortality and migration. But, by assumption (8), the population in any age group cannot become negative at any time. In order to satisfy this assumption, emigration will have to be naturally restricted by the initial age structure and also fertility and mortality conditions. Thus the values of u and $a(x)$ must satisfy the inequalities:

$$\sum_{\alpha}^{\beta} [m(x)p(x, t - 1)] > -u \qquad (3.28)$$

and

$$p(x-1, t-1) > -\frac{a(x-1)}{S(x-1)} \text{ for } x = 1, 2, \ldots, w \qquad (3.29)$$

where $p(x, t-1)$ denotes the proportion of the population aged x at time $(t-1)$, and u and $a(x)$ are negative quantities. If these inequalities are not satisfied, then it means that the given conditions of emigration cannot prevail in the given population under the given conditions of fertility and mortality. Such a situation is called an incompatible situation. Also, it may be noted that in demographic applications the first inequality holds good if the other inequalities given by eqn (3.29) are satisfied. This can be seen using eqns (3.19), (3.20) and (3.25).

Thus, for assumption (8) to be satisfied in this case, the inequalities (3.29) must be satisfied for each initial cohorts $P(x, 0)$, $x = 0, 1, 2, \ldots$ $(w-1)$ at the different time periods, $t = 1, 2, \ldots$, as it passes through the age range x to w years. When the age cohort $P(x, 0)$ reaches finally age w in the year $t = (w-x)$, it must be greater than or equal to zero. This will be guaranteed if and only if the following inequality is satisfied for all x:

$$p(x,0) \geqslant - \left[\frac{\sum_{y=0}^{w-x-1} a(x+y)\dfrac{S(x+y+1)}{h_y}\dfrac{S(x+y+2)}{h_{y+1}}\cdots\dfrac{S(x+w-x-1)}{h_{w-x-2}}}{S(x)\dfrac{S(x+1)}{h_0}\dfrac{S(x+2)}{h_1}\cdots\dfrac{S(w-1)}{h_{w-x-2}}} \right]$$

where

$$h_y = \left\{\sum_0^w P(x, y+1)\right\} \bigg/ \left\{\sum_0^w P(x, y)\right\}. \qquad (3.30)$$

The inequality (3.30) could easily be derived by writing down the equation for $P(w, w-x)$ in terms of the initial cohort $P(x, 0)$.

Further, the relationship between u and $a(x)$ on the one hand, and $S(x)$ and $m(x)$ on the other must be such that the matrix L_M becomes a matrix of positive elements when raised to some power and that the sums of its rows are all positive, i.e.

$$-(w+1)u > \sum_\alpha^\beta m(x) \qquad (3.31)$$

and

$$-(w+1)a(x) > S(x) \text{ for } x = 0, 1, 2, \ldots, (w-1). \qquad (3.32)$$

(It may be recalled that u and $a(x)$ are negative quantities). If these conditions are not satisfied, then again an incompatible situation arises at least in the long run, because in that case either the dominant root of L_M would become negative or if it is positive the characteristic vector associated with it contains negative elements (Brauer, 1961).

When the above conditions are satisfied, then we conclude from the theory of power positive matrices that L_M has a unique positive dominant root and a corresponding vector of positive elements exists. Fortunately, these conditions are generally satisfied in demographic applications. Hence it may be concluded that an equilibrium state population is evolved in this case also.

Sometimes, however, it may be that the net emigration rate is very high or the age composition of the net migrants is abnormally concentrated in some ages or both, then an incompatible situation arises in the long run. An example of such a situation is the one in which the migration conditions of the First World War years 1915–16 are assumed to operate constantly, along with the fertility and mortality conditions of 1911 in Australia (see Table 3.1).

(b) Suppose some $n(x)$ are zero and others are all positive. This happens when there is overall net immigration, but it does not affect some of the ages. If $n > 0$, the L_M is a non-negative square matrix. It will be power positive if there is at least one age $\leq \beta$ years at which $n(x) \neq 0$. Then, from the properties of irreducible non-negative square matrices, it follows that L_M has a unique real positive dominant root and associated with it there exists a characteristic vector of positive elements. This proves the existence of an equilibrium state population in this case.

If $n < 0$ and $n(x) \neq 0$ for at least one age $\leq \beta$ years, we can argue as in (a) above and infer that in demographic applications in general, an equilibrium state population exists.

(c) Next, suppose $n(x)$ are zero for all ages $\leq \beta$ years. In this case migration affects only the populations at ages beyond the reproductive period. Then, the matrix L_M can be partitioned in the same way as the matrix L. Also, it can easily be shown by writing the growth equations for successive t, that the population at each age above β years becomes in the course of time a linear function of the populations at ages $\leq \beta$ bears whether $n > 0$ or $n < 0$, provided the absolute value of n is less than 1. In demographic applications n is necessarily less than 1 when it is negative (i.e. emigration) and is generally less than 1 when it is positive (n may be greater than 1 in the case of new settlements). Hence as in the case with no migration it can be asserted that an equilibrium state population exists.

(d) Lastly, suppose $n(x) \gtreqless 0$ which happens when there is net immigration at some ages, no migration at some, and net emigration at others. Then L_M will have some $a(x)$ negative, some zero and others positive.

However, if assumption (8) is satisfied, L_M must be power positive and must have positive row sums. This guarantees the existence of a unique real positive dominant root and a corresponding vector of positive elements. Hence an equilibrium state population is evolved ultimately in this case also.

Thus, in general, the equilibrium-state population exists.

3.3.2 Growth rate and age distribution of the equilibrium-state population

Now we shall consider the changes in the growth rate and the age distribution of the resulting equilibrium-state population. From the discussions in Section 3.2, it is clear that the constant growth rate (i.e. the intrinsic growth rate) of the equilibrium state population is given by λ_1, the unique real positive dominant root of the matrix L_M, and its constant age distribution by the corresponding characteristic vector of positive elements.

Comparing the value of λ_1 in the presence of migration with that in the absence of migration, the effects of different types of migration on the growth rate of the equilibrium state population can be inferred. Using the theory of matrices regarding the changes in their elements (or from demographic considerations), it is not difficult to prove that, as compared to the case with no migration, λ_1 increases if there is overall net immigration (i.e. $n > 0$) and decreases when there is overall net emigration (i.e. $n < 0$), provided $n(x) \geq 0$ for all x including at least one age $x \leq \beta$ years for which $n(x) > 0$. If $n(x) = 0$ for all ages $\leq \beta$ years, then λ_1 will remain the same as in the absence of migration whether $n > 0$ or $n < 0$, assuming that the absolute value of n is less than 1. If $n(x) \gtreqless 0$, λ_1 may increase, decrease, or remain the same depending on the relative magnitudes of $n(x)$ at the different ages and the magnitude of n.

However, very little is known about the changes in the characteristic vector associated with λ_1. It is therefore difficult to draw any conclusions regarding the comparative picture of the equilibrium state age distributions. However, it is possible to find explicit relationships between the resulting equilibrium-state age distribution and the operating schedules of fertility, mortality, and migration. This is discussed in the next chapter.

3.3.3 The duration of convergence (i.e. the time required for convergence)

As already discussed in the case with no migration, the duration of convergence of an arbitrary age distribution to the equilibrium-state age distribution (i.e. the time required for "forgetting" the initial form of the age distribution) depends on the first two dominant characteristic roots, λ_1 and λ_2, of the matrix L_M. But from matrix algebra very little is known about the changes in λ_2 resulting from any changes in the elements of the matrix L_M. Accordingly, it is difficult to infer the changes in the duration of convergence, using the theory of matrices. Therefore, an attempt is made here to analyse the effects of migration on the duration of convergence, using the theory of weighted averages.

Let t_1 and t_0 be respectively the duration of convergence in the absence of migration, and in the presence of migration. Then $t_0 \lessgtr t_1$ according as $n \lessgtr 0$, when $n(x) \geq 0$ for all x.

In order to prove this proposition, let us consider a hypothetical population which had at time $t = 0$ the same size as the population under study but had the equilibrium-state age distribution that would result from the operation of constant fertility, mortality and migration schedules. Then define the population ratios at time t as:

$$R(x, t) = P(x, t)/W(x, t) \tag{3.33}$$

where $W(x, t)$ is the population aged x at time t in the hypothetical population. Let $R(t)$ and $r(t)$ be the maximum and minimum of these ratios.

Now, the population ratios at time $(t + 1)$ when there is no migration are:

$$R(0, t + 1) = \frac{\sum\limits_{\alpha}^{\beta} m(x)R(x, t)W(x, t)}{\sum\limits_{\alpha}^{\beta} m(x)W(x, t)} \tag{3.34}$$

and

$$R(x, t + 1) = \frac{S(x - 1)R(x - 1, t)W(x - 1, t)}{S(x - 1)W(x - 1, t)} \tag{3.35}$$

$$= R(x - 1, t) \text{ for } x = 1, 2, \ldots, w.$$

On the other hand, when there is migration these ratios are given by:

$$R(0, t + 1) = \frac{\sum\limits_{\alpha}^{\beta} m(x)R(x, t)W(x, t) + u \sum\limits_{0}^{w} R(x, t)W(x, t)}{\sum\limits_{\alpha}^{\beta} m(x)W(x, t) + u \sum\limits_{0}^{w} W(x, t)}$$

$$= \frac{\sum\limits_{0}^{w} (m(x) + u)R(x, t)W(x, t)}{\sum\limits_{0}^{w} (m(x) + u)W(x, t)} \tag{3.36}$$

since $m(x)$ is zero outside the age range α and β years, and

$$R(x, t+1) = \frac{S(x-1)R(x-1, t)W(x-1, t) + a(x-1)\sum_0^w R(x, t)W(x, t)}{S(x-1)W(x-1, t) + a(x-1)\sum_0^w W(x, t)}$$

$$\text{for } x = 1, 2, \ldots, w. \tag{3.37}$$

From eqn (3.34) it is easy to infer that $R(0, t+1)$, being the weighted average of $R(x_1 t)$ for $\alpha \leq x \leq \beta$, is definitely less than the greatest and definitely greater than the smallest of these ratios. But the greatest of these ratios is $\leq R(t)$ and the smallest $\geq r(t)$. Therefore, we conclude that $R(0, t+1)$ is $<R(t)$ and $>r(t)$. We shall call this effect the averaging effect. Since $m(x)$ is strictly positive (not equal to zero) for at least two consecutive ages, this averaging effect necessarily goes on taking place until all the ratios at ages $\leq \beta$ years become equal in the natural process of ageing. Once these ratios are all equal, the same ratio is reproduced at age 0, year after year. The ratios at ages other than 0 do not change; but are shifted to the older ages as the cohorts attain the respective older ages.

Thus a change in $d(t) = R(t) - r(t)$, in the case with no migration, must have to come through the dropping off of the ratio at age w as the oldest age cohort dies out. The value of $d(t)$ may not change for several years, i.e. until the cohorts having the ratios $R(t)$ and/or $r(t)$ die out. Due to the natural process of ageing and the ultimate death of the age cohorts, the population ratios at all ages become equal in the course of time after the same ratio is reproduced at age 0, year after year. When this happens $R(t) = r(t)$, and the age distribution of the population under study will be the same as the equilibrium-state age distribution and thus the initial form of the age distribution of the population under study will be changed and become the same as the equilibrium-state age distribution. Hence, it is said that the initial form of the age distribution of the population is "forgotten".

Following the argument here, we shall examine the effect of migration on the duration of convergence. As before, several possibilities are distinguished.

(a) Suppose $n(x) > 0$ for all x. If $n > 0$, it can be inferred from eqns (3.36) and (3.37), that the averaging effect occurs at all ages and involves all ratios from ages 0 to w. Also, it may be noted that there will actually be double averaging in this case—once at ages other than 0 and again at age 0. Thus, $R(t+1)$ is surely less than $R(t)$ and $r(t+1)$ surely greater than $r(t)$, unless $R(t) = r(t)$ when $R(t+1) = r(t+1) = R(t) = r(t)$. Hence $d(t)$ decreases every year and the duration of convergence is thus decreased as compared to the case with no migration. Therefore $t_0 < t_1$ in this case.

If $n = 0$, then there is no migration and therefore $t_0 = t_1$.

If $n < 0$ (i.e. there is emigration at all ages), the averaging effect must have to come through the zeroth age since the effect of emigration is only to cause reduction in the size of an age cohort. In fact, emigration has the same effect as additional mortality. Emigration in any age group cannot therefore exceed the size of that age group at any time as required by assumption (8). Hence, at least some of the coefficients in eqn (3.36) must remain positive as the zero age cohort advances over the age range. Thus the averaging effect continues to take place, but the number of ages involved in the process, or the weight attached to the age cohort under consideration, goes on reducing due to emigration. Therefore the process of convergence is delayed and $t_0 > t_1$. This argument is supported by the numerical illustrations given in Section 3.5.

So far, it is assumed that $n(x) > 0$ for all x. Now, we have to consider the case in which $n(x)$ is zero at some ages, i.e. $n(x) \geq 0$. If $n > 0$ in this situation, then the averaging effect obviously takes place only at those ages for which $n(x) > 0$. Also, if there is at least one age $\leq \beta$ years at which $n(x) > 0$, the double averaging effect at age 0, described above, occurs to some extent; otherwise the averaging effect occurs only once. Thus t_0 will be less than that in the case with no migration, but greater than that in the case with $n(x) > 0$ at all ages. On the other hand, if $n < 0$, t_0 will be greater than that in the case with no migration, but less than that in the case with $n(x) > 0$ at all ages since the deductions would not take place at the ages where $n(x) = 0$. If $n = 0$, there is no migration and $t_0 = t_1$ again.

(b) Suppose $n(x) \gtreqless 0$, then no definite conclusion follows regarding the relative value of t_0 as compared to t_1. It would depend on the relative magnitudes of the $n(x)$ values at the different ages. This is because if $n > 0$, for instance, there will be the averaging effect at ages where $n(x) > 0$, and that effect is reduced at ages where $n(x) < 0$. The net result of these counteracting effects will depend on the magnitude of the $n(x)$ values at the different ages and the value of n.

(c) Another question of importance is: How would t_0 change when n changes keeping $n(x)$ fixed? If $n > 0$, we may clearly infer from eqn (3.36) that the relative weight given to a particular age cohort under consideration as compared to the rest decreases with increasing n. This has the effect of making the averaging more effective and $d(t)$ tends to zero faster. Hence, as n increases, t_0 decreases. If $n < 0$, the deductions increase as the absolute value of n increases and, hence, t_0 increases.

3.3.4 A special case

So far, it is implicitly assumed that the initial age distribution is not a stable one with respect to the operating schedules of fertility and mortality. If it is, then the duration of convergence is zero in the absence of migration. But, when migration is introduced, the stable state is disturbed and it takes some time before the new equilibrium state is established. In this case, therefore, $t_0 > t_1$ whether there is net immigration or net emigration. The equilibrium-state age distribution will also be different from the stable one.

However, if the age composition of the net migrants is identical with the same stable age distribution, then the duration is zero and the equilibrium-state age distribution will also be the same.

If only the age composition of the net migrants is identical with the stable age distribution but the initial age distribution is not, then the duration changes as in the general case but the equilibrium-state age distribution will be identical with the stable one.

3.3.5 Effects of using age-specific net migration rates

Before closing this discussion, we shall briefly refer to the effects of migration when the age-specific net migration rates are used. Though Lopez indicated that the convergence to an equilibrium state takes place in this case, no detailed analysis seems to have yet been presented regarding the effects of migration on the duration of convergence and on the intrinsic growth rate. Following the procedure adopted in the case with no migration, we can show that, when the age-specific net migration rates are defined as in Section 1.8, the population growth depends on a matrix M' which is obtained by substituting $(S(b) + u')$ and $(S(x) + a'(x))$ respectively for $S(b)$ and $S(x)$ in the matrix M. Hence, as long as u' and $a'(x)$ are either positive or are less than $S(b)$ and $S(x)$ respectively, the whole theory of stable populations becomes applicable in this case also. Since the power to which M' is to be raised to obtain a positive matrix, is the same as that required for M, and the averaging effect does not also occur at the older ages, the duration of convergence would remain approximately the same as in the absence of migration whether there is immigration or emigration, or both. But the effects of migration on the intrinsic growth rate would be in the same direction as discussed earlier in this section. If we assume that the Pearson Type III curve could be used to approximate the modified net maternity function

$$F'(x) = [(S(b) + u')(S(0) + a'(0)) \ldots (S(x-1)$$
$$+ a'(x-1))]f(x) \tag{3.38}$$

the duration of convergence as well as the intrinsic growth rate can be calculated from the total density, R_0, the mean and the coefficient of variation of the modified net maternity function. However, if the age-specific net migration rates are the same at all ages, the duration of convergence and the age distribution of the equilibrium state population would be the same as in the absence of migration because the age-sex composition of net migrants would be changing in the same manner as the transient age distribution of the population, but the intrinsic growth rate changes to the extent of the common rate of net migration (Pollard, 1966). If the initial age distribution is identical with the stable one, then it is not affected by the occurrence of migration at an equal rate at all ages. Hence, in this case, the duration of convergence is reduced to zero, but the intrinsic growth rate changes to the extent of the common net migration rate.

3.4 The two-sex case

So far, we have assumed that the population consisted of only one-sex— either males or females. Now, the results are extended to the case where the population has both males and females. First, we shall discuss the female dominance case and then examine briefly the case with equal dominance. If male dominance is assumed, the same conclusions as those in the case of the female dominance, would follow with the terms "female" and "male" suitably interchanged.

3.4.1 Female dominance with no migration

Using the subscripts m and f to distinguish the male and the female populations and assuming $f_f(x)$ to be the age-specific birth rate for females aged x years, taking births of both sexes and s to be the male proportion at birth, the growth eqns (3.2) and (3.3) can be written as follows in the case where there is no migration:

$$P_f(0, t) = (1 - s)S_f(b) \sum_{\alpha}^{\beta} \tfrac{1}{2}[P_f(x, t - 1) + S_f(x - 1)P_f(x - 1, t - 1)]f_f(x)$$

$$P_f(x, t) = S_f(x - 1)P_f(x - 1, t - 1), \quad \text{for} \quad x = 1, 2, \ldots, w$$

$$P_m(0, t) = s\, S_m(b) \sum_{\alpha}^{\beta} \tfrac{1}{2}[P_f(x, t - 1) + S_f(x - 1)P_f(x - 1, t - 1)]f_f(x)$$

and

$$P_m(x, t) = S_m(x - 1)P_m(x - 1, t - 1), \quad \text{for} \quad x = 1, 2, \ldots, w. \quad (3.39)$$

If the population vector has, now, females by age as the first $(w + 1)$

elements and the males by age as the next $(w + 1)$ elements, the growth equations could be written as the matrix equation:

$$(P_t) = L'(P_{t-1}) \tag{3.40}$$

where the matrix L' is as shown on p. 77.

Thus, in this case, the intrinsic growth rate and the duration of the convergence are determined by the characteristic roots of the matrix L'.

This matrix can be partitioned into four parts by dividing at the $(w + 1)$th row and at the $(w + 1)$th column as shown on p. 77. Hence, following the argument in Section 3.2, it could be inferred that, at any time, the changes in the male population will not have any effect on the female population at any age. Further, it can easily be shown that in $(w + 1)$ years, the male populations at all ages and the female populations at ages beyond β years, become linear functions of the female populations at ages below β years. Thus the intrinsic growth rate and the duration of convergence, in this case, would be the same as for the female population at ages below β years provided that the duration of convergence is greater than $(w + 1)$ years. Hence they depend on the characteristic roots of the matrix M, and could be calculated from the matrix roots or from the approximate formulas (3.15) and (3.15a). If, however, the initial age–sex distribution is the same as the stable age–sex distribution resulting from the given fertility and mortality conditions, then the duration of convergence is zero.

3.4.2 Female dominance with migration

In this case, the growth equations can easily be written by referring to the one-sex model and the case with no migration discussed in Section 3.4.1. The population projection matrix now becomes the matrix L'_M on p. 78 where

$$u_f = (1 - s)S_f(b) \sum_\alpha^\beta \tfrac{1}{2}[a_f(x - 1)f_f(x)] + n(1 - s') \left[\frac{1 + S_f(0)}{4}\right] n_f(0),$$

s' being the male proportion among the net migrants;

$$u_m = sS_m(b) \sum_\alpha^\beta \tfrac{1}{2}[a_f(x - 1)f_f(x)] + ns' \left[\frac{1 + S_m(0)}{4}\right] n_m(0);$$

$$a_f(x) = \tfrac{1}{4}[(1 + S_f(x))n_f(x) + (1 + S_f(x + 1))n_f(x + 1)] n (1 - s');$$

and

$$a_m(x) = \tfrac{1}{4}[(1 + S_m(x))n_m(x) + (1 + S_m(x + 1))n_m(x + 1)]ns'.$$

Since, in this case also, the male populations at all ages become linear functions of the female populations at ages below β years in $(w + 1)$ years,

$$
L' =
\begin{bmatrix}
0 & 0 & \cdots & 0 & m_f(\alpha) & \cdot & m_f(\beta) & 0 & \cdots & 0 & 0 & 0 & \cdots & 0 \\
S_f(0) & 0 & \cdots & 0 & 0 & \cdot & 0 & 0 & \cdots & 0 & 0 & 0 & \cdots & 0 \\
0 & S_f(1) & \cdots & 0 & 0 & \cdot & 0 & 0 & \cdots & 0 & 0 & 0 & \cdots & 0 \\
\cdot & \cdot & \cdot & \cdot & \cdot & \cdot & \cdot & \cdot & \cdot & \cdot & \cdot & \cdot & \cdot & \cdot \\
0 & 0 & \cdots & S_f(w-1) & 0 & \cdot & 0 & 0 & \cdots & 0 & 0 & 0 & \cdots & 0 \\
0 & 0 & \cdots & 0 & m'_f(\alpha) & \cdot & m'_f(\beta) & 0 & \cdots & 0 & 0 & 0 & \cdots & 0 \\
0 & 0 & \cdots & 0 & 0 & \cdot & 0 & S_m(0) & \cdots & 0 & 0 & 0 & \cdots & 0 \\
0 & 0 & \cdots & 0 & 0 & \cdot & 0 & 0 & S_m(1) & \cdots & 0 & 0 & \cdots & 0 \\
\cdot & \cdot & \cdot & \cdot & \cdot & \cdot & \cdot & \cdot & \cdot & \cdot & \cdot & \cdot & \cdot & \cdot \\
0 & 0 & \cdots & 0 & 0 & \cdot & 0 & 0 & \cdots & 0 & 0 & 0 & \cdots & S_m(w-1)
\end{bmatrix}
$$

in which $m_f(x) = \dfrac{1-s}{2}[f_f(x) + S_f(x)f_f(x+1)]S_f(b)$

and $m'_f(x) = \dfrac{s}{2}[f_f(x) + S_f(x)f_f(x+1)]S_m(b)$.

$$
L'_M=\begin{bmatrix}
\substack{u_f\\[2pt] [S_f(0)+a_f(0)]} & \cdot & \substack{[m_f(\alpha)+u_f]\\[2pt] a_f(0)} & \cdot & \substack{[m_f(\beta)+u_f]\\[2pt] a_f(0)} & \cdot & \substack{u_f\\[2pt] a_f(0)} & \substack{u_f\\[2pt] a_f(0)} & \substack{u_f\\[2pt] a_f(0)} & \substack{u_f\\[2pt] a_f(0)} & \substack{u_f\\[2pt] a_f(0)} \\[10pt]
a_f(w-1) & \cdot & a_f(w-1) & \cdot & a_f(w-1) & \cdot & \substack{[S_f(w-1)\\[2pt] +a_f(w-1)]} & a_f(w-1) & a_f(w-1) & a_f(w-1) & a_f(w-1) \\[10pt]
\substack{u_m\\[2pt] a_m(0)} & \cdot & \substack{[m'_f(\alpha)+u_m]\\[2pt] a_m(0)} & \cdot & \substack{[m'_f(\beta)+u_m]\\[2pt] a_m(0)} & \cdot & \substack{u_m\\[2pt] a_m(0)} & \substack{u_m\\[2pt] a_m(0)} & [S_m(0)+a_m(0)] & \substack{u_m\\[2pt] a_m(0)} & \substack{u_m\\[2pt] a_m(0)} \\[10pt]
\cdot & & \cdot & & \cdot & & \cdot & & \cdot & & \cdot \\[10pt]
a_m(w-1) & \cdot & a_m(w-1) & \cdot & a_m(w-1) & \cdot & a_m(w-1) & a_m(w-1) & a_m(w-1) & \substack{[S_m(w-1)\\[2pt] +a_m(w-1)]} & a_m(w-1)
\end{bmatrix}
$$

migration, if it affects only the male population, will not have any effect
on the duration of convergence or on the intrinsic growth rate, provided
the duration is greater than $(w + 1)$ years. But the age–sex distribution of
the equilibrium state population changes due to the effect of migration on
the male population as compared to the results in the absence of migration.
However, if the initial age–sex distribution is the stable one, then the
occurrence of migration into the male population affects the duration of
convergence to the extent of $(w + 1)$ years, which is the time required for
the male populations at all ages to become functions of the female populations at ages below β years. The age–sex distribution of the equilibrium
state population is also changed, though the intrinsic growth rate itself is
not changed. When migration affects the female population, the effects
would be as discussed in the case of the one-sex model (see Section 3.3.2).

If the age–sex-specific net migration rates are used, the duration of
convergence and the intrinsic growth rate depend on the characteristic
roots of the matrix M' and could be calculated from the matrix roots or
from the approximate formulae (3.15) and (3.15a). The other results could
easily be inferred from those discussed under the one-sex model.

3.4.3 Equal dominance of the sexes

Before closing this analytical discussion, we shall refer briefly to the case
where both the sexes are taken into consideration for calculating the
number of births. Among the earlier authors who attempted this, A. H.
Pollard (1948), related the female births to males and the male births to
females, while Goodman (1967) assumed female dominance in a portion
δ of the year and male dominance in the remaining part $(1 - \delta)$ of the
year. Yntema (1952, Chap. 3), proposed the use of age–sex specific birth
rates instead of age-specific ones, by relating births to a combination of
the male and the female populations at each age in the reproductive ages.

We argue in a manner similar to that of A. H. Pollard and state that
each birth (male or female) will have a mother of certain age i and a father
of certain age j. Thus the same event could be related once with the mother
and again with the father. Hence if we calculate the number of births
during a year using the birth rates for males as well as for females we must
get two times the number of births that would actually occur. Hence half
of the total number of births obtained by using male and female age-
specific birth rates, must be a better estimate of the number of births
during the year. This procedure is called here, the equal dominance method
because males and females are given equal weight in obtaining the births.

Although the procedure seems to suffer from the defect that it gives
some births even when persons of only one sex exist in the population, this
artificial situation cannot result if the initial population contains members

of both sexes. This is because the population of each sex at each age becomes in course of time, a function not only of the population of the same sex but also that of the other, unless the sex ratio at birth is abnormal so that births of only one sex occur always.

If we use the equal dominance method the growth equations change only in respect of the population at age 0 years for males and females. These equations can now be written as:

$$P_f(0, t) = (1 - s)S_f(b)B(t)$$

and

$$P_m(0, t) = sS_m(b)B(t) \tag{3.24}$$

with

$$B(t) = \sum_{\alpha'}^{\beta'} \tfrac{1}{2}[\tfrac{1}{2}\{P_f(x, t - 1) + S_f(x - 1)P_f(x - 1, t - 1)\}f_f(x)$$
$$+ \tfrac{1}{2}\{P_m(x, t - 1) + S_m(x - 1)P_m(x - 1, t - 1)\}f_m(x)]$$

where α' and β' are the youngest and the oldest ages at which births occur among males and/or females and $f_m(x)$ is the birth rate for males aged x years.

Accordingly, the elements of the first row and the $(w + 2)$th row of the projection matrix L', change and they can now be written as follows:

First row:

$$0 \; . \; 0 \; m_f(\alpha') \; . \; m_f(\beta') \; 0 \; . \; 0 \; 0 \; 0 \; . \; 0 \; m_m(\alpha') \; . \; m_m(\beta') \; 0 \; . \; 0 \; 0$$

and the $(w + 2)$th row:

$$0 \; . \; 0 \; m_f'(\alpha') \; . \; m_f'(\beta') \; 0 \; . \; 0 \; 0 \; 0 \; . \; 0 \; m_m'(\alpha') \; . \; m_m'(\beta') \; 0 \; . \; 0 \; 0$$

where

$$m_f(x) \text{ and } m_f'(x) \text{ are half of those in } L',$$

and

$$m_m(x) = \tfrac{1}{2}(1 - s)S_f(b)[\tfrac{1}{2}\{f_m(x) + S_m(x)f_m(x + 1)\}]$$

$$m_m'(x) = \tfrac{1}{2}sS_m(b)[\tfrac{1}{2}\{f_m(x) + S_m(x)f_m(x + 1)\}].$$

The other elements of the matrix remain the same as in L'. Let us denote this matrix as L''.

The matrix L'' can be partitioned at $(\beta' + 1)$th, $(w + 1)$th and $(w + 1 + \beta' + 1)$th rows and columns and be written as follows:

$$L'' = \begin{bmatrix} Q & 0 & R & 0 \\ A & B & 0 & 0 \\ Q_1 & 0 & R_1 & 0 \\ 0 & 0 & A_1 & B_1 \end{bmatrix}.$$

It may be shown by matrix multiplication that the first row and the third row of any power of this matrix would be independent of the elements in the second and fourth rows. Thus, as in the case of the one-sex model, we can conclude that the changes in the population above β' years either among males or among females will not have any effect on the populations below that age. But the populations at ages above β' years become, in the course of time, the survivors of the populations below the age β' years. Hence the convergence in this case, depends on the matrix

$$\begin{bmatrix} Q & R \\ Q_1 & R_1 \end{bmatrix}$$

which is the projection matrix if we consider the female and the male populations up to the age β' years only. Since the fertility rate for males at age β' years can be assumed to be positive (because the oldest age at which reproduction occurs is generally higher in the case of males than in the case of females), the above matrix is a non-negative square matrix which will be power positive. It will have, therefore, a unique positive dominant characteristic root and an associated characteristic vector of positive elements. Thus, we conclude that the convergence to the equilibrium state age–sex distribution occurs in this case. The duration of convergence and the intrinsic growth rate may be obtained from the dominant characteristic roots of the above matrix. Alternatively, these may be computed from the combined net maternity function using formulas (3.15) and (3.15a), if we assume that the Pearson Type III curve will be a good fit in this case also.

If migration is introduced into the process, the values of u_f and u_m change as follows:

$$u_f = \frac{(1-s)}{2} S_f(b) \sum_{\alpha'}^{\beta'} \tfrac{1}{2}[a_f(x-1)f_f(x) + a_m(x-1)f_m(x)]$$
$$+ n(1-s') \left(\frac{1 + S_f(0)}{4}\right) n_f(0)$$

and

$$u_m = \frac{s}{2} S_m(b) \sum_{\alpha'}^{\beta'} \tfrac{1}{2}[a_f(x - 1)f_f(x) + a_m(x - 1)f_m(x)]$$

$$+ n s' \left(\frac{1 + S_m(0)}{4}\right) n_m(0).$$

The elements of the matrix L'_M can be written down easily by adding the migration coefficients: u_f, u_m, $a_f(x)$ and $a_m(x)$, to the respective elements of the matrix L'' as in the case of female dominance. It may be observed that the structure of the matrix L'_M remains the same as in the case of female dominance. Therefore, similar conclusions follow with the exception that duration as well as the intrinsic growth rate would change when migration affects the male or the female population at ages below β' years, where the corresponding fertility rates are not zero. These may be obtained from the first two dominant characteristic roots of the new matrix.

In this case also, the effects of migration when the age–sex-specific net migration rates are used, may easily be inferred.

3.5 Numerical illustrations

For purposes of illustration of the analytical conclusions, the three initial populations—1911 obs., 1911 stb., and 1966 obs. (see Chapter 2)—were projected successively under the same constant conditions of fertility, mortality and migration. At each age x years, a growth index was computed as the ratio of the population at age x at time t to the population at the same age at time $(t - 1)$. These growth indexes were then compared among themselves and the maximum (MaxGI) and the minimum (MinGI) growth indexes were recorded for each of the three populations at every five year interval of time. When the difference between the MaxGI and the MinGI became less than 0.00009, the process was terminated and each of the age–sex distributions was taken to have reached the equilibrium state. The limit of 0.00009 was arbitrarily chosen. It was observed that the other indicators such as the ADI and the SRDI between the percentages and the sex ratios in five year age groups at time t and those in the same age groups at time $(t - 1)$, reduced to zero long before the difference between MaxGI and MinGI became less than the specified limit. An advantage in computing the MaxGI and MinGI is that the graphs of MaxGI and MinGI over time would not only show the nature of the process of convergence but also the magnitude of the intrinsic growth rate resulting from the given fertility, mortality and migration conditions.

The value of t, thus obtained, was used to verify the conclusions arrived at by employing the matrix method or the approximate formulas resulting from it. It must, however, be mentioned here that the value of t obtained by the direct projection method is conditioned by the nature of the initial age–sex distribution while the value of t computed from the matrix roots or from formula (3.15) is not. This fact should be borne in mind in studying the illustrations presented here.

(i) *Effect of migration on the duration of convergence*

Table 3.1 compares the results obtained under the different assumed conditions. The four situations of migration were purposely selected for reasons detailed in Section 2.3.3 (p. 45). The following points may be observed from the table. Except when the initial age–sex structure was the stable one, the values of t obtained from the matrix roots were fairly close to those observed in the actual projections with the same order of approximation. The approximate formula (3.15) gave quite satisfactory results as far as the estimation of the intrinsic growth rate was concerned. But it yielded somewhat higher values of t both when no migration was assumed and when the age–sex-specific net migration rates were used. That formula is not directly applicable in the other case. It appears that the time limit given by formula (3.15) may be taken as a safe value of t for any arbitrary age–sex distribution.

When the age–sex composition of net migrants contained positive values at all ages, there was a definite decrease in the value of t as could be seen in the cases when the 1911 vital rates and the 1911–12 migration condition or the 1966 vital rates and the 1965–66 migration condition were assumed. When the same migration situations were specified by age–sex-specific net migration rates, the duration increased in the first case and remained the same in the second case as compared to the case with no migration. The migration situation of the war years 1915–16 was shown to be incompatible with the vital rates situation in 1911, when migration was specified by the net migration rate and age–sex composition of net migrants. When the same situation was specified by the age–sex-specific net migration rates, the duration turned out to be the same as that in the absence of migration. But the resultant age–sex distribution became abnormal compared with that in the absence of migration (see Chapter 4). In 1945–46, both the male and the female populations experienced emigration at almost all ages. In this case the duration increased, as expected, when migration was specified by the net migration rate and the age–sex composition of net migrants. On the other hand, the duration remained almost the same when the situation was specified by age–sex-specific net migration rates.

Table 3.1 Effect of migration on the duration of convergence of age–sex distributions to an equilibrium state age–sex distribution

| | Prevailing conditions | | | From actual projections — Value of t (in No. of years) | | | From matrix roots | | | From the moments of the net maternity function | | | | |
	Mortality (1)	Fertility (2)	Migration (3)	1911 obs. (4)	1911 stb. (5)	1966 obs. (6)	λ_1 (7)	λ_2 (8)	Value of t (in No. of Years) with $\varepsilon = 0.00009$ (9)	R_0 (10)	μ (11)	σ^2 (12)	Value of t (in No. of Years) with $\varepsilon = 0.00009$ (13)	Estimate of λ_1 (14)
							No migration							
1	1911	1911	0	245	95	240	1.01219	0.95804 ±0.19791i	274	1.43783	30.28	42.21	308	1.01217
2	1966	1966	0	235	215	245	1.01159	0.94914 ±0.22559i	258	1.36608	27.31	33.13	289	1.01154
						Migration specified by a net migration rate and an age–sex composition of net migrants								
3	1911	1911	1911–12	170	145	175	1.03044	0.95756 ±0.19801i	178					
4	1911	1911	1915–16	x	x	x	1.01292	0.95798 ±0.19797i	x					
5	1911	1911	1945–46	260	190	255	1.01002	0.95808 ±0.19789i	292					
6	1966	1966	1965–66	195	175	195	1.02180	0.94912 ±0.22561i	202					
						Migration specified by age–sex-specific net migration rates								
7	1911	1911	1911–12	245	195	255	1.02723	0.97324 ±0.19995i	280	2.26943	31.04	42.84	320	1.02727
8	1911	1911	1915–16	245	160	240	1.01347	0.95907 ±0.19879i	273	1.49359	30.27	42.03	308	1.01346
9	1911	1911	1945–46	245	175	240	1.00997	0.95579 ±0.19741i	273	1.34640	30.18	42.22	306	1.00995
10	1966	1966	1965–66	235	215	245	1.02213	0.95940 ±0.22683i	258	1.82187	27.75	34.32	288	1.02214

Note: 1. The figures in columns (1), (2), (3) are the calendar years to which the mortality and fertility rates, and the migration data relate. The respective data were those observed in Australia.

2. x denotes that the situation was not compatible. Percentages in some age groups of the equilibrium state population became negative.

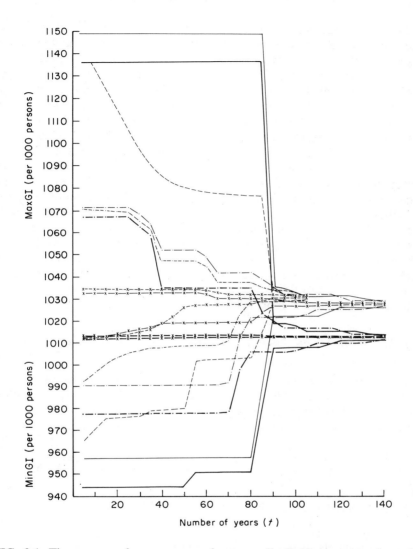

FIG. 3.1. The process of convergence of age–sex distributions as seen from the convergenc of MaxGI and MinGI for females under constant schedules of fertility, mortality and migration, when migration is specified in two different ways. Mortality: As in 1911. Fertility: As in 1911. Migration: (i) No migration: ———— 1911 obs. pop.; ×–×–×–×–×–× 1911 stb. pop.; ——— 1966 obs. pop. (ii) Net migration rate and age–sex composition of net migrants as observed in Australia, 1911–12: ——————— 1911 obs. pop.; ×–×–×–×–×–× 1911 stb. pop.; --------- 1966 obs. pop. (iii) Age–sex-specific net migration rates as observed in Australia, 1911–12: ——————— 1911 obs. pop.; ×–×–×–×–×–× 1911 stb. pop.; ——— 1966 obs. pop.

Figure 3.1 depicts the nature of the process of convergence as seen from the convergence of the MaxGI and MinGI when the fertility and mortality rates for 1911 and net migration conditions of 1911–12 were assumed. It shows a clear similarity in the processes when there was no migration and when migration was specified by age–sex-specific net migration rates. For the 1911 stb. population the difference between MaxGI and MinGI should have been negligible from the beginning when there was no migration. But since a slightly different sex ratio at birth (105.22 males per 100 females) was used in the computation of the 1911 stb. age–sex structure than the one (105 males per 100 females) used in the actual projections, a small difference is found to exist and this continues for one lifetime, i.e. 86 years. The figure also indicates that the large differences in the initial age–sex distributions reduced as soon as the cohorts alive at the initial point of time died out; but the smaller variations induced by the initial differences took a long time to disappear. When the migration was specified by the net migration rate and an age–sex composition of the net migrants, the differences started getting reduced even in the lifetime of the cohorts alive at the initial point of time, and the convergence was accelerated. Thus the numerical examples support our analytical conclusions.

(ii) *Changes in the duration of convergence due to the changes in the net migration rate*

A comparison of the values of t when migration observed during 1911–12 and 1965–66, were assumed to operate, suggested that the duration increased with the decrease in the value of the net immigration rate. But during these two years the age–sex composition of net migrants was also

Table 3.2 Changes in the duration of convergence of age–sex distributions to an equilibrium state age–sex distribution due to the changes in the net migration rate

Prevailing conditions Mortality—1911 Fertility—1911 Net migrants age–sex Composition—1962–66 Net migration rate: (per cent)	Value of t (in no. of years) from actual projections		
	1911 obs.	1911 stb.	1966 obs.
−1.0	365	280	360
0.0	245	95	240
0.5	210	145	210
1.0	185	145	195
5.0	110	100	115

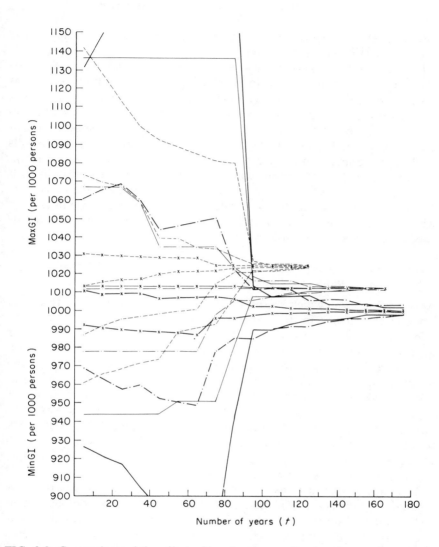

FIG. 3.2. Comparison of the effect of immigration and emigration on the process of convergence of age–sex distributions as seen from the convergence of MaxGI and MinGI for females under constant schedules of fertility, mortality and migration. Mortality: As in 1911. Fertility: As in 1911. Migration: (i) No migration: —·—·— 1911 obs. pop.; ×-×-×-×-×-×- 1911 stb. pop.; ———— 1966 obs. pop. (ii) One per cent immigration with age and sex composition of net migrants in Australia 1962–66: —·······—1911 obs. pop.; ×-×-×-×-×-×- 1911 stb. pop.; – – – – – – 1966 obs. pop. (iii) One per cent emigration with age and sex composition of net migrants in Australia 1962–66: —·—·— 1911 obs. pop.; ×-×-×-×-×-×- 1911 stb. pop.; ———— 1966 obs. pop.

different. Hence, the increase could not be attributed specifically to the decrease in the net migration rate.

To examine this aspect, the age–sex composition of net migrants during 1962–66, which contained positive values at all ages for both sexes, was assumed to remain the same and different hypothetical net migration rates were used with it. It may, however, be noted that it is the values of u and $a(x)$ derived from the net migration rate and the age–sex composition that are important in the study of the process of population growth. The results of these experiments are given in Table 3.2. It shows that the net immigration reduced the duration, while net emigration increased it. Also it can be seen that the duration decreased with the increase in the magnitude of the net migration rate. Figure 3.2 describes the processes of convergence when net immigration, net emigration and no migration were assumed. It supports the above conclusions.

(iii) *Changes in the duration of convergence due to the changes in the age–sex composition of net migrants*

Another question which arises from the above experimental results is whether the change in the age–sex composition of net migrants has any effect on the duration of the process of convergence. For studying this question, a net migration rate of 1 per cent was kept constant and several hypothetical age–sex compositions of net migrants were tried and the results are presented in Table 3.3. Again the conclusion that net immigration reduces the duration if it affected some ages below β years, is well supported. But the table indicates that the changes in the age–sex compositions had only a small effect on the duration unless they were such that the structure of the projection matrix changed, as it happened when the age–sex composition had special features such as no female migrants at all ages or at ages below β years, and so on.

The larger value of t observed when the 1925 age–sex distribution was assumed, needs some explanation. Though the age–sex composition in 1925 contained positive values at all ages for females, the proportions at about fifteen ages in the old age range, i.e. above 60 years, were negative for males. Therefore the projection matrix was not really a positive matrix as it was when the other (for example, the 1962–66 or the 1911 stb. population, etc.) age–sex compositions were assumed. Hence the duration increased in this case as compared with the other cases.

(iv) *Duration of convergence under equal dominance*

The duration of convergence and the intrinsic growth rate change, in this case, to the extent that the fertility and mortality rates and the effect of

Table 3.3 Changes in the duration of convergence of age–sex distributions to an equilibrium state age–sex distribution due to the changes in the age–sex composition of net migrants

Prevailing conditions Mortality—1911 Fertility—1911 Net migration rate—1 per cent Age–sex composition of net migrants:	Value of t (in no. of years) from actual projections		
	1911 obs.	1911 stb.	1966 obs.
1 Same as in 1962–66	185	145	195
2 Same as in 1925	205	165	205
3 Same as 1911 stb. population	185	95	190
4 Same as 1966 obs. population	190	115	190
5 Same as 1911 life table population	195	130	190
6 Same as 1911 life table population with no female migrants	245	165 (95 females only)	240
7 Same as 1911 life table populations with no male migrants	200	160	195
8 1962–66, with no female migrants below the age 49 years	225	160	225
9 1962–66, with female migrants only at age 0 years below the age 49 years	225	185	210

Note: A comparison of these age compositions of net migrants and the sex compositions associated with them is given in Chapter 2.

migration are different for males from those for females. Table 3.4 shows that the duration decreased under equal dominance both when there was no migration and when there was migration. In the case of no migration, it was perhaps the slight increase in the value of the coefficient of variation of the combined net maternity function as compared to that of the net maternity function for females, that made the duration decrease. While in the case where migration was included, the decrease was caused by the greater impact of immigration on the male population than on the female population. However, this observation need not be true in general. The duration, obviously, depends on the characteristics of the combined net maternity function and the effect of migration on both the male and the female populations.

3.6 Summary

The process of convergence of arbitrary age–sex distributions to an equilibrium state age–sex distribution has been investigated in this chapter. In the case with no migration, a relatively simple formula is obtained to

Table 3.4 Duration of convergence of age–sex distributions to an equilibrium state age–sex distribution when equal dominance is assumed

Prevailing conditions			From actual projections value of t			From matrix roots		
Mortality (1)	Fertility (2)	Migration (3)	1911 obs. (4)	1911 stb. (5)	1966 obs. (6)	λ_1 (7)	λ_2 (8)	Value of t (in no. of years) (9)
			No migration					
1911	1911	0	235	180	225	1.01135	0.95742 ±0.18817i	260
			Migration specified by a net rate and age–sex composition of net migrants					
1911	1911	1911–12	155	155	165	1.03504	0.95661 ±0.18848i	156

Note: See note (1) to Table 3.1.

calculate the time required for the convergence (i.e. the duration of convergence) in terms of the characteristics of the net maternity function.

It is shown that the convergence also occurs when migration is included into the process of population change using an overall net migration rate and an age–sex composition of net migrants. The duration of convergence is reduced when the migration schedule is such that the intrinsic growth rate is increased, as compared to the case with no migration. The opposite result holds good if the migration schedule is such that the intrinsic growth rate is decreased. But no definite conclusion follows if the migration schedule is such that the intrinsic growth rate remains the same as in the absence of migration. The duration of convergence and the intrinsic growth rate can be computed from the first two dominant roots of the projection matrix.

Further, it is observed that, for a given age–sex composition of net migrants containing positive values at all ages, the duration of convergence decreases as the net migration rate increases. On the other hand, for a given net migration rate, the changes in the age–sex composition of the net migrants produce only small changes in the duration of convergence unless the changes are such that the structure of the projection matrix is changed.

Alternatively, if age–sex-specific net migration rates are used in the process of population change, the duration of convergence remains approximately the same as in the absence of migration, though the intrinsic growth rate follows a similar trend as in the case where a net migration rate and an age–sex composition of net migrants are utilized.

4

GROWTH AND AGE STRUCTURE OF EQUILIBRIUM-STATE POPULATION

4.1 Introduction

In the previous chapter, the main concern has been to see whether or not the equilibrium-state population results, and how the duration of convergence is affected, when migration is introduced into the process of population change. However, the relationship between population change—the changes in the growth rate and age–sex composition—and the components of change—fertility, mortality and migration—has not been investigated. This relationship is examined in this chapter.

It has been shown in Chapter 3 that when a set of single schedules of fertility, mortality and migration operates constantly over time, a constant growth rate and an unchanging age–sex distribution (i.e. equilibrium-state age–sex distribution) are evolved. If these results are obtained from the dominant characteristic root and the associated characteristic vector of the population projection matrix, the relationships between these factors and the given schedules are not explicitly shown. Hence, by using an elementary approach which avoids the use of matrix algebra, we shall derive formulas (in Section 4.2) that would reveal clearly the nature of this relationship. Numerical examples are presented to illustrate the formulas and to study the changes in these characteristics of the equilibrium-state population in relation to the changes in the operating schedules of fertility, mortality, and migration.

Namboodiri (1969b) has shown that, when a sequence of k schedules of fertility and mortality operates repeatedly over time on a closed population, a stable set of k growth rates and age–sex distributions is evolved. He has named this set as the "cyclical" model of population change, and has examined the relationship of this set with the operating conditions. In this chapter (in Section 4.3), the procedure adopted by Namboodiri is slightly modified to facilitate the inclusion of migration, and the population change resulting from the repeated operation of a sequence of k schedules of fertility, mortality and migration is studied. The set of growth rates and age–sex distributions which results when migration is introduced as one of the components in the process of population change, is called here the equilibrium-state cycle to distinguish it from the "cyclical" model obtained in the absence of migration. The model seems to be useful in investigating the implications of the operation of certain observed or assumed conditions and also in obtaining the growth rate and the age–sex distribution of the equilibrium-state population by iteration.

4.2 Equilibrium-state population of one sex

An equilibrium-state population, as defined in this study, possesses a constant growth rate and an unchanging age–sex distribution. This property is used here as the basis for deriving the required relationships. Following the practice in the previous chapters, we shall deal with the one-sex model first and then extend the results to the two-sex case.

4.2.1 The stable population (i.e. the case with no migration)

When there is no migration, the equilibrium-state population is the same as the stable population which is already well known in the literature. Its age composition could be computed from the following formulas derived by Goodman (1968):

$$\left[P(x, t)/\sum_0^w P(x, t) \right] = [s(x)/\lambda^x]/\left[\sum_0^w (s(x)/\lambda^x) \right] \tag{4.1}$$

where

$$s(x) = 1, \text{ if } x = 0,$$

and

$$= S(0)S(1) \ldots S(x-1), \text{ if } x > 0 \tag{4.2}$$

and λ is obtained from the equation:

$$\lambda^{\beta+1} - \sum_\alpha^\beta m(x)s(x)\lambda^{\beta-x} = 0. \tag{4.3}$$

It may be noticed that eqn (4.3) is the same as the characteristic equation of the matrix M (see Section 3.2). This equation has only one real positive root since there is only one change of sign in the coefficients (Burnside and Panton, 1960). Hence, either by using matrix algebra or by solving eqn (4.3) by any other iterative methods, we can obtain the unique positive root of this equation and thus obtain the age composition. Then r, the intrinsic growth rate of the stable population, may be calculated from the relation $\lambda = e^{rd}$ where d is the interval of the age groups. Usually, d is taken as equal to 1 or 5 years of age.

4.2.2 The equilibrium-state population (i.e. the case with migration)

In this case, the population growth is given by the set of equations:

$$P(0, t) = \sum_{\alpha}^{\beta} m(x) P(x, t - 1) + u \sum_{0}^{w} P(x, t - 1) \tag{4.4}$$

$$P(x, t) = S(x - 1) P(x - 1, t - 1) + a(x - 1) \sum_{0}^{w} P(x, t - 1),$$

$$\text{for } x = 1, 2, \ldots w \tag{4.5}$$

where $m(x)$, u and $a(x)$ are as defined in Sections 3.2 and 3.3.

Since we are interested in the equilibrium-state population, we have:

$$p(x) = \left[P(x, t)/\sum_{0}^{w} P(x, t) \right] = \left[P(x, t - 1)/\sum_{0}^{w} P(x, t - 1) \right]$$

$$\text{for } x = 0, 1, 2, \ldots, w \tag{4.6}$$

and

$$\left[\sum_{0}^{w} P(x, t) \right] \Big/ \left[\sum_{0}^{w} P(x, t - 1) \right] = \lambda, \text{ a constant independent of } t. \tag{4.7}$$

Now the problem is to find the values of $p(x)$ and λ in terms of the $S(x)$, $m(x)$, u and $a(x)$ which are known and are assumed to remain constant over time. From eqns (4.4), (4.6) and (4.7), the following equations can easily be derived:

$$[P(0, t)/P(0, t - 1)] = \left[\sum_{0}^{w} P(x, t - 1) \right] \Big/ \left[\sum_{0}^{w} P(x, t - 2) \right] = \lambda. \tag{4.8}$$

By successive application of eqn (4.8), we get:

$$[P(0, t)]/[P(0, t - x)] = \lambda^{x}. \tag{4.9}$$

Now substituting for $P(x - 1, t - 1)$ in eqn (4.5), we have:

$$P(x, t) = S(x - 1)S(x - 2)P(x - 2, t - 2)$$
$$+ S(x - 1)a(x - 2) \sum_0^w P(x, t - 2) + a(x - 1) \sum_0^w P(x, t - 1) \qquad (4.10)$$

and continuing in a similar manner, we obtain:

$$P(x, t) = s(x)P(0, t - x)$$
$$+ \sum_{\xi=0}^{x-1} a(\xi)S(\xi + 1) \ldots S(x - 1) \left[\sum_0^w P(x, t - x + \xi) \right]$$

for $x = 1, 2, \ldots, w$. $\qquad (4.11)$

Dividing both sides of eqn (4.11) by $P(0, t)$ and using the fact that $p(0)$ is constant over time, we have:

$$[P(x, t)/P(0, t)] = [s(x)/\lambda^x] + \frac{1}{p(0)} \left[\sum_{\xi=0}^{x-1} A(\xi, x)/\lambda^{x-\xi} \right] \qquad (4.12)$$

where $A(\xi,x) = a(\xi)S(\xi + 1)S(\xi + 2) \ldots S(x - 1)$, for $x = 1, 2, \ldots, w$. But $p(0)$ is unknown. To obtain $p(0)$, we use the definition of $p(0)$ and write:

$$[1/p(0)] = 1 + \sum_1^w \left[s(x)/\lambda^x + \frac{1}{p(0)} \sum_{\xi=0}^{x-1} A(\xi, x)/\lambda^{x-\xi} \right].$$

This yields the value of $p(0)$ as:

$$p(0) = \frac{1 - \sum_1^w \sum_{\xi=0}^{x-1} [A(\xi, x)/\lambda^{x-\xi}]}{1 + \sum_1^w [s(x)/\lambda^x]}. \qquad (4.13)$$

The proportions of populations at other ages can be calculated from the following relationship, which is easily established:

$$\left[P(x, t)/\sum_0^w P(x, t) \right] = [P(x, t)/P(0, t)]p(0). \qquad (4.14)$$

Now, if we know the value of λ, our problem is solved. The value of λ can be computed by matrix methods, since it is the dominant characteristic root of the population matrix L_M (see Section 3.3). However, we can obtain λ from eqn (4.4). On dividing both sides of that equation by $P(0, t)$, we get:

$$1 = \sum_{\alpha}^{\beta} m(x) \left[\frac{P(x, t-1)}{P(0, t-1)} \frac{P(0, t-1)}{P(0, t)} \right] + u \sum_{0}^{w} \left[\frac{P(x, t-1)}{P(0, t-1)} \frac{P(0, t-1)}{P(0, t)} \right]$$

which on substitution for the terms on the right-hand side, and simplification, gives the polynomial equation in λ:

$$\lambda^{\beta+1} - [u/p(0)]\lambda^{\beta}$$

$$- \sum_{\alpha}^{\beta} \left[m(x)s(x)\lambda^{\beta-x} + \{1/p(0)\} \sum_{\xi=0}^{x-1} m(x)A(\xi, x)\lambda^{\beta-x+\xi} \right] = 0. \quad (4.15)$$

The last term in eqn (4.15) is

$$- [s(\beta) + \{A(0, \beta)/p(0)\}]m(\beta),$$

which can be written as

$$- [\{S(1)S(2) \ldots S(\beta-1)\}/p(0)][S(0)p(0) + a(0)]m(\beta)$$

and will be negative under assumption (8) whether $a(0)$ is positive or negative. Thus eqn (4.15) has at least one positive real root. In particular cases, however, there may be more than one positive root. Then the positive root which has the largest value is taken as the value of λ.

Thus by solving eqn (4.15) we can obtain the value of λ. But in this equation $p(0)$ is also not known and it is dependent on λ. Hence we start with a trial value of λ, e.g. the value obtained without including migration plus the net migration rate, calculate $p(0)$ and estimate λ; and continue the process of iteration till values of λ and $p(0)$ become constant to the desired approximation. Alternatively, we may obtain the value of λ from the matrix methods and use it in computing the other values. In practice, it may be preferable to obtain λ from the matrix methods since the coefficients of the above polynomial change in every iteration and the calculation of λ from the polynomial itself involves an iteration procedure.

It may be noticed from eqn (4.15) that, if migration affects only ages beyond β years, the values of u, $A(\xi, x)$ in the equation become zero, and hence the equation becomes the same as eqn (4.3) and the value of λ would remain the same as in the case with no migration (see Section 3.3).

4.3 The two-sex model

The formulas for the two-sex case can be derived by a simple extension of the argument given for the one-sex case. In the two-sex model we note that the age–sex distribution is unchanging and the growth rates for the male and the female populations are the same. Hence we have to obtain in this case not only the age distributions of each sex, but also the sex composition in the age groups as well as in the total population. We shall first consider the two-sex model with female dominance and then discuss the case with equal dominance. The suffixes m and f are used to distinguish males and females.

4.3.1 Two-sex model with no migration

Goodman (1967) has discussed in detail the case when there is no migration and has obtained the following formulas:

$$[P_f(x, t)/P_f(0, t)] = [s_f(x)/\lambda^x], \text{ for } x = 1, 2, \ldots, w \qquad (4.16)$$

$$[P_m(0, t)/P_f(0, t)] = \text{SR}(0) = \sum_\alpha^\beta m_f'(x)s_f(x)/\lambda^{x+1} \qquad (4.17)$$

and

$$[P_m(x, t)/P_f(0, t)] = [s_m(x)/\lambda^x] \text{ SR}(0), \text{ for } x = 1, 2, \ldots, w \qquad (4.18)$$

where $m_f'(x) = (s/2)[f_f(x) + S_f(x)f_f(x + 1)]S_m(b)$ with s as the male proportion at birth and SR(0) the sex ratio in the age group 0 years. The sex ratios at other ages are obtained as follows:

$$\text{SR}(x) = \text{SR}(0)[s_m(x)/s_f(x)] \qquad (4.19)$$

and the sex ratio in the total population is shown to be:

$$\text{SR} = \text{SR}(0) \left[\sum_0^w s_m(x)/\lambda^x \right] \Big/ \left[\sum_0^w s_f(x)/\lambda^x \right]. \qquad (4.20)$$

From eqns (4.16) to (4.18), the age structures for males and females can easily be computed provided the value of λ is known. The value of λ can either be obtained as the dominant characteristic root of the projection matrix L', or by solving the following equation:

$$\lambda^{\beta+1} - \sum_\alpha^\beta m_f(x)s_f(x)\lambda^{\beta-x} = 0 \qquad (4.21)$$

where $m_f(x) = \frac{1}{2}(1 - s)[f_f(x) + S_f(x)f_f(x + 1)]S_f(b)$.

4.3.2 Two-sex model with migration

For convenience, let us write down the growth equations for this model:

$$P_f(0, t) = \sum_\alpha^\beta m_f(x)P_f(x, t - 1) + u_f \sum_0^w [P_f(x, t - 1) + P_m(x, t - 1)] \quad (4.22)$$

$$P_m(0, t) = \sum_\alpha^\beta m_f'(x)P_f(x, t - 1)$$

$$+ u_m \sum_0^w [P_f(x, t - 1) + P_m(x, t - 1)] \quad (4.23)$$

$$P_f(x, t) = S_f(x -)P_f(x - 1, t - 1)$$

$$+ a_f(x - 1) \sum_0^w [P_f(x, t - 1) + P_m(x, t - 1)] \quad (4.24)$$

and

$$P_m(x, t) = S_m(x - 1)P_m(x - 1, t - 1)$$

$$+ a_m(x - 1) \sum_0^w [P_f(x, t - 1) + P_m(x, t - 1)]$$

for $x = 1, 2, \ldots, w$. $\quad (4.25)$

Assuming that the population is an equilibrium-state population, it can be shown that:

$$\frac{P_f(0, t)}{P_f(0, t - 1)} = \frac{P_m(0, t)}{P_m(0, t - 1)} = \frac{\sum_0^w [P_f(x, t - 1) + P_m(x, t - 1)]}{\sum_0^w [P_f(x, t - 2) + P_m(x, t - 2)]} = \lambda. \quad (4.26)$$

By the repeated application of eqn (4.26), we obtain:

$$[P_f(0, t)/P_f(0, t - x)] = [P_m(0, t)/P_m(0, t - x)] = \lambda^x. \quad (4.27)$$

Proceeding as in the one-sex model, we get from eqn (4.24):

$$[P_f(x, t)/P_f(0, t)] = [s_f(x)/\lambda^x] + (1/f_p(0)) \sum_{\xi=0}^{x-1} [A_f(\xi, x)/\lambda^{x-\xi}]$$

for $x = 1, 2, \ldots, w$ $\quad (4.28)$

where $f_p(0)$ is the proportion of the female population at age 0 years to the total population of both sexes, and is constant over time for the equilibrium state population.

From equation (4.25) we can similarly obtain:

$$[P_m(x, t)/P_f(0, t)] = \text{SR}(0)[s_m(x)/\lambda^x] + \frac{1}{f_p(0)} \sum_{\xi=0}^{x-1} [A_m(\xi, x)/\lambda^{x-\xi}]$$

for $x = 1, 2, \ldots, w$. (4.29)

On dividing both sides of the eqn (4.23) by $P_f(0, t)$ we get:

$$(P_m(0, t)/P_f(0, t)] = \text{SR}(0) = \sum_{\alpha}^{\beta} \left[m_f'(x)s_f(x)/\lambda^{x+1} \right.$$

$$\left. + \frac{1}{f_p(0)} \sum_{\xi=0}^{x-1} m_f'(x)A_f(\xi, x)/\lambda^{x-\xi+1} \right] + \frac{1}{\lambda} \left(\frac{u_m}{f_p(0)} \right). \quad (4.30)$$

Equations (4.28), (4.29) and (4.30) give the population in all the age–sex groups in terms of the population in the first age group for females. From these we can easily compute the age distributions for males and females, the sex ratios in the age groups and the sex ratio in the total population, as we did in the case with no migration. It may be noted that the formulas given by Goodman (1967b) are particular cases of the above ones and could be derived by putting the migration coefficients equal to zero.

However, all these formulas are dependent on λ and $f_p(0)$ which are still unknown. We shall derive, now, expressions to compute these. To obtain $f_p(0)$ we use the relationship:

$$\sum_{0}^{w} [P_f(x, t) + P_m(x, t)] = P_f(0, t) \left[1 + \frac{P_m(0, t)}{P_f(0, t)} + \sum_{1}^{w} \left(\frac{P_f(x, t)}{P_f(0, t)} + \frac{P_m(x, t)}{P_f(0, t)} \right) \right].$$

Substituting the respective expressions for the terms in parenthesis on the right-hand side and simplifying, we get:

$$f_p(0) = \frac{1 - \left[\sum_{\alpha}^{\beta} \sum_{\xi=0}^{x-1} \frac{m_f'(x)A_f(\xi, x)}{\lambda^{x-\xi+1}} + \frac{u_m}{\lambda} \right] \left(1 + \sum_{1}^{w} \frac{s_m(x)}{\lambda^x} \right)}{\left[1 + \sum_{1}^{w} \frac{s_f(x)}{\lambda^x} \right] + \left[1 + \sum_{1}^{w} \frac{s_m(x)}{\lambda^x} \right] \left(\sum_{\alpha}^{\beta} \frac{m_f'(x)s_f(x)}{\lambda^{x+1}} \right)}.$$

$$\frac{- \sum_{1}^{w} \sum_{\xi=0}^{x-1} \left[\frac{A_f(\xi, x) + A_m(\xi, x)}{\lambda^{x-\xi}} \right]}{\left[1 + \sum_{1}^{w} \frac{s_f(x)}{\lambda^x} \right] + \left[1 + \sum_{1}^{w} \frac{s_m(x)}{\lambda^x} \right] \left(\sum_{\alpha}^{\beta} \frac{m_f'(x)s_f(x)}{\lambda^{x+1}} \right)}. \quad (4.31)$$

For calculating the value of λ, we obtain, using eqn (4.22), the polynomial equation:

$$\lambda^{\beta+1} - \left(\frac{u_f}{f_p(0)}\right)\lambda^\beta - \sum_\alpha^\beta \left[m_f(x)s_f(x)\lambda^{\beta-x}\right.$$

$$\left. + \frac{1}{f_p(0)}\sum_{\xi=0}^{x-1}m_f(x)A_f(\xi,x)\lambda^{\beta-x+\xi}\right] = 0. \tag{4.32}$$

As in the one-sex model, we can show that this equation has at least one positive root provided that $S_f(0)f_p(0) > a_f(0)$ whenever $a_f(0)$ is negative. Hence the values of λ and $f_p(0)$ can be iterated from eqns (4.31) and (4.32). Again, λ may preferably be obtained from the matrix roots. It can also be seen from eqn (4.32) that, if migration does not affect the female population at any of the ages below β years, it will not have any effect on the intrinsic growth rate.

4.3.3 Two-sex model with equal dominance

When equal dominance is assumed, the number of births changes and accordingly the equations for $SR(0)$, $f_p(0)$ and λ change. The new expressions for these can easily be derived by proceeding as in the case with female dominance.

When the migration is specified by a net migration rate and an age–sex composition of net migrants, the growth equations for the female and the male populations at age 0 years are as given below:

$$P_f(0,t) = \sum_{\alpha'}^{\beta'}\tfrac{1}{2}[m_f(x)P_f(x,t-1) + m_m(x)P_m(x,t-1)]$$

$$+ u_f\sum_0^w [P_f(x,t-1) - P_m(x,t-1)]$$

and

$$P_m(0,t) = \sum_{\alpha'}^{\beta'}\tfrac{1}{2}[m_f'(x)P_f(x,t-1) + m_m'(x)P_m(x,t-1)]$$

$$+ u_m\sum_0^w [P_f(x,t-1) + P_m(x,t-1)].$$

Consequently, the respective formulas for $SR(0)$, $f_p(0)$ and λ are as follows:

Let

$$D = 1 - \frac{1}{2} \sum_{\alpha'}^{\beta'} [m'_m(x)s_m(x)/\lambda^{x+1}].$$

Then

$$SR(0) = \frac{1}{D} \left[\frac{1}{2} \sum_{\alpha'}^{\beta'} \frac{m'_f(x)s_f(x)}{\lambda^{x+1}} + \frac{1}{f_p(0)} \right.$$

$$\left. \times \left\{ \frac{1}{2} \sum_{\alpha'}^{\beta'} \sum_{\xi=0}^{x-1} \left(\frac{m'_f(x)A_f(\xi, x) + m'_m(x)A_m(\xi, x)}{\lambda^{x-\xi+1}} \right) + (u_m/\lambda) \right\} \right] \quad (4.33)$$

$$f_p(0) = \frac{\left[1 - \frac{1}{D} \left\{ 1 + \sum_1^w \frac{s_m(x)}{\lambda^x} \right\} \left\{ \frac{1}{2} \sum_{\alpha'}^{\beta'} \sum_{\xi=0}^{x-1} \left(\frac{m'_f(x)A_f(\xi, x) + m'_m(x)A_m(\xi, x)}{\lambda^{x-\xi+1}} \right) + \left(\frac{u_m}{\lambda} \right) \right\} \right]}{\left\{ 1 + \sum_1^w \frac{s_f(x)}{\lambda^x} \right\} + \frac{1}{D} \left\{ 1 + \sum_1^w \frac{s_m(x)}{\lambda^x} \right\} \left[\frac{1}{2} \sum_{\alpha'}^{\beta'} \frac{m'_f(x)s_f(x)}{\lambda^{x+1}} \right]}$$

$$\frac{- \sum_1^w \sum_{\xi=0}^{x-1} \frac{A_f(\xi, x) + A_m(\xi, x)}{\lambda^{x-\xi}}}{\left\{ 1 + \sum_1^w \frac{s_f(x)}{\lambda^x} \right\} + \frac{1}{D} \left\{ 1 + \sum_1^w \frac{s_m(x)}{\lambda^x} \right\} \left[\frac{1}{2} \sum_{\alpha'}^{\beta'} \frac{m'_f(x)s_f(x)}{\lambda^{x+1}} \right]} \quad (4.34)$$

and the polynomial equation in λ:

$$\lambda^{\beta'+1} - \left(\frac{u_f}{f_p(0)} \right) \lambda^{\beta'} - \frac{1}{2} \sum_{\alpha'}^{\beta'} \left[\{m_f(x)s_f(x) + SR(0)m_m(x)s_m(x)\}\lambda^{\beta'-x} \right.$$

$$\left. + \frac{1}{f_p(0)} \sum_{\xi=0}^{x-1} \{m_f(x)A_f(\xi, x) + m_m(x)A_m(\xi, x)\}\lambda^{\beta'-x+\xi} \right] = 0 \quad (4.35)$$

where α' and β' are the youngest and the oldest ages at which reproduction occurs among males and/or among females.

From the considerations given in the case of the one-sex model, eqn (4.35) also has at least one positive root provided $S_f(0)f_p(0) > a_f(0)$, and $S_m(0)f_p(0) > a_m(0)$ whenever $a_f(0)$ and/or $a_m(0)$ are negative. Therefore, the values of $SR(0)$, $f_p(0)$ and λ may be obtained by iteration. Alternatively, perhaps preferably, we may obtain λ from the matrix roots and compute $SR(0)$ and $f_p(0)$ from the above expressions. Once these three quantities are known, we proceed as in the case with the female dominance to calculate the age distributions for males and females, the sex ratios in the age groups and the sex ratio in the total population.

The corresponding formulas when no migration is assumed, are obtained by substituting zero for the migration coefficients in the above expressions. They may be seen to be the same as those given by Goodman (1967b) with $\delta = \frac{1}{2}$.

4.4 Numerical illustrations

We shall use the two-sex models to test the formulas derived here. Since the formulas for the case with no migration are well known and, in fact, could be taken as particular cases of those derived here, we do not attempt to illustrate them. Though the case in which the age–sex-specific net migration rates are used in the process of population growth is not considered in the theoretical investigations because the formulas applicable in the case with no migration are directly applicable in that case, we do compare the equilibrium-state populations resulting from the use of the two procedures for specifying the migration situation.

Further, the effect of changing the set of fertility, mortality and migration schedules on the characteristics of the equilibrium-state population, an aspect which has not been considered in the analytical work, is examined using the results of empirical experiments. Though expressions could be obtained to take account of these effects of the changes of schedules, we have not attempted to do so because the resulting formulas will be too cumbersome and, in any case, the changes in the equilibrium-state populations depend on the observed changes in the components and will have to be studied separately in each case.

Finally, the changes in the characteristics of the equilibrium state populations are separated into the effects of the changes in the schedules of fertility, mortality and migration, adopting a method similar to the one used by Keyfitz (1968b) to decompose the changes in the characteristics of the stable populations. Such a decomposition indicates in a given situation, the relative weights of the effects of the changes in the schedules of the components, on the characteristics of the equilibrium state populations.

(i) *Age–sex distributions and the growth rates resulting from given sets of fertility, mortality and migration conditions*

From the actual projections which were carried out to illustrate the convergence of the age–sex distributions of the three initial populations (see Section 3.5), the age–sex distributions and the growth rates of the equilibrium-state populations resulting from the given schedules, when

Table 4.1 The age–sex distribution of the equilibrium state population that would result from the fertility and mortality rates of 1911, and the net migration rate and the age–sex composition of net migrants during 1911–12 in Australia

| Age groups | When female dominance is assumed | | | | | | When equal dominance is assumed | | | | | |
| | From actual projections | | | From the formulas derived in Section 4.3.2 | | | From actual projections | | | From the formulas derived in Section 4.3.3 | | |
	Male	Female	Sex ratio (per 100)	Male	Female	Sex ratio (per 100)	Male	Female	Sex ratio (per 100)	Male	Female	Sex ratio (per 100)
0–4	9.22	11.52	104.34	9.20	11.50	104.66	10.66	13.11	104.18	10.64	13.08	104.50
5–9	8.64	10.47	107.65	8.63	10.45	107.96	9.65	11.55	107.10	9.64	11.52	107.40
10–14	8.24	9.72	110.64	8.24	9.71	110.94	8.91	10.40	109.86	8.91	10.39	110.15
15–19	8.36	9.00	121.18	8.35	8.99	121.48	8.76	9.37	119.82	8.75	9.36	120.11
20–24	8.88	8.45	137.05	8.88	8.45	137.34	9.04	8.57	135.23	9.04	8.57	135.52
25–29	9.13	8.04	148.15	9.13	8.04	148.42	9.09	7.96	146.38	9.09	7.96	146.65
30–34	8.84	7.57	152.29	8.84	7.58	152.53	8.63	7.34	150.74	8.63	7.34	150.98
35–39	8.14	6.94	152.97	8.14	6.94	153.19	7.80	6.59	151.57	7.80	6.60	151.79
40–44	7.18	6.16	152.00	7.18	6.17	152.21	6.75	5.74	150.69	6.76	5.75	150.90
45–49	6.14	5.35	149.67	6.14	5.36	149.86	5.66	4.89	148.40	5.67	4.90	148.60
50–54	5.08	4.54	146.12	5.09	4.55	146.31	4.60	4.07	144.87	4.61	4.08	145.05
55–59	4.07	3.75	141.53	4.07	3.76	141.71	3.61	3.30	140.24	3.61	3.30	140.41
60–64	3.12	3.00	135.67	3.13	3.01	135.84	2.71	2.58	134.31	2.71	2.59	134.48
65–69	2.24	2.28	128.52	2.25	2.28	128.68	1.90	1.92	127.13	1.91	1.93	127.29
70–74	1.45	1.58	119.89	1.46	1.59	120.04	1.21	1.31	118.53	1.21	1.31	118.68
75–79	0.80	0.95	109.31	0.80	0.95	109.45	0.65	0.77	107.98	0.65	0.77	108.12
80–84	0.35	0.47	96.37	0.35	0.47	96.50	0.28	0.37	95.14	0.28	0.37	95.26
85+	0.13	0.21	83.52	0.13	0.21	79.03	0.10	0.16	82.48	0.10	0.17	78.06
Total	100.00	100.00	130.46	100.00	100.00	130.73	100.00	100.00	128.18	100.00	100.00	128.45
Growth index	1.03050	1.03050	—	1.03044	1.03044	—	1.03512	1.03512	—	1.03504	1.03504	—

Note: The growth index used in the formulas of Section 4.3.2 was the matrix root given in Table 3.1; and the one used in the formulas of Section 4.3.3 was the matrix root given in Table 3.4.

female dominance was assumed and when equal dominance was assumed, were obtained. Then the formulas derived in Sections 4.3.2 and 4.3.3 were used to compute the corresponding age–sex structures of the equilibrium state populations utilizing the values of λ from the characteristic roots of the matrix L_M of Sections 3.4.2 and 3.4.3.

Table 4.1 compares the equilibrium state age–sex distributions obtained by the two procedures. It can be seen that the values are quite close, both when the female dominance is assumed and when the equal dominance is assumed. The significant difference found in the sex ratio in the age group (85+) may be due to the different procedures used in obtaining the proportion in that age group in the actual projections and in applying the formulas. For applying the formulas, it was necessary to keep the width of the age interval the same throughout the age range. Hence single year survival rates up to 99 years were used in the formulas to get the population proportion and the sex ratio in the age group (85+), whereas in the actual projections the group (84+) was projected as a group to (85+). In those old age groups the survival rates for females were higher than for males.

(ii) *Effect of migration on the characteristics of the equilibrium state population*

The comparison of the age distributions presented in Table 4.2, and that of the sex distributions and the growth rates presented in Table 4.3, reveals that the use of the net migration rate and the age–sex composition of net migrants made a substantial difference in the characteristics of the equilibrium state populations as against the use of the age–sex-specific net migration rates, when the net migrants age–sex composition was very different from that of the stable population resulting from the given vital rates, as it was during 1911–12. Otherwise the differences were small, as revealed by the situation in 1965–66. It must, however, be mentioned that the magnitude of the difference is also dependent on the magnitude of the net migration. For instance, during 1945–46, the net migration was small and thus the differences were quite small, though the age–sex composition of the net migrants was not close to that of the stable population. For the case in which the 1915–16 net migration situation was assumed, the use of the net migration rate and the age–sex composition of net migrants showed that the situation was incompatible with the vital rates of 1911. But when the same situation was specified by the age–sex-specific net migration rates, the age–sex distribution of the equilibrium state population became very unusual showing exceptionally high proportion of males under 15 years of age and abnormally low sex ratios in all age groups. In fact, negative values would not, generally, result in this case.

Table 4.2 Comparison of the age distributions of the equilibrium state populations resulting from the specified fertility, mortality and migration conditions

Prevailing conditions			Male age distribution (per cent)				Mean age	Female age distribution (per cent)				Mean age
Mortality	Fertility	Migration	0–14	15–44	45–64	65+		0–14	15–44	45–64	65+	
			No migration									
1911	1911	0	31.54	44.73	17.38	6.35	29.16	30.61	43.68	17.84	7.86	30.23
1966	1966	0	29.17	44.02	19.17	7.64	30.88	27.55	42.13	19.45	10.87	32.92
			Migration specified by a net migration rate and an age–sex composition of net migrants									
1911	1911	1911–12	26.10	50.52	18.41	4.97	30.31	31.71	46.16	16.64	5.48	28.60
1911	1911	1915–16	x	x	x	x	x	x	x	x	x	x
1911	1911	1945–46	30.48	44.67	18.06	6.79	29.83	30.59	43.49	17.81	8.11	30.34
1966	1966	1965–66	29.66	45.43	18.51	6.41	30.05	28.59	43.63	18.66	9.12	31.65
			Migration specified by a set of age–sex-specific net migration rates									
1911	1911	1911–12	23.84	49.16	20.94	6.07	32.17	31.19	45.40	17.29	6.12	29.19
1911	1911	1915–16	62.81	32.94	3.37	0.88	14.70	31.17	44.40	17.20	7.24	29.61
1911	1911	1945–46	30.48	44.61	18.10	6.82	29.86	30.51	43.43	17.90	8.17	30.41
1966	1966	1965–66	29.45	45.51	18.65	6.39	30.16	28.34	43.67	18.85	9.14	31.79

Note: See notes (1) and (2) to Table 3.1.

Table 4.3 Comparison of the sex compositions and the growth rates of the equilibrium state populations resulting from the specified fertility, mortality and migration conditions

Prevailing conditions			Sex ratios in age groups (Males per 100 females)				Sex ratio in total population	Growth rate[a] (per 1000)
Mortality	Fertility	Migration	0–14	15–44	45–64	65+		
			No migration					
1911	1911	0	102.97	102.32	97.35	80.70	99.93	12.10
1966	1966	0	104.43	103.06	97.20	69.32	98.63	11.50
		Migration specified by a net migration rate and an age–sex composition of net migrants						
1911	1911	1911–12	107.37	142.78	144.34	118.25	130.46	30.05
1911	1911	1915–16	x	x	x	x	x	x
1911	1911	1945–46	102.84	105.98	104.61	86.37	103.18	10.02
1966	1966	1965–66	104.54	104.93	100.00	70.76	100.78	21.65
		Migration specified by a set of age–sex-specific net migration rates						
1911	1911	1911–12	106.99	151.60	169.47	138.74	139.99	26.91
1911	1911	1915–16	85.23	31.38	8.30	5.15	42.29	13.38
1911	1911	1945–46	102.82	105.73	104.11	85.93	102.94	9.94
1966	1966	1965–66	104.52	104.81	99.49	70.35	100.58	21.92

Note: See notes (1) and (2) to Table 3.1.
[a] This was computed from actual projections, using the mid-year population as the base.

(iii) *Changes in the characteristics of the equilibrium—state populations
due to the changes in the net migration rate and in the age–sex
composition of net migrants*

In attempting an empirical investigation of this kind, it is necessary to
mention at the outset that the effects observed will be true to the particular
situations under consideration.

The results presented in Table 4.4 indicate a slowly increasing trend in
the proportion in the age group (0–14) and in the sex ratio in the total
population, and a decreasing trend in the old age proportion and in the
mean age, associated with an increasing trend in the magnitude of the net
migration rate from −1 per cent to 5 per cent, when the age–sex composition
of net migrants was as in Australia during 1962–66. It may be recalled that
this age–sex composition of net migrants was comparatively nearer to the
smooth age–sex distribution of the stable population resulting from the
vital rates of 1911 (see Section 2.4). But, even in this case, heavy net
migration such as the uncommon rate of immigration of 5 per cent, changed
the age–sex distribution of the equilibrium-state population to a marked
extent as compared to that in the case with no migration.

On the other hand, when the age–sex composition of the net migrants
was significantly different from the stable age–sex distribution resulting
from the given vital rates, as in the experiments 2, 6, 7, 8 and 9 under (ii)
in Table 4.4, the age–sex distribution of the resulting equilibrium-state
population was also significantly different. When the age–sex distribution
of the net migrants was identical with the stable one, the age–sex distribution
of the resulting equilibrium-state population was also identical with the
stable one. But the growth rate changed to the extent of the net migration
rate.

These experiments indicate that a migration stream in which the balance
of the sexes is not too uneven, and in which there is not very heavy
concentration of net migrants in certain age groups, is more beneficial from
the point of view of the growth of the population and in obtaining a normal
age–sex distribution in the population. Perhaps this is desirable from the
social point of view as well.

(iv) *Decomposition of the changes in the characteristics of the
equilibrium-state populations into the effects of the changes in the
components*

The fertility, mortality and migration schedules in Australia changed sub-
stantially from 1911 to 1966. If we compute the equilibrium-state populations corresponding to these two situations observed at two points of

Table 4.4 Changes in some characteristics of the equilibrium-state populations due to the changes in the net migration rate and in the age–sex composition of net migrants

Prevailing conditions Mortality—1911 Fertility—1911 Migration—	Proportion in young age group (0–14 years)		Proportion in old age group (65 years and over)		Mean age		Sex ratio (per 100) in total population	Growth rate[a] (per 1000)
	Male	Female	Male	Female	Male	Female		
(i) Age-sex composition of 1962–66 and the net rate (per cent) as:								
−1.0	31.28	29.75	7.74	9.49	29.95	31.34	97.59	00.01
0.0	31.54	30.61	6.35	7.86	29.16	30.23	99.93	12.10
0.5	31.73	30.97	5.76	7.23	28.77	29.77	100.68	17.95
1.0	31.93	31.30	5.25	6.68	28.40	29.36	101.24	23.71
5.0	33.31	32.89	2.96	4.41	26.30	27.34	103.01	66.43
(ii) Net rate of 1 per cent and age–sex composition								
1. Same as in 1962–66	31.93	31.30	5.25	6.68	28.40	29.36	101.24	23.71
2. Same as in 1925	26.14	30.78	6.31	6.99	31.32	29.83	122.27	20.26
3. Same as 1911 stb. population	31.53	30.61	6.36	7.87	29.17	30.24	99.98	21.98
4. Same as 1966 obs. population	31.04	30.29	6.76	8.30	29.60	30.58	100.58	21.24
5. Same as 1911 life table population	30.68	29.68	7.27	9.01	30.03	31.22	99.59	20.47
6. Same as 1911 life table population with no female migrants	21.01	30.61	11.65	7.87	36.26	30.23	171.08	12.10
7. Same as 1911 life table population with no male migrants	41.34	29.17	3.32	9.59	23.72	31.75	66.63	26.18
8. 1962–66, with no female migrants below age 49 years	24.39	26.00	8.19	16.73	33.03	36.13	120.84	12.10
9. 1962–66, with female migrants only at age 0 years below age 49 years	25.65	27.90	7.61	14.74	32.20	34.43	116.02	14.10

[a] This was computed from actual projections using mid-year population as base.

Table 4.5 Decomposition of the changes in the mean age and in the proportion in the old age group (65 years and over) of the equilibrium-state age–sex distribution into those due to changes in fertility, mortality and migration

| | Mean age | | | | Proportion in the old age group (65+) years | | | |
| | Male | | Female | | Male | | Female | |
Source of change	Absolute value (no. of years)	Percentage	Absolute value (no. of years)	Percentage	Absolute value (per 100)	Percentage	Absolute value (per 100)	Percentage
Value under initial conditions	30.31	—	28.60	—	4.97	—	5.48	—
Change in mortality	−0.45	−173.08	0.01	0.33	−0.16	−11.11	0.58	15.93
Change in fertility	1.74	669.23	1.87	61.31	0.94	65.28	1.10	30.22
Change in migration	−1.68	−646.15	0.82	26.88	0.50	34.72	1.34	36.81
Interaction of the changes in:								
Fertility and mortality	0.00		0.06	1.97	−0.01	−0.69	0.13	3.57
Mortality and migration	−0.07	−26.92	0.06	1.97	−0.04	−2.78	0.14	3.85
Fertility and migration	0.22	84.61	0.22	7.21	0.23	15.97	0.32	8.79
Fertility, mortality and migration	−0.02	−7.69	0.01	0.33	−0.02	−1.39	0.03	0.83
Total change	−0.26	−100.00	3.05	100.00	1.44	100.00	3.64	100.00
Value under final conditions	30.05	—	31.65	—	6.41	—	9.12	—

time, their characteristics would naturally be different. For instance, the mean age for males which was 30.31 under the 1911 conditions decreased to 30.05 years under the conditions of 1966, while the mean age for females increased from 28.60 years to 31.65 years. Just by comparing these results, we are tempted to conclude that, probably, none of the changes in the components had any significant effect on the mean age for males. But, this observed change is the sum of all the changes produced by the differences in the values of the components in 1911 and in 1966. Hence it would be interesting to decompose this observed change in the characteristics of the equilibrium-state populations into the effect of the change in each component separately and the effects of the interaction of the changes in the different components. This is attempted here.

The details of the procedure adopted for decomposing the observed change are given in Chapter 6 and will not be presented here.

Table 4.5 gives the decomposition of the changes in the mean age and the proportion in the old age group (65+), for males and females. The proportion in the old age group was chosen for no particular reason except that the relative variation was large in that group. It is clear from the table that the large increase in the mean age for males, produced by the decrease in fertility was offset by a large decrease due to the change in the migration conditions and thus, the net result was a very small change in the mean age. Change in the mortality conditions decreased the mean age for males to some extent, but did not have any effect on the mean age for the females. It may be observed that, in the case of the females, the changes in all the components and hence their interactions, had an effect of increasing the mean age and the proportion in the old age group with fertility playing the most important part. However, the analysis of the proportion in the old age group for females and that of the mean age for males showed that migration, depending upon its characteristics, could be as important a factor in changing the age distributions as fertility is. Interaction effects, in general, were found to be comparatively small.

From the analysis presented in Table 4.6, we observe that the sole reason for the decrease in the proportion of males was the change in the migration conditions, i.e. the decrease in the sex ratio among net migrants, though fertility and mortality contributed by a small extent to increase it. The decline in mortality increased the growth rate, but the decline in fertility decreased it almost to the same extent so that the growth rate became smaller in 1966 than in 1911 to the extent of the decrease in the effect of migration. The interaction effects were, again, comparatively small.

Thus the decomposition of the changes in the characteristics of the equilibrium-state populations gives a better understanding of the mechanisms effecting the change.

Table 4.6 Decomposition of the changes in the proportion of males and in the intrinsic growth rate in the equilibrium-state age–sex distribution into those due to changes in fertility, mortality and migration

Source of change	Proportion of males		Growth rate	
	Absolute value (per 100)	Percentage	Absolute value (per 1000)	Percentage
Value under initial conditions	56.61	—	30.06	—
Change in mortality	−0.21	−3.27	4.55	54.04
Change in fertility	0.48	7.48	−4.31	−51.19
Change in migration	−6.17	−96.11	−8.38	−99.53
Interaction of the changes in:				
Fertility and mortality	−0.08	−1.25	0.00	0.00
Mortality and migration	0.12	1.87	0.09	1.07
Fertility and migration	−0.56	−8.72	−0.39	−4.63
Fertility, mortality and migration	0.00	0.00	0.02	0.24
Total change	−6.42	−100.00	−8.42	−100.00
Value under final conditions	50.19		21.64	

4.5 Cyclical model of population change

In this section we shall examine how the growth rate and the age–sex distributions change when a sequence of k schedules of fertility, mortality and migration conditions operates repeatedly over a long period of time. This model is called "cyclical" because the growth rates and the age–sex distributions show, after a sufficiently long period of time, a fixed pattern of change, i.e. a pattern which will repeat itself cyclically.

Let $f(x, i)$ be the age-specific fertility rate at age x in the i-th fertility schedule; $S(b, i)$ and $[S(x, i), x = 0, 1, \ldots, (w - 1)]$ the survival rates in the i-th mortality schedule; and $u(i)$ and $a(x, i)$ respectively, the values of u and $a(x)$ as defined in Section 3.3, in the i-th migration schedule.

From a practical point of view, it would be unrealistic to assume that the survival rates change in a cyclical manner. While fertility and migration have shown trends which can roughly be considered as cyclical, mortality has rarely followed such a pattern. However, if migration is included into the survival rates using a set of age–sex-specific net migration rates, then the survival rates may show this kind of cyclical change. Hence the formulas obtained in the case with no migration using these survival rates could be employed without change in the case where age–sex-specific net migration rates are used, so that there would be no need to consider that case separately.

4.5.1 The case with no migration

Namboodiri (1969b, p. 288) proposed this model and demonstrated that

> For any arbitrary female population, closed to migration, the age distribution below the end of the childbearing period and the growth rates of the different age groups will eventually show a fixed pattern of change, i.e. one which will repeat itself cyclically.

We shall follow his argument briefly and slightly modify the procedures to make them suitable for the present purpose.

The age structure at the end of the k-th period in the first cycle is given by:

$$P^*(1, k) = M(k)M(k-1) \ldots M(1)P^*(0, 0) \qquad (4.36)$$

where $M(i)$, $i = 1, 2, \ldots, k$ represent the projection matrices corresponding to the k schedules of fertility and mortality; $P^*(T, i)$ a column vector representing the distribution by age of the population at the end of the period in which the i-th schedules are operating in the T-th cycle; and $P^*(0, 0)$ is the population vector giving the distribution by age of the initial population.

If we continue beyond the k-th schedule, then by our assumption, the first schedule follows and the others in the cycle are repeated. Hence after m repetitions of the cycle, we have:

$$P^*(m, k) = (M^*)^m p^*(0, 0) \qquad (4.37)$$

where $M^* = M(k)M(k-1) \ldots M(2)M(1)$.

Since $M(i)$ are the population projection matrices, it follows from the considerations given in Chapter 3 that M^* is a power positive matrix. Hence it has a unique real positive characteristic root whose value is greater than the absolute value of any other characteristic root (Brauer, 1961).

As m becomes large the vector $P^*(m, k)$ becomes proportional to a constant volumn vector C. In fact, we can write:

$$P^*(T, k) = [a^T r P^*(0, 0)]C \qquad (4.38)$$

where T is one large value of m and a^T is a scalar, and r is a row vector and thus $[a^T r P^*(0, 0)]$ is a scalar multiplier (Namboodiri, 1969b, p. 289).

From this it is easy to prove that:

$$P^*(T + t, i) = a^t P^*(T, i) \tag{4.39}$$

which means that the proportionate age distributions at the end of the different periods within the $(T + 1)$-th, $(T + 2)$-th, etc. cycles are the same as those within the cycle T. Thus the age structures repeat themselves in all the subsequent cycles.

If $P(T + t, i, x)$ is the x-th element of the vector $P^*(T + t, i)$, then this denotes the population at age x years at the end of the i-th period in the $(T + t)$-th cycle and from eqn (4.39) it can be written as:

$$P(T + t, i, x) = a^t P(T, i, x), \qquad \text{for } x = 0, 1, 2, \ldots, \beta$$
$$i = 1, 2, 3, \ldots, k$$
$$t = 0, 1, 2, \ldots . \tag{4.40}$$

To extend this result to the ages beyond β years, we have to simply make use of the fact that the populations at ages above β years become linear functions of those at ages below β years. The coefficients of these functions being determined entirely by the given fertility and mortality conditions, would repeat in the respective period within each cycle. Hence the age distributions including the whole age range repeat within each cycle.

However, eqn (4.40) does not suggest anything about the relationship between the populations at the end of the different periods within the cycle $(T + t)$. To obtain this relationship which would enable the computation of the age structures at the end of the different periods if one is known, Namboodiri (1969b) defined k growth multipliers and using those multipliers, he obtained the relative numbers of females in the different age groups at the end of the i-th period in the $(T + t)$-th cycle. He has also suggested an iteration procedure to compute the growth multipliers (Namboodiri, 1969a).

At this stage we depart slightly from Namboodiri and define $R(i + 1)$ as the growth index at age 0 years, i.e. the ratio of the population at age 0 years at the end of the $(i + 1)$-th period to the population at the same age at the end of the i-th period in the T-th cycle, viz.

$$R(i + 1) = [P(T, i + 1, 0)/P(T, i, 0)], i = 1, 2, \ldots, (k - 1)$$

and

$$R(1) = R(k + 1) = [P(T + 1, 1, 0)/P(T, k, 0)]. \tag{4.41}$$

It may be noted that $R(i)$ as defined here would be the same as the growth multipliers used by Namboodiri if the survival rates are assumed to be the same for all the periods within the cycle. In fact, Namboodiri made this assumption. But, for our purpose here, we cannot assume this.

Now, we shall obtain the age structures and the growth multipliers at the end of each period within a cycle in terms of the given sequence of fertility and mortality schedules. For this purpose we may proceed in two alternate ways. We may make use of the fact that the equilibrium state age structure which results from a set of fertility and mortality conditions is independent of the initial age structure with which we begin, and employ an iteration procedure to obtain the age structures and the growth indexes at the end of the different periods within any equilibrium-state cycle. Or else, we may first obtain the matrix multiplication M^* and calculate using this matrix, the equilibrium-state age structure at the end of the k-th period and use this in computing the age structures and growth indexes at the end of the other periods. In either case, therefore, we can assume that one age distribution is known.

Hence, let $\phi(T, i, x) = [P(T, i, x)/P(T, i, 0)]$ be the ratio of the population at age x years to the population at age 0 years at the end of the i-th period in the T-th cycle. Obviously, $\phi(T, i, 0) = 1.0$.

The eqns of population growth from period i to $(i + 1)$ are:

$$P(T, i + 1, 0) = \sum_{\alpha}^{\beta} [m(x, i + 1)P(T, i, x)]$$

and

$$P(T, i + 1, x) = S(x - 1, i + 1)P(T, i, x - 1),$$

$$\text{for } x = 1, 2, \ldots, w \tag{4.42}$$

where $m(x, i + 1)$ are computed from the fertility rates $f(x, i + 1)$ as in eqn (3.5).

On dividing both sides of the first equation in (4.42) by $P(T, i + 1, 0)$, we have:

$$\phi(T, i + 1, 0) = 1.0$$

and

$$R(i + 1) = \sum_{\alpha}^{\beta} m(x, i + 1)\phi(T, i, x) \tag{4.43}$$

and on dividing the second equation in (4.42) by $P(T, i + 1, 0)$, we get:

$$\phi(T, i + 1, x) = [S(x - 1, i + 1)\phi(T, i, x - 1)]/R(i + 1). \tag{4.44}$$

From the $\phi(T, i + 1, x)$ values we can easily obtain the age distribution of the population at the end of the $(i + 1)$-th period in the T-th cycle. It may be noted that eqn (4.44) is true for any age x years and not merely for ages below β years.

The growth indexes of the population at each of the other ages and of the total population could be computed from the following equations:

$$\text{GI}(i + 1, x) = P(T, i + 1, x)/P(T, i, x) = [\phi(T, i + 1, x)/\phi(T, i, x)]\{R(i + 1)\},$$

for $x = 1, 2, \ldots, w$

and

$$\text{GI}(i + 1) = \frac{\sum_0^w P(T, i + 1, x)}{\sum_0^w P(T, i, x)} = \frac{\sum_1^w \phi(T, i + 1, x)}{\sum_1^w \phi(T, i, x)} R(i + 1). \qquad (4.45)$$

It is not difficult to see that, as Namboodiri (1969b) has shown, the growth indexes for age 0 years are $R(1), R(2), \ldots, R(k)$; for age 1 year $R(k), R(1), R(2), \ldots, R(k - 1)$; for age 2 years $R(k - 1), R(k), R(1), \ldots, R(k - 2)$; and so on, provided the survival rates are the same for all the periods. Otherwise these would be affected to the extent of the product of the ratios of the survival rates at the different ages from one period to the other. For example, the growth index at age 1 year would be

$$\text{GI}(i + 1, 1) = \left[\frac{\phi(T, i + 1, 1)}{\phi(T, i, 1)}\right] R(i + 1) = \frac{S(0, i + 1)}{S(0, i)} R(i) \qquad (4.46)$$

at age 2 years would be

$$\text{GI}(i + 1, 2) = \left[\frac{\phi(T, i + 1, 2)}{\phi(T, i, 2)}\right] R(i + 1) = \frac{S(1, i + 1)}{S(1, i)} \frac{S(0, i)}{S(0, i - 1)} R(i - 1)$$

$$(4.47)$$

and so on.

Thus, starting with any arbitrary age structure we can obtain the set of growth indexes $R(2), R(3), \ldots, R(k), R(k + 1)$ and the corresponding age structures. Then $R(1)$ is put equal to $R(k + 1)$ and the initial age distribution is replaced by the age distribution corresponding to $R(k + 1)$, and the process is repeated. If $R(k + 1)$ now obtained, differs from $R(1)$ by less than an assumed small quantity, then we say that the equilibrium state cycle has evolved and the set of growth indexes and the age distributions already obtained, is the set we are looking for. If $R(k + 1)$ is not equal to $R(1)$, then $R(1)$ is again replaced by the new value of $R(k + 1)$ and the initial age distribution by the age distribution corresponding to the new value of $R(k + 1)$, and the whole process is repeated. When the effect of the initial age structure is thus eliminated, the equilibrium state cycle evolves. However, in testing for the attainment of the equilibrium state, it would be necessary to compare the age distributions of the first period with that of the $(k + 1)$-th period or to compare the growth indexes at all ages in the two periods, because $R(i)$ are dependent only on the age distributions up to the age β years.

We can conveniently use this iteration procedure to compute the intrinsic growth rate and the associated age distribution of the stable population without using the matrix methods. The model could also be useful in studying the implications of a sequence of k fertility and mortality schedules.

4.5.2 The case with migration

In the proof of the cyclical model given by Namboodiri (1969b), the matrix M^* could be any general power positive matrix, as he has indicated at the end of his paper. Hence, if we replace $M(i)$ by the projection matrix $L_M(i)$, which is as in Section 3.3, we can write:

$$M^* = L_M(k)L_M(k - 1) \ldots L_M(2)L_M(1) \qquad (4.48)$$

and from the results discussed in Chapters 3 (and those in Chapter 5), and those given by Namboodiri we conclude that, in this case also, a cyclical model evolves. The only problem we have to resolve, therefore, is to obtain expressions which would enable us to compute the age distributions at the end of the different periods within an equilibrium state cycle T. For this purpose, we assume, as in Section 4.5.1, that one age structure is known. Let

$$f_p(T, i, 0) = \left[P(T, i, 0) / \left\{ \sum_0^w P(T, i, x) \right\} \right]$$

be the proportion of the population at age 0 years and $\phi(T, i, x) = [P(T, i, x)/P(T, i, 0)]$, the ratio of the population at age x years to the population at age 0 years at the end of the i-th period in the T-th cycle. Obviously $\phi(T, i, 0) = 1.0$. Also, let $R(i + 1) = [P(T, i + 1, 0)/P(T, i, 0)]$ be the growth index for the age 0 years. It may be noted that, when the ratio of the number of migrant children aged 0 years to the number of births during the period, is constant from period to period and the survival rates are also the same, this growth index would again, be equal to the growth multiplier defined by Namboodiri.

If we write down the equations of population growth for convenience, we have:

$$P(T, i + 1, 0) = \sum_{\alpha}^{\beta} m(x, i + 1)P(T, i, x) + u(i + 1) \sum_{0}^{w} P(T, i, x)$$

and

$$P(T, i + 1, x) = S(x - 1, i + 1)P(T, i, x - 1) + a(x - 1, i + 1) \sum_{0}^{w} P(T, i, x).$$

(4.49)

We have on dividing both sides of the first equation by $P(T, i + 1, 0)$:

$$\phi(T, i + 1, 0) = 1.0$$

and

$$R(i + 1) = \sum_{\alpha}^{\beta} m(x, i + 1)\phi(T, i, x) + u(i + 1)/f_p(T, i, 0); \quad (4.50)$$

and on dividing both sides of the second equation by $P(T, i + 1, 0)$, we get:

$$\phi(T, i + 1, x) = [S(x - 1, i + 1)\phi(T, i, x - 1)$$
$$+ a(x - 1, i + 1)/f_p(T, i, 0)]/R(i + 1). \quad (4.51)$$

The growth index of the population at age x years and that of the total population are given by:

$$GI(i + 1, x) = \frac{P(T, i + 1, x)}{P(T, i, x)} = \left[\frac{\phi(T, i + 1, x)}{\phi(T, i, x)}\right] R(i + 1)$$

and

$$GI(i + 1) = \frac{\sum_{0}^{w} P(T, i + 1, x)}{\sum_{0}^{w} P(T, i, x)} = \left[\frac{f_p(T, i, 0)}{f_p(T, i + 1, 0)}\right] R(i + 1). \quad (4.52)$$

Thus all values required to continue the procedure to the $(i + 2)$-th period are available if we know $f_p(T, i + 1, 0)$. This can be obtained using the equation which follows from the definition of $f_p(T, i + 1, 0)$, i.e.

$$f_p(T, i + 1, 0) = \left[P(T, i + 1, 0) / \sum_0^w P(T, i + 1, x) \right]$$

$$= \left[1 / \sum_0^w \phi(T, i + 1, x) \right]. \tag{4.54}$$

From these equations we can compute the complete set of age structures and the growth indexes for all the periods within any cycle T. It is not difficult to see that the expressions given by Namboodiri can be obtained from those given here, by putting the migration coefficients equal to zero and assuming constant survival rates for the different periods. Since it has been shown that the age distributions repeat in all equilibrium-state cycles, we can see from eqns (5.50), (5.52) and (5.53) that the growth indexes also repeat in these cycles. We make use of this fact to obtain, simultaneously the parameters $R(1), R(2), \ldots, R(k)$ of the equilibrium-state cycle and the age structures within that cycle using the method of iteration already described.

4.6 The two-sex cyclical model

In order to extend our results to the two-sex case, we merely note that the matrices $M(i)$ can be replaced by projection matrices appropriate to the two-sex case and still the results will hold good. Hence, as in Section (4.5.2), we shall deal here only with the problem of obtaining the growth indexes and the age–sex structures at the end of the different periods within any cycle T. It is assumed that one age–sex distribution is known and formulas which can be derived to obtain the required age–sex structures and the growth indexes by the iteration procedure. Again the suffixes m and f are used to distinguish the male and the female populations.

4.6.1 Two-sex model with female dominance

First, consider the case with no migration. Let $R(i + 1) = [P_f(T, i + 1, 0)/P_f(T, i, 0)]$ be the growth index for the female population at age 0 years, and let $\phi_f(T, i, x)$ and $\phi_m(T, i, x)$ be the ratios of the female and the male populations at age x years to the female population at age 0 years at the end of the i-th period. Let $SR(x, i)$ be the sex ratio at age x years at the end of the i-th period.

The equations of population growth in this case, are:

$$P_f(T, i + 1, 0) = \sum_{\alpha}^{\beta} m_f(x, i + 1)P_f(T, i, x)$$

$$P_m(T, i + 1, 0) = \sum_{\alpha}^{\beta} m_f'(x, i + 1)P_f(T, i, x)$$

$$P_f(T, i + 1, x) = S_f(x - 1, i + 1)P_f(T, i, x - 1)$$

and

$$P_m(T, i + 1, x) = S_m(x - 1, i + 1)P_m(T, i, x - 1),$$

$$\text{for } x = 1, 2, \ldots, w \tag{4.55}$$

where $m_f(x, i + 1)$ and $m_f'(x, i + 1)$ are obtained from the corresponding fertility rates, $f_f(x, i + 1)$, as in Section 3.4.1.

Proceeding as in the case of the one-sex model, we get from the first equation:

$$\phi(T, i + 1, 0) = 1.0$$

and

$$R(i + 1) = \sum_{\alpha}^{\beta} m_f(x, i + 1) \, \phi_f(T, i, x) \tag{4.56}$$

From the second equation:

$$\phi_m(T, i + 1, 0) = SR(0, i + 1)$$

$$= \left[\sum_{\alpha}^{\beta} m_f'(x, i + 1) \, \phi_f(T, i, x) \right] / R(i + 1) \tag{4.57}$$

and from the last two equations:

$$\phi_f(T, i + 1, x) = [S_f(x - 1, i + 1) \, \phi_f(T, i, x - 1)]/R(i + 1)$$

and

$$\phi_m(T, i + 1, x) = [S_m(x - 1, i + 1) \, \phi_m(T, i, x - 1)]/R(i + 1),$$

$$\text{for } x = 1, 2, \ldots, w. \tag{4.58}$$

From the values of $\phi_f(T, i + 1, x)$ and $\phi_m(T, i + 1, x)$ we can compute the age distributions for females and males.

Now the sex ratios by age can be calculated from the equation:

$$SR(x, i + 1) = [\phi_m(T, i + 1, x)/\phi_f(T, i + 1, x)],$$

$$\text{for } x = 1, 2, \ldots, w \tag{4.60}$$

and the sex ratio in the total population by:

$$SR(i + 1) = \left[\sum_0^w \phi_m(T, i + 1, x)\right] \Big/ \left[\sum_0^w \phi_m(T, i + 1, x)\right]. \tag{4.61}$$

The growth indexes for the populations at age x years are obtained as:

For females:

$$GI_f(i + 1, x) = \frac{\phi_f(T, i + 1, x)}{\phi_f(T, i, x)} R(i + 1)$$

For males:

$$GI_m(i + 1, x) = \frac{\phi_m(T, i + 1, x)}{\phi_m(T, i, x)} R(i + 1) \tag{4.63}$$

and for the female and the male populations at all ages, respectively:

$$GI_f(i + 1) = \frac{\sum_0^w \phi_f(T, i + 1, x)}{\sum_0^w \phi_f(t, i, x)} R(i + 1) \tag{4.64}$$

and

$$GI_m(i + 1) = \frac{\sum_0^w \phi_m(T, i + 1, x)}{\sum_0^w \phi_m(T, i, x)} R(i + 1). \tag{4.65}$$

Finally, the growth index for the total population is given by:

$$GI(i + 1) = \frac{\sum_0^w [\phi_m(T, i + 1, x) + \phi_f(T, i + 1, x)]}{\sum_0^w [\phi_m(T, i, x) + \phi_f(T, i, x)]} R(i + 1). \tag{4.66}$$

As in the case of the one-sex model, we can use these equations to continue the process and thus obtain the growth indexes and the corresponding age–sex distributions at the end of the different periods within an equilibrium state cycle. From the equations derived here, it is easy to conclude that, since the same set of one schedule of each of the components operates repeatedly in the case of the equilibrium state population, the age–sex distributions remain constant and hence all the growth indexes become equal. Further, if the survival rates and the sex ratio at birth, are assumed to be constant for all the periods within a cycle, we can infer from the discussion given in the case of the one-sex model, that the growth index at each age is one of the growth indexes $R(1)$, $R(2)$, . . . , $R(k)$ and is the same for males and females. Hence, the sex ratios at all ages would remain identical in all the periods.

When migration is introduced, the corresponding expressions can be obtained without difficulty from those derived in the one-sex case and those given above in this section. Let

$$f_p(T, i, 0) = P_f(T, i, 0) / \sum_0^w [P_f(T, i, x) + P_m(T, i, x)]$$

be the proportion of the female population at age 0 years to the total population, and $\phi_f(T, i, x)$ and $\phi_m(T, i, x)$ the ratios of the female and the male populations at age x years to the female population at age 0 years at the end of the i-th period.

The population growth equations, in this case, are as follows:

$$P_f(T, i+1, 0) = \sum_\alpha^\beta m_f(x, i+1) P_f(T, i, x)$$

$$+ u_f(i+1) \sum_0^w [P_f(T, i, x) + P_m(T, i, x)]$$

$$P_m(T, i+1, 0) = \sum_\alpha^\beta m_f'(x, i+1) P_f(T, i, x)$$

$$+ u_m(i+1) \sum_0^w [P_f(T, i, x) + P_m(T, i, x)]$$

$$P_f(T, i+1, x) = S_f(x-1, i+1) P_f(T, i, x-1)$$

$$+ a_f(x-1, i+1) \sum_0^w [P_f(T, i, x) + P_m(T, i, x)]$$

and

$$P_m(T, i+1, x) = S_m(x-1, i+1)P_m(T, i, x-1)$$

$$+ a_m(x-1, i+1) \sum_0^w [P_f(T, i, x) + P_m(T, i, x)],$$

for $x = 1, 2, \ldots, w$. (4.67)

As in the case of the one-sex model, on dividing both sides of each of the above equations by $P_f(T, i+1, 0)$, we get:

from the first equation:

$$\phi_f(T, i+1, 0) = 1.0$$

and

$$R(i+1) = \sum_\alpha^\beta m_f(x, i+1)\phi_f(T, i, x) + [u_f(i+1)/f_p(T, i, 0)]; \quad (4.68)$$

from the second equation:

$$\phi_m(T, i+1, 0) = SR(0, i+1)$$

$$= \left[\sum_\alpha^\beta m_f'(x, i+1)\phi_f(T, i, x) + \{u_m(i+1)/f_p(T, i, 0)\}\right]/R(i+1);$$

(4.69)

from the third equation:

$$\phi_f(T, i+1, x) = [S_f(x-1, i+1)\phi_f(T, i, x-1)$$

$$+ a_f(x-1, i+1)/f_p(T, i, 0)]/R(i+1) \quad (4.70)$$

and from the fourth equation:

$$\phi_m(T, i+1, x) = [S_m(x-1, i+1)\phi_m(T, i, x-1)$$

$$+ a_m(x-1, i+1)/f_p(T, i, 0)]/R(i+1). \quad (4.71)$$

Finally, using the values of $\phi_f(T, i+1, x)$ and $\phi_m(T, i+1, x)$ calculated above, we obtain the proportion of the female population at age 0 years as:

$$f_p(T, i+1, 0) = \left[1/\sum_0^w \{\phi_f(T, i+1, x) + \phi_m(T, i+1, x)\}\right]. \quad (4.72)$$

Thus we have the set of quantities necessary to continue the process to the $(i + 2)$-th period and so on.

From the values of $\phi_f(T, i + 1, x)$ and $\phi_m(T, i + 1, x)$ we can get the age distributions for females and males, the sex composition and the growth indexes using the respective formulas in the case with no migration.

The formulas derived here can be used to obtain the intrinsic growth rate and the age–sex distribution of the equilibrium state population by the method of iteration described in Section 4.5.1. From eqn (4.68) it is clear that the growth rate of the equilibrium state population will not be changed by migration if migration does not affect the female ages below β years.

4.6.2 Two-sex model with equal dominance

When equal dominance is assumed the only growth equations that change are those which depend on the fertility rates. Hence, considering the case in which migration is included into the process of population growth, we have:

$$P_f(T, i + 1, 0) = \frac{1}{2} \sum_{\alpha'}^{\beta'} [m_f(x, i + 1)P_f(T, i, x) + m_m(x, i + 1)P_m(T, i, x)]$$

$$+ u_f(i + 1) \sum_0^w [P_f(T, i, x) + P_m(T, i, x)]$$

and

$$P_m(T, i + 1, 0) = \frac{1}{2} \sum_{\alpha'}^{\beta'} [m_f'(x, i + 1)P_f(T, i, x) + m_m'(x, i + 1)P_m(T, i, x)]$$

$$+ u_m(i + 1) \sum_0^w [P_f(T, i, x) + P_m(T, i, x)] \quad (4.73)$$

where $m_m(x, i + 1)$ and $m_m'(x, i + 1)$ are obtained from the fertility rates by age of males; $u_f(i + 1)$ and $u_m(i + 1)$ are suitably modified as explained in Section 3.4.3. From the first equation of (4.73), we have:

$$\phi_f(T, i + 1, 0) = 1.0$$

and

$$R(i + 1) = \frac{1}{2} \sum_{\alpha'}^{\beta'} [m_f(x, i + 1)\phi_f(T, i, x) + m_m(x, i + 1)\phi_m(T, i, x)]$$

$$+ [u_f(i + 1)/f_p(T, i, 0)]. \quad (4.74)$$

From the second we get:

$$\phi_m(T, i+1, 0) = SR(0, i+1) = \left[\frac{1}{2}\sum_{\alpha'}^{\beta'}\{m_f'(x, i+1)\phi_f(T, i, x)\right.$$

$$\left. + m_m'(x, i+1)\phi_m(T, i, x)\} + \{u_m(i+1)/f_p(T, i, 0)\}\right]/R(i+1). \quad (4.75)$$

The other formulas needed for continuing the process are the same as in the case where female dominance is assumed. The set of formulas applicable in the case with no migration can be obtained simply by putting the migration coefficients equal to zero in the above equations.

4.7 Numerical illustrations

Numerical examples are presented here to examine whether the formulas derived lead in particular cases, to the conclusions that have been drawn from them, and utilize the iteration procedure to compute the age–sex distribution and the growth rate of an equilibrium state population. In these experiments, the 1911 obs. age–sex distribution was taken as the arbitrary initial age–sex distribution. The fertility, mortality and migration conditions were assumed as follows: (1) the fertility rates as in the sequence of hypothetical fertility rates (see Section 2.4); (2) the survival rates as observed in Australia in 1966 remaining constant; and (3) the net migration rate as given by the absolute value of the cosine function [0.01 cos 0.0628318 $(i-1)$] with the age–sex composition of net migrants as observed in Australia during 1962–66. These assumptions meant that the mortality schedule remained constant, the fertility and the migration schedules repeated every fifty years so that the rates for the first year and the fifty-first year were the same, and so on. Thus we expect that a cycle of fifty years would evolve from these conditions. Though the formulas are strictly applicable only when all the age groups have the same interval, in the numerical calculations we may make a small adjustment as in the usual population projections, to take account of the last open end age interval. Such an adjustment was made in the examples presented here. The process was discontinued when the difference between $R(1)$ and $R(51)$ became less than $\varepsilon = 0.00009$.

Table 4.7 gives the fifty values of the growth indexes for the female population at age 0 years, which may be called the parameters of the cyclical model, because the other quantities are functions of these indexes and the known values of fertility, mortality and migration schedules. The growth indexes for the total population (males and females together) are also presented for a comparison of the trend in the two sets of growth indexes.

Table 4.7 Growth indexes for the female population at age 0 years and for the total population in the different periods within an equilibrium-state cycle

Period i	No migration		With migration	
	Female age 0	Total population	Female age 0	Total population
1	1.00577	1.01312	1.02252	1.02508
2	1.01057	1.01310	1.02737	1.02520
3	0.99843	1.01281	1.01475	1.02499
4	0.99080	1.01236	1.00599	1.02454
5	0.97563	1.01161	0.98945	1.02370
6	0.96825	1.01074	0.98069	1.02267
7	0.97763	1.01009	0.98880	1.02182
8	0.99644	1.00983	1.00631	1.02131
9	1.01773	1.00996	1.02665	1.02118
10	1.05505	1.01080	1.06295	1.02174
11	1.05479	1.01164	1.06149	1.02224
12	1.03469	1.01209	1.04038	1.02229
13	1.03124	1.01246	1.03635	1.02221
14	1.01524	1.01249	1.01990	1.02175
15	1.01251	1.01246	1.01700	1.02120
16	1.01357	1.01244	1.01797	1.02065
17	1.00030	1.01214	1.00458	1.01980
18	1.00269	1.01190	1.00698	1.01899
19	1.01074	1.01184	1.01504	1.01835
20	1.00560	1.01166	1.00982	1.01759
21	0.98601	1.01109	0.99010	1.01641
22	0.98902	1.01060	0.99303	1.01531
23	0.95629	1.00948	0.96006	1.01357
24	0.94532	1.00823	0.94883	1.01168
25	0.96928	1.00750	0.97249	1.01032
26	0.97268	1.00688	0.97540	1.00904
27	0.98912	1.00655	0.99121	1.00806
28	1.01132	1.00660	1.01405	1.00871
29	1.01462	1.00670	1.01822	1.00943
30	1.00962	1.00673	1.01390	1.01006
31	1.01180	1.00679	1.01663	1.01073
32	1.01796	1.00697	1.02321	1.01149
33	1.04048	1.00751	1.04612	1.01262
34	1.02928	1.00788	1.03511	1.01355
35	1.06383	1.00887	1.07003	1.01508
36	1.05009	1.00964	1.05645	1.01638
37	1.05249	1.01049	1.05915	1.01773
38	1.08046	1.01192	1.08766	1.01965
39	1.05634	1.01292	1.06390	1.02110
40	1.01593	1.01304	1.02384	1.02163
41	1.01091	1.01304	1.01953	1.02203
42	1.01996	1.01325	1.02949	1.02262
43	1.00972	1.01322	1.02007	1.02295
44	1.02351	1.01350	1.03495	1.02358
45	1.01183	1.01350	1.02417	1.02392
46	1.00405	1.01332	1.01734	1.02406
47	1.01082	1.01330	1.02519	1.02433
48	1.01018	1.01327	1.02545	1.02458
49	1.01675	1.01338	1.03288	1.02495
50	1.00577	1.01325	1.02228	1.02503

Note: The mortality, fertility and migration schedules assumed were: survival rates of 1966 remaining constant, hypothetical fertility rates having the continuing trend similar to the one observed during 1911–61 and net migration rate given by the absolute value of 0.01 (cos $0.0628318(i-1)$) with the age–sex composition of net migrants in Australia during 1962–66.

Table 4.8 Growth indexes for the populations at single years of age for selected ages during certain periods within an equilibrium state cycle

Age	MALE Period i						FEMALE Period i					
	1	11	21	31	41	51	1	11	21	31	41	51
	With no migration											
0	1.00577	1.05479	0.98600	1.01180	1.01090	1.00577	1.00578	1.05479	0.98600	1.01180	1.01091	1.00578
10	1.01090	1.00574	1.05479	0.98600	1.01180	1.01090	1.01090	1.00574	1.05479	0.98600	1.01180	1.01090
20	1.01180	1.01093	1.00574	1.05478	0.98600	1.01180	1.01180	1.01093	1.00574	1.05478	0.98600	1.01180
30	0.98600	1.01180	1.01093	1.00574	1.05478	0.98600	0.98600	1.01180	1.01093	1.00574	1.05478	0.98600
40	1.05478	0.98594	1.01180	1.01093	1.00574	1.05478	1.05478	0.98595	1.01180	1.01093	1.00574	1.05478
50	1.00574	1.05492	0.98594	1.01180	1.01093	1.00574	1.00574	1.05493	0.98595	1.01180	1.01093	1.00574
60	1.01093	1.00559	1.05492	0.98594	1.01180	1.01093	1.01093	1.00559	1.05493	0.98595	1.01180	1.01093
70	1.01180	1.01097	1.00559	1.05493	0.98594	1.01180	1.01180	1.01096	1.00559	1.05493	0.98595	1.01180
80	0.98594	1.01206	1.01097	1.00559	1.05492	0.98594	0.98595	1.01206	1.01096	1.00559	1.05492	0.98595
85+	1.01862	0.97779	1.03210	1.01777	0.99181	1.01862	1.01835	0.97934	1.03006	1.01848	0.99318	1.01835
Total	1.01325	1.01150	1.01101	1.00675	1.01320	1.01325	1.01299	1.01178	1.01117	1.00683	1.01289	1.01299
	With migration											
0	1.02251	1.06152	0.99012	1.01659	1.01951	1.02251	1.02252	1.06149	0.99010	1.01663	1.01953	1.02252
10	1.02241	1.02088	1.05249	0.98883	1.02427	1.02241	1.02233	1.02095	1.05282	0.98884	1.02402	1.02233
20	1.02722	1.02029	1.01495	1.05222	0.99688	1.02722	1.02675	1.02037	1.01549	1.05251	0.99620	1.02675
30	1.00344	1.02381	1.01338	1.01282	1.05740	1.00344	1.00265	1.02346	1.01360	1.01374	1.05750	1.00265
40	1.05678	1.00385	1.01793	1.01167	1.01811	1.05678	1.05690	1.00321	1.01737	1.01147	1.01923	1.05690
50	1.01978	1.05418	1.00187	1.01586	1.01472	1.01978	1.02077	1.05443	1.00136	1.01546	1.01439	1.02077
60	1.01564	1.01938	1.05191	1.00142	1.01766	1.01564	1.01574	1.02009	1.05103	1.00099	1.01814	1.01574
70	1.01858	1.01537	1.01789	1.05145	1.00311	1.01858	1.01958	1.01542	1.01790	1.04994	1.00358	1.01958
80	1.00406	1.01835	1.01431	1.01747	1.05231	1.00406	1.00454	1.01941	1.01444	1.01711	1.05084	1.00454
85+	1.02651	0.99998	1.02874	1.01979	1.00788	1.02651	1.02544	1.00141	1.02841	1.02036	1.00804	1.02544
Total	1.02524	1.02224	1.01633	1.01057	1.02213	1.02524	1.02492	1.02224	1.01649	1.01088	1.02193	1.02492

Note: See note to Table 4.7.

Table 4.9 Age structures at the end of certain periods within an equilibrium state cycle

With no migration

Age groups	MALE Period i						FEMALE Period i					
	1	11	21	31	41	51	1	11	21	31	41	51
0–4	11.13	9.73	10.49	8.29	10.90	11.13	10.52	9.19	9.89	7.80	10.27	10.52
5–9	10.51	9.96	10.06	8.77	8.46	10.51	9.94	9.41	9.48	8.26	7.97	9.94
10–14	9.48	9.89	8.59	9.68	7.44	9.48	8.97	9.35	8.11	9.12	7.02	8.97
15–19	7.35	9.34	8.79	9.28	7.87	7.35	6.97	8.85	8.31	8.76	7.44	6.97
20–24	6.43	8.37	8.68	7.87	8.63	6.43	6.13	7.97	8.25	7.47	8.20	6.13
25–29	6.78	6.47	8.16	8.02	8.24	6.78	6.49	6.19	7.79	7.65	7.87	6.49
30–34	7.43	5.66	7.32	7.93	7.00	7.43	7.14	5.43	7.01	7.58	6.70	7.14
35–39	7.08	5.95	5.65	7.44	7.12	7.08	6.83	5.74	5.43	7.14	6.84	6.83
40–44	5.97	6.48	4.90	6.63	6.98	5.97	5.79	6.29	4.74	6.40	6.75	5.79
45–49	5.98	6.09	5.08	5.04	6.46	5.98	5.86	5.96	4.96	4.91	6.30	5.86
50–54	5.73	5.01	5.40	4.26	5.61	5.73	5.70	4.98	5.36	4.22	5.57	5.70
55–59	5.08	4.80	4.86	4.23	4.09	5.08	5.21	4.93	4.98	4.33	4.19	5.21
60–64	4.12	4.30	3.73	4.20	3.23	4.12	4.47	4.66	4.04	4.54	3.49	4.47
65–69	2.70	3.42	3.20	3.40	2.87	2.70	3.19	4.05	3.79	4.01	3.40	3.19
70–74	1.82	2.38	2.45	2.23	2.44	1.82	2.43	3.18	3.28	2.97	3.26	2.43
75–79	1.27	1.23	1.55	1.51	1.56	1.27	2.01	1.94	2.43	2.38	2.46	2.01
80–84	0.78	0.59	0.77	0.83	0.74	0.78	1.48	1.12	1.46	1.57	1.39	1.48
85+	0.38	0.33	0.31	0.40	0.39	0.38	0.87	0.77	0.71	0.90	0.89	0.87
Total	100.00	100.00	100.00	100.00	100.00	100.00	100.00	100.00	100.00	100.00	100.00	100.00

0–4	11.38	10.15	10.54	8.34	10.97	11.38	10.86	9.70	10.07	7.94	10.44	10.86
5–9	10.60	10.36	10.24	8.75	8.64	10.60	10.10	9.89	9.77	8.33	8.21	10.10
10–14	9.54	10.00	8.94	9.61	7.58	9.54	9.08	9.54	8.52	9.16	7.20	9.08
15–19	7.61	9.27	9.02	9.33	7.87	7.61	7.20	8.80	8.59	8.89	7.46	7.20
20–24	6.87	8.49	8.74	8.12	8.63	6.87	6.53	8.08	8.33	7.76	8.24	6.53
25–29	7.20	7.09	8.21	8.20	8.43	7.20	6.85	6.73	7.83	7.84	8.07	6.85
30–34	7.65	6.39	7.53	7.92	7.33	7.65	7.37	6.11	7.20	7.59	7.06	7.37
35–39	7.24	6.38	6.22	7.41	7.23	7.24	7.03	6.17	5.97	7.10	6.99	7.03
40–44	6.16	6.50	5.49	6.72	6.85	6.16	6.02	6.35	5.31	6.47	6.62	6.02
45–49	5.85	5.94	5.31	5.46	6.24	5.85	5.74	5.85	5.20	5.30	6.05	5.74
50–54	5.27	4.84	5.17	4.68	5.45	5.27	5.25	4.85	5.17	4.63	5.38	5.25
55–59	4.54	4.33	4.48	4.32	4.23	4.54	4.68	4.49	4.64	4.43	4.33	4.68
60–64	3.69	3.63	3.40	3.93	3.37	3.69	4.06	4.00	3.75	4.27	3.68	4.06
65–69	2.58	2.80	2.72	3.05	2.78	2.58	3.11	3.39	3.30	3.65	3.33	3.11
70–74	1.76	1.95	1.95	1.98	2.17	1.76	2.41	2.68	2.68	2.70	2.93	2.41
75–79	1.14	1.08	1.19	1.25	1.33	1.14	1.83	1.75	1.93	2.02	2.12	1.83
80–84	0.63	0.53	0.60	0.64	0.62	0.63	1.21	1.02	1.15	1.25	1.19	1.21
85+	0.29	0.26	0.25	0.30	0.30	0.29	0.67	0.61	0.59	0.70	0.70	0.67
Total	100.00	100.00	100.00	100.00	100.00	100.00	100.00	100.00	100.00	100.00	100.00	100.00

Note: See note to Table 4.7.

Comparing the corresponding values of the parameters in Table 4.7 with the growth indexes of the populations at selected ages given in Table 4.8, it may be observed that, when migration was absent, the growth indexes at the respective ages were equal to the parameters in the years in which these cohorts were born. For instance, if we take the first period, the growth indexes for ages 0, 10, 20, 30 and 40 years were the parameters respectively, for the first (i.e. fifty-first), forty-first, thirty-first, twenty-first and eleventh periods; and the index for age 50 years was the same as for age 0 years, for 60 years the same as for 10 years and so on. These results are true to the approximation we have used. Thus taking a still smaller value of ε, we could obtain the values as close to each other as we desire. It may also be seen that the growth indexes, as we expected, were the same for males and females when there was no migration. The effect of this was that, in this case, the sex ratios at all ages remained unchanged from period to period within the cycle (see Table 4.10).

When migration was introduced, none of these results followed. This consequence was also expected from the formulas derived here. At age 0 years the sex ratio remained the same even in the presence of migration because the effect of migration was comparatively small on this age and because a constant sex ratio among the net migrants was used in the model. A similar comment holds good for some of the old age groups. If we had taken different age–sex compositions of net migrants for the different periods the results would have been different.

The age distributions for males and females resulting from the cyclical model in the absence and in the presence of migration, are presented in Table 4.9 at intervals of 10 years of age for selected periods, for convenience of presentation. Comparing the two results, it can be seen that the effect of introducing migration, in this case, was to increase the proportions in the younger age groups and to decrease those in the old age groups. However, it must be noted that this effect of migration is not true in general, and, in fact, the effect depends as in the case of the equilibrium state populations, on the magnitudes of the net migration rates and the natures of the age–sex compositions of the net migrants within the cycle.

Finally, the procedure of iteration using the cyclical model, was used to compute the equilibrium state age–sex distribution resulting from the operation of the fertility and mortality rates observed in Australia in 1911 and the migration condition as in Australia during 1911–12. It was observed that the percentage age distributions and the sex ratios in five year age groups and the intrinsic growth rate (per 1000 persons) were almost identical with those obtained from the actual projections up to the second decimal point. The main advantage in using this iteration procedure is that we may start with any arbitrary age–sex distribution and obtain the equilibrium

Table 4.10   Sex structures at the end of certain periods within an equilibrium state cycle

Males per 100 females

Age groups	No migration period i						With migration period i					
	1	11	21	31	41	51	1	11	21	31	41	51
0–4	104.50	104.50	104.49	104.50	104.50	104.50	104.50	104.50	104.49	104.50	104.50	104.50
5–9	104.42	104.42	104.42	104.41	104.42	104.42	104.68	104.66	104.55	104.46	104.65	104.68
10–14	104.34	104.34	104.34	104.34	104.34	104.34	104.81	104.80	104.68	104.42	104.70	104.81
15–19	104.14	104.13	104.13	104.13	104.12	104.14	105.47	105.25	104.88	104.43	104.90	105.47
20–24	103.59	103.59	103.59	103.59	103.58	103.59	104.97	104.95	104.66	104.04	104.13	104.97
25–29	103.13	103.15	103.14	103.14	103.14	103.13	104.77	105.25	104.68	104.03	103.95	104.77
30–34	102.78	102.78	102.79	102.78	102.79	102.78	103.59	104.47	104.41	103.90	103.32	103.59
35–39	102.37	102.36	102.38	102.37	102.37	102.37	102.63	103.25	103.94	103.82	102.91	102.63
40–44	101.81	101.80	101.80	101.81	101.80	101.81	102.18	102.38	103.18	103.35	102.84	102.18
45–49	100.85	100.87	100.84	100.88	100.86	100.85	101.74	101.47	101.93	102.45	102.48	101.74
50–54	99.21	99.23	99.20	99.21	99.24	99.21	100.21	99.68	99.88	100.56	100.66	100.21
55–59	96.17	96.12	96.17	96.08	96.22	96.17	96.88	96.19	96.32	97.04	97.11	96.88
60–64	91.11	91.03	91.09	91.01	91.04	91.11	90.89	90.45	90.53	91.41	91.22	90.89
65–69	83.43	83.32	83.21	83.33	83.13	83.43	82.61	82.44	82.29	83.25	83.15	82.61
70–74	73.72	73.83	73.71	73.80	73.68	73.72	73.01	72.81	72.69	73.19	73.69	73.01
75–79	62.42	62.81	62.67	62.53	62.68	62.42	62.23	61.87	61.81	61.83	62.52	62.23
80–84	52.00	52.04	52.14	52.03	52.13	52.00	52.02	51.60	51.43	51.32	51.75	52.02
85+	43.03	42.64	42.96	43.17	42.87	43.03	43.03	42.82	42.61	42.59	42.51	43.03
Total	98.76	98.68	98.45	98.31	98.45	98.76	99.77	99.88	99.81	99.49	99.48	99.77

Note: See note to Table 4.7.

state age–sex distribution and the growth rate, simultaneously, to any desired degree of approximation without using the matrix methods. If the initial age–sex distribution chosen is close to the equilibrium state one, the iteration will be faster.

4.8 Summary

The problem of population change under the operation of a constant set of fertility, mortality and migration conditions has been studied in this chapter in two situations: (1) when the set contains a single schedule of each of the components of change—the equilibrium state model; and (2) when the set contains k schedules of each of the components of change—the cyclical model. Since the formulas under the assumption of no migration in the equilibrium state model have been derived by Goodman, more emphasis is given to the case where migration is included into the process of population growth using a net migration rate and an age–sex composition of net migrants.

In the cyclical model, the formulas derived by Namboodiri are slightly modified to facilitate the inclusion of migration and then extended to the two-sex case.

In each case, numerical illustrations are presented to check the formulas and to compare the structures of the resultant populations. From the numerical illustrations, it is observed that the age–sex composition of migrants plays an important role in determining the shape of the age–sex distributions of the equilibrium state population. For instance, the closer the age–sex composition of net migrants is to the age–sex distribution of the stable population resulting from the given schedules of fertility and mortality rates, the closer will be the resultant age–sex distribution of the equilibrium state population to the stable one.

The case in which age–sex-specific net migration rates are used in the process of population growth, is not presented separately, because the formulas applicable in the case with no migration can be used without change in that case.

Part III

POPULATION CHANGE UNDER VARYING CONDITIONS

5

WEAK ERGODICITY OF THE AGE–SEX DISTRIBUTIONS

5.1 Introduction

Weak ergodicity of an age–sex distribution is its property to "forget" and to become independent of its original shape in the remote past, when subjected to a set of age-specific fertility and mortality rates probably varying over time but satisfying certain conditions. It means that, after a sufficiently long period of time, the age–sex distribution of the population is determined entirely by the history of the age-specific vital rates. This theorem which was conjectured by Coale (1957a, pp. 83–89), was proved by Lopez (1961). Recently, McFarland (1969) has given a new elementary proof of the theorem and has suggested a method of computing the time required to "forget" the original shape of the age structure in terms of the oldest and the youngest ages at which child bearing takes place. These authors have concentrated mainly on closed populations. However, Lopez indicated that the weak ergodicity property holds good in the presence of migration, if migration is specified by a set of age-specific net migration rates, when it could be easily incorporated into the survival rates. Although McFarland made a passing remark that, unless conscious efforts are made to maintain a particular initial age–sex distribution through selective migration, migration could only speed up the process by which the initial age distribution is "forgotten", he did not attempt to demonstrate the same.

In this chapter, therefore, an attempt is made to examine whether this property holds good when migration specified by a net migration rate and an age–sex composition of net migrants is introduced into the process of

135

population change and to investigate the possible effects of the presence of migration on the duration of the process of convergence (i.e. the time required for the "forgetting" of the initial age structure), as compared to the case with no migration.

The weak ergodicity theorem is often stated in terms of two arbitrary populations as follows: Two populations with different age structures, when subjected to identical histories of age-specific vital rates, the rates possibly varying over time, will eventually have age structures which remain arbitrarily close to one another even though both may be changing over time. They will have, therefore, the same current crude rates of birth, death and growth. The same formulation will be used in the present investigation as it is convenient for analytical exposition.

Hence, in this chapter, the duration of convergence is defined as the number of years needed for the difference between any two arbitrary age distributions to become less than a preassigned small quantity, from the time both are subjected to identical histories of fertility, mortality and migration conditions.

We start, as in the previous chapters, with the one-sex model with no migration, then introduce migration and, finally, extend the results to the two-sex model which is our ultimate concern. The process of population change is again represented by matrix multiplication, instead of by a birth series (Lopez, 1967), because it facilitates the inclusion of migration into the process.

5.2 Convergence of age distributions

Let the two female (or male) populations be denoted by V and W so that at time t $V(x, t)$ and $W(x, t)$ are the numbers at age x years and $V(t)$ and $W(t)$ the total numbers at all ages in the two populations. We assume that, at the initial point of time, the age cohorts $V(x, t)$ and $W(x, t)$ are all positive. This is not a restrictive assumption because, if there is at least one non-zero cohort below the oldest age at which reproduction takes place, the whole age range gets filled up in course of time, and we can consider that point of time as the initial point. If no such cohort exists in any one of the populations, then that population becomes extinct and can not be considered further.

5.2.1 Convergence in the absence of migration

When there is no migration, the population growth of the two populations from $t = 0$ to $t = t$ years can be written down in matrix notation, as discussed in Section 3.2:

$$(V_t) = L(t - 1)L(t - 2) \ldots L(1)L(0)(V_0)$$

and

$$(W_t) = L(t - 1)L(t - 2) \ldots L(1)L(0)(W_0)$$

$$(5.1)$$

where (V_t) and (W_t) denote the population vectors at time t, and $L(t)$ is the population projection matrix:

$$\begin{bmatrix} 0 & 0 & . & 0 & m(\alpha, t) & . & m(\beta, t) & 0 & . & 0 & 0 \\ S(0, t) & 0 & . & 0 & 0 & . & 0 & 0 & . & 0 & 0 \\ 0 & S(1, t) & . & 0 & 0 & . & 0 & 0 & . & 0 & 0 \\ . & . & . & . & . & . & . & . & . & . & . \\ 0 & 0 & . & 0 & 0 & . & 0 & 0 & . & S(w - 1, t) & 0 \end{bmatrix}$$

where $m(x, t) = \frac{1}{2}[f(x, t) + S(x, t)f(x + 1, t)]S(b, t)$.

Lopez (1961) considered first the ages up to β years and proved that:

$$\lim_{t \to \infty} \left\{ \frac{V(x, t)}{W(x, t)} - \frac{V(y, t)}{W(y, t)} \right\} = 0 \tag{5.2}$$

for any two ages x and y years.

This means that the two populations tend to have identical age structures. The essential steps in his proof are presented below:

(1) The following lemma is proved: There is a sufficiently large positive integer k such that the product of k or more matrices $M(t)$, is a strictly positive matrix where $M(t)$ is the matrix:

$$\begin{bmatrix} 0 & 0 & . & 0 & m(\alpha, t) & . & m(\beta - 1, t) & m(\beta, t) \\ S(0, t) & 0 & . & 0 & 0 & . & 0 & 0 \\ 0 & S(1, t) & . & 0 & 0 & . & 0 & 0 \\ . & . & . & . & . & . & . & . \\ 0 & 0 & . & 0 & 0 & . & S(\beta - 1, t) & 0 \end{bmatrix} .$$

(2) The projection process is, then, carried in lumped steps of k years apart, k being the positive integer satisfying the lemma. At each lumped step T, the ratios $[V(x, T)/W(x, T)]$ are calculated for all x. Let r_T be the minimum and R_T the maximum of these ratios. Then it is proved that the

sequence of minima in the successive lumped steps, i.e. $r_0, r_1, \ldots$, is bounded and monotonically increasing, whereas the sequence of maxima, i.e. $R_0, R_1, \ldots$, is bounded and monotonically decreasing. Both sequences are therefore convergent.

(3) Finally, it is shown that the limits to which these two sequences converge are the same, thereby proving the weak ergodicity theorem.

After establishing that the weak ergodicity theorem holds good for the truncated age distribution excluding ages above β years, he demonstrated that the same holds good for the entire age range, from the fact that the populations at ages above β years are the survivors of those below β years. The details of the rigorous proofs of the three steps are given in Lopez (1961, pp. 50–57) and to an extent in Keyfitz (1968a, pp. 89–94) and are not repeated here.

For examining the duration of the process of convergence (i.e. the time required for the two age distributions to become arbitrarily close to each other), we shall again use the arguments involving the weighted averages as in Chapter 3. This will be taken up in Section 5.2.3.

5.2.2 Convergence in the presence of migration

Considering the case with migration, the population growth can be represented, as in Section 3.3, by the matrix equations:

$$(V_t) = L_M(t - 1)L_M(t - 2) \ldots L_M(0)(V_0),$$

$$(W_t) = L_M(t - 1) \ldots L_M(0)(W_0) \tag{5.3}$$

where $L_M(t)$ is the matrix shown on p.139.

Before proceeding further, it is shown that, as in the case where there is no migration, the populations at ages beyond β years (the oldest age at which reproduction occurs) become in course of time linear functions of the populations at ages below β years. This was claimed in Section 3.3 also (see Chapter 3). Let us assume that there is net migration at all ages above β years. Then the population at age $(\beta + 1)$ years at $t = 1$ could be obtained as follows:

$$V(\beta + 1, 1) = S(\beta, 0)V(\beta, 0) + a(\beta, 0) \sum_{0}^{w} V(x, 0)$$

$$= \left[a(\beta, 0) \sum_{0}^{\beta - 1} V(x, 0) \right] + [(S(\beta, 0) + a(\beta, 0))V(\beta, 0)]$$

$$+ a(\beta, 0) \sum_{\beta + 1}^{w} V(x, 0). \tag{5.4}$$

$$L_M(t) = \begin{bmatrix}
u(t) & [m(\alpha,t)+u(t)] & [m(\beta,t)+u(t)] & \cdot & u(t) & u(t) \\
[S(0,t)+a(0,t)] & a(0,t) & a(0,t) & \cdot & a(0,t) & a(0,t) \\
a(1,t) & a(1,t) & a(1,t) & \cdot & a(1,t) & a(1,t) \\
 & [S(1,t)+a(1,t)] & & & & \\
\cdot & \cdot & \cdot & \cdot & \cdot & \cdot \\
a(w-1,t) & a(w-1,t) & a(w-1,t) & \cdot & [S(w-1,t)+a(w-1,t)] & a(w-1,t)
\end{bmatrix}$$

(5.5)

with
$$u(t) = \left[S(b,t) \sum_{\alpha}^{\beta} \tfrac{1}{2}[a(x-1,t)f(x,t)] + \left(\frac{1+S(0,t)}{4} \right) n(0,t) \right] n(t)$$

and
$$a(x,t) = \tfrac{1}{4}[(1+S(x,t))n(x,t) + (1+S(x+1,t))n(x+1,t)]n(t).$$

(5.6)

At $t = 2$, we have:

$$V(\beta+1,2) = \left[a(\beta,1) \sum_0^{\beta-1} V(x,1) \right] + [(S(\beta,1) + a(\beta,1))V(\beta,1)]$$

$$+ a(\beta,1)V(\beta+1,1) + a(\beta,1) \sum_{\beta+2}^{w} V(x,1)$$

$$= \left[a(\beta,1) \sum_0^{\beta-1} V(x,1) \right] + [(S(\beta,1) + a(\beta,1))V(\beta,1)]$$

$$+ a(\beta,1)a(\beta,0) \sum_0^{\beta-1} V(x,0) + a(\beta,1)[(S(\beta,0) + a(\beta,0))V(\beta,0)]$$

$$+ a(\beta,1)a(\beta,0) \sum_{\beta+1}^{w} V(x,0) + a(\beta,1) \sum_{\beta+2}^{w} V(x,1).$$

$$(5.7)$$

Continuing further we can show that, as the original cohorts die out, the population at age $(\beta + 1)$ years becomes a linear function of the populations at ages below β years. Similarly, it follows that the populations at other ages above β years become functions of the populations at ages below β years. The coefficients of these functions are determined entirely by the mortality and migration schedules in the different periods of time.

Hence if the populations below the age β years become eventually proportional in the two populations which are subjected to the same set of fertility, mortality and migration conditions, so do the populations at the ages above β years, in the two populations.

(a) Now, for examining the effects of introducing migration, let us consider first the extreme cases, as in Chapter 3. Suppose $n(x, t)$ and $n(t)$ are all positive for all x and t. This implies that there is net immigration at all ages in all successive years. Then $u(t)$ and all $a(x, t)$ are positive for all x and t. Hence the matrix $L_M(t)$ has all its elements positive and could be taken as the lumped matrix we are seeking. Thus the lemma proved by Lopez as the first requirement for the convergence of the age distributions of the two populations V and W, is satisfied for $k = 1$. Once the lemma is satisfied, the other two steps needed to prove convergence of the age distributions follow from the proofs given by Lopez. Therefore we conclude that the theorem of weak ergodicity holds good in this case as well.

On the other hand, if there is emigration at all ages during the successive years, i.e. all $n(x, t)$ are positive but $n(t)$ is negative, then $u(t)$ and all $a(x, t)$ become negative. It may be noted that the case where all $n(x, t)$ are negative and $n(t)$ is positive is not admissible from the practical point of view. Also, from assumption (8), it is necessary that $n(t)$ be sufficiently

small so that the population will be able to sustain this continuous emigration, which means that at no time, the population at any age becomes
negative. This requires that there is at least one positive element in each
of the rows of the matrix $L_M(t)$ for all t such that the vectors of the products
$L_M(t)(V_t)$ and $L_M(t)(W_t)$ are strictly positive. By examining the matrix
$L_M(t)$, it is not difficult to see that the positive elements are the subdiagonal
elements corresponding to $S(0, t)$, $S(1, t)$, $S(2, t)$, . . . , $S(w - 1, t)$ as in the
matrix $L(t)$ and some elements, $m(x, t)$, in the first row corresponding to
the fertility rates. We assume that $m(x, t)$ will remain strictly positive for
at least two fixed consecutive values of x, for all t.

Thus the positive elements remain at fixed positions in all the matrices
being multiplied, as in the case with no migration. Hence, from the results
proved by Lopez, it is possible to infer, without actual multiplication
(however, see the following paragraph) that a number k exists such that
the product of the elements of the k matrices passes through positive paths
and thus a lumped matrix of positive elements could be obtained. But, in
this case, we cannot partition the matrix $L_M(t)$ as we partitioned the matrix
$L(t)$ and consider only the ages below β years. Further, the matrix $L_M(t)$
may contain a smaller number of positive elements in the first row than
the matrix $M(t)$ because at some of the ages at the beginning and at the
end of the reproductive life the fertility rates are very small and therefore,
some of these elements may become negative. Hence it would require a
larger k to obtain a lumped matrix of positive elements than would be
required in the case of the matrix $M(t)$. However, the existence of a lumped
matrix of positive elements proves the weak ergodicity theorem in this
case.

The question that remains to be settled in this case of continuous
emigration, is whether the result would be applicable even when t is not
a multiple of k as it does in the case when there is no migration or when
there is continuous immigration. Following the procedure adopted by
Lopez (1961, pp. 65–67), let the product of the lumped matrices,
$H(T, T + 1)$, tend to the matrix B which has the following form:

$$\begin{bmatrix} k_0 b_t(0) & k_1 b_t(0) & . & . & . & k_w b_t(0) \\ k_0 b_t(1) & k_1 b_t(1) & . & . & . & k_w b_t(1) \\ . & . & . & . & . & . \\ k_0 b_t(w) & k_1 b_t(w) & . & . & . & k_w b_t(w) \end{bmatrix}$$

when t is a multiple of k, the size of the lump. The numbers $b_t(x)$ keep
changing in general as the number t of factor matrices varies. To see what
happens when t is not a multiple of k, we shall pre-multiply the matrix B

by a matrix of the type $L_M(t)$ with $u(t)$ and $a(x, t)$ being negative. Then we obtain the matrix B' given below:

$$\begin{bmatrix} k_0 b_{t+1}(0) & k_1 b_{t+1}(0) & . & . & . & k_w b_{t+1}(0) \\ k_0 b_{t+1}(1) & k_1 b_{t+1}(1) & . & . & . & k_w b_{t+1}(1) \\ & & \cdot & \cdot & \cdot & \\ k_0 b_{t+1}(w) & k_1 b_{t+1}(w) & . & . & . & k_w b_{t+1}(w) \end{bmatrix}$$

in which

$$b_{t+1}(0) = \sum_{\alpha}^{\beta} m(x, t) b_t(x) + u(t) \sum_0^w b_t(x) \tag{5.8}$$

and

$$b_{t+1}(x) = S(x-1, t) b_t(x-1) + a(x-1, t) \sum_0^w b_t(x),$$

$$\text{for } x = 1, 2, \ldots, w. \tag{5.9}$$

The product matrix B is a matrix of positive elements and hence $b_t(x)$ are positive. Therefore, $b_{t+1}(x)$ must be positive from the requirements of assumption (8). Hence, by comparing the matrices B and B', we conclude that when the emigration rates are such that condition (8) is always satisfied, then the matrix product $\prod_{i=0}^{t-1} L_M(i)$ will tend, as t becomes large, to a matrix of the form as B whether t is a multiple of k or not and therefore the weak ergodicity theorem holds good.

(b) In the considerations so far, we have assumed that $n(x, t)$ are positive for all x though varying over time while $n(t)$ is either positive for all t or negative for all t. But if we allow $n(x, t)$ to assume zeros for some x, which means that we relax the condition that migration affects all ages, then there can arise several situations. For instance, if we consider an extreme case where migration occurs at only one age every year, this age may remain the same or change over time apart from the fact that the magnitude of the migration effect may change. In the case of the equilibrium state conditions considered in Chapter 3, the ages at which migration occurs are automatically fixed for all t, once the migration schedule is specified. But in the present case, this is not so, unless we introduce additional assumptions. This does not seem to be necessary because the subdiagonal elements corresponding to the survival rates and at least two of the elements of the first row corresponding to the fertility rates which we have assumed to be at fixed ages will remain at fixed positions over time and are positive. Their magnitude may vary over time. Therefore, if only immigration occurs for all t at some ages including at least one age below β years, it would only increase the number of positive elements in the matrices. Hence the convergence occurs.

On the other hand, if only emigration occurs for all t at some ages including at least one age below β years, we can infer from a similar argument as in (a) above that the convergence does take place.

(c) When $n(x, t)$ and $n(t)$ assume positive, negative and/or zero values for any x and for any t, which implies that immigration, emigration and no migration can occur at any age and at any time, the fact that in each of the projection matrices we have at least one positive element in a fixed position in each row except in the first one where, actually, two are always positive at fixed positions, suggests that the convergence should take place sooner or later, unless there is a systematic trend in immigration and emigration such that the effects become compensatory at different ages in the different years.

(d) Special cases: Now, consider the special case in which the net migration affects only the ages beyond the oldest age of reproduction. Then we cannot find a lumped matrix with positive elements for any value of k, as can be seen from the following. Let the matrix $L_M(t)$ be written as follows:

$$\begin{bmatrix} M(t) & 0 \\ A(M, t) & B(M, t) \end{bmatrix}.$$

Multiplying two matrices of this form we have:

$$\begin{bmatrix} M(2) & 0 \\ A(M, 2) & B(M, 2) \end{bmatrix} \begin{bmatrix} M(1) & 0 \\ A(M, 1) & B(M, 1) \end{bmatrix}$$

$$= \begin{bmatrix} M(2)M(1) & 0 \\ [A(M, 2)M(1) + B(M, 2)A(M, 1)] & B(M, 2)B(M, 1) \end{bmatrix}. \quad (5.10)$$

We can see that the right-hand side of eqn (5.10) is of the same form as $L_M(t)$ and continuing in this manner it can be shown that we cannot get a lumped matrix containing all positive elements. But, if we multiply the matrix $L_M(t)$ in the form given in eqn (5.10) by the initial population vector, we can see that, as in the case with no migration, the population change above the age β years has no effect on the population growth below the age β years. Therefore, the convergence of the truncated age distribution below β years can be considered first, as in the case with no migration, and then extend to the other ages. As far as the truncated age distribution is concerned, the situation is the same as in the case with no migration and hence the convergence occurs.

The question is therefore, whether the weak ergodicity property holds good in this case if all the ages are included, as it does when there is no migration. It has already been shown that the populations at ages beyond β years become linear functions of the populations at ages below β years, even in the presence of migration, and the coefficients of these functions are determined entirely by the mortality and migration conditions. Since these schedules are common to the populations V and W, and since the cohorts at ages below β years become proportional with the increase in t, the populations at ages beyond β years also become proportional. Hence the theorem holds good for the whole age range.

Next, consider another special case in which migration affects only the ages below β years. In this situation we may note that, in course of time, the population at ages above β years become the survivors of the populations at ages below β years. The situation remains the same as in the general case except that now, the averaging effect of immigration or the deductions due to emigration occur only up to age β years. Hence, from the earlier discussion, the convergence follows.

If, alternatively, we use the age-specific net migration rates in the process of population change, the convergence of the age distributions depends on the matrices $M'(t)$ which have the same structures as the matrices $M(t)$. Hence the weak ergodicity theorem holds good, but the duration of convergence will remain the same as in the case with no migration.

5.3 The duration of convergence

The duration of convergence of any two age distributions (i.e. the number of years needed for the two age distributions to become arbitrarily close to each other) depends as much on the initial differences between the two age distributions as on the nature of the variations in fertility, mortality and migration schedules. We shall examine in this section the comparative picture of this duration in the presence of migration as against that in the absence of the same. In general, the "forgetting" of the initial shape of the age distribution happens gradually as the initial cohorts die out and are replaced by cohorts which are not replicas of the old ones; each one arises from a combination of the earlier cohorts.

The procedure employed in Chapter 3 for this purpose in the case of constant conditions can be adopted here without much change. As before, let the population ratio at age x at time t be defined as:

$$R(x, t) = V(x, t)/W(x, t), \qquad \text{for } x = 0, 1, \ldots, w. \qquad (5.11)$$

Let $R(t)$ and $r(t)$ be the maximum and minimum of these ratios. Then, the population ratios at time $(t + 1)$ for the different age cohorts are:

$$R(0, t + 1) = \frac{V(0, t + 1)}{W(0, t + 1)} = \frac{\sum\limits_{\alpha}^{\beta} m(x, t)R(x, t)W(x, t)}{\sum\limits_{\alpha}^{\beta} m(x, t)W(x, t)} \qquad (5.12)$$

and

$$R(x, t + 1) = \frac{S(x - 1, t)R(x - 1, t)W(x - 1, t)}{S(x - 1, t)W(x - 1, t)}$$

$$= R(x - 1, t), \qquad \text{for } x = 1, 2, \ldots, w. \qquad (5.13)$$

Hence, as in the case of constant conditions, the averaging effect takes place only at age 0, and any change in $d(t) = R(t) - r(t)$ must come through this and the dropping off of the ratio at the end age, w.

Now, introduce migration and examine the population ratios at time $(t + 1)$:

$$R(0, t + 1) = \frac{\sum\limits_{\alpha}^{\beta} m(x, t)R(x, t)W(x, t) + u(t)\sum\limits_{0}^{w} R(x, t)W(x, t)}{\sum\limits_{\alpha}^{\beta} m(x, t)W(x, t) + u(t)\sum\limits_{0}^{w} W(x, t)}$$

$$= \frac{\sum\limits_{0}^{w} (m(x, t) + u_t)R(x, t)W(x, t)}{\sum\limits_{0}^{w} (m(x, t) + u_t)W(x, t)} \qquad (5.14)$$

and

$R(x, t + 1)$

$$= \frac{S(x - 1, t)R(x - 1, t)W(x - 1, t) + a(x - 1, t)\sum\limits_{0}^{w} R(x, t)W(x, t)}{S(x - 1, t)W(x - 1, t) + a(x - 1, t)\sum\limits_{0}^{w} W(x, t)}. \qquad (5.15)$$

Comparing these equations with eqns (3.36) and (3.37), it is not difficult to see that the results proved there follow in this case also. Therefore, it may be concluded that the duration of convergence in the presence of migration (i.e., t_0) is less than, or equal to, or more than the duration in the absence of migration (i.e., t_1) according as $n(t) \gtreqless 0$ when $n(x, t) \geq 0$ for all x and t.

However, if $n(x, t)$ and $n(t)$ both assume positive, negative and/or zero values for any x and t, then the duration of convergence could be less than, equal to, or greater than that in the case with no migration, depending on the number of years each of the situations prevails and the age range affected by immigration or emigration or no migration in each case, as well as the magnitudes of the corresponding $n(t)$.

In the special situation in which migration affects only the ages beyond the oldest age of reproduction (see Section 5.2.2(d)) also, the duration will be less in the presence of immigration than that in the case of no migration, since the averaging effect occurs every year, in this case, at ages beyond β years. But, this duration would obviously be greater than in the case where there is immigration at all ages. However, if emigration occurs at these ages, it is not very clear how the duration would change. A safe conclusion would be that the duration will not be less than that in the case with no migration.

However, it may be argued that the weights of some of the age cohorts included in the averaging which occurs at age 0, are reduced or offset by the deductions caused by the emigration and hence the duration will be longer than that in the case with no migration and less than that in the presence of emigration at all ages.

By similar reasoning it may be concluded that, in any other special situation when migration affects only the ages below β years, the duration of convergence will be smaller in the case of immigration than when there is no migration, but larger than when immigration occurs at all ages. The opposite results follow if there is emigration at these ages.

Finally, when the age-specific net migration rates are used in the process of population change, the situation becomes similar to the one with no migration. For instance, the population ratio at time $(t + 1)$ will be:

$$R(x + 1, t + 1) = \frac{V(x + 1, t + 1)}{W(x + 1, t + 1)} = \frac{(S(x, t) + a(x, t))V(x, t)}{(S(x, t) + a(x, t))W(x, t)}$$

$$= \frac{V(x, t)}{W(x, t)} = R(x, t) \tag{5.16}$$

and hence the ratio for a cohort will not change until that cohort dies ultimately, as in the absence of migration. Thus the changes in the population ratios must come through the newborn cohorts only, and the duration of convergence will be approximately the same as in the case with no migration. Any difference in the duration must arise only due to the change in the relative weights of the different cohorts involved in the population ratio at age zero.

5.4 Corollaries

As a corollary to the weak ergodicity theorem, McFarland (1969) has shown that the two populations subjected to identical fertility and mortality conditions will tend to have the same birth, death and growth rates. It is not difficult to see that the same holds good when migration is introduced into the process.

Further, we shall show that the age cohorts in the two populations will have the same growth rates. We know from the weak ergodicity theorem that, when t is sufficiently large,

$$\frac{V(x, t)}{W(x, t)} = R', \text{ a constant for all } x.$$

Then

$$\frac{V(x + 1, t + 1)}{V(x + 1, t)} = \frac{S(x, t)V(x, t) + a(x, t) \sum_{0}^{w} V(x, t)}{V(x + 1, t)}$$

$$= \frac{S(x, t)R'W(x, t) + a(x, t) \sum_{0}^{w} R'W(x, t)}{R'W(x + 1, t)}$$

$$= \frac{W(x + 1, t + 1)}{W(x + 1, t)}. \tag{5.17}$$

The proofs in the case with no migration and when age–sex-specific net migration rates are used, follow easily.

Thus the equality of the growth rates for each age can be used as the criterion for recognizing the weak ergodicity in any practical situation. Further, the graphs of the MaxGI and MinGI could be used to depict the process of convergence as in the case of constant conditions (see, for instance, Fig. 5.1 in Section 5.6). It may be noted, however, that, in the present case, MaxGI and MinGI which coincide and become constant over time when the operating conditions are constant (see Chapter 3), will not only be different from each other but also will be changing over time. Therefore, if we are looking at only MaxGI and MinGI but not at the growth indexes at all ages, it may happen that the age distributions might not have converged even though MaxGI and MinGI for the two populations differ by an arbitrarily small quantity. This happens because the growth indexes at different ages may actually be different within the same maximum and minimum limits. Hence, in practice, we must either test for the equality of growth indexes at all ages or use other indicators such as the ADI and SRDI in conjunction with the MaxGI and MinGI to test the occurrence of convergence.

5.5 Extension to the two-sex case

The results discussed in the case of the one-sex model could easily be extended to infer the convergence of age–sex distributions and the related changes in the duration of convergence.

We shall consider first the female dominance and then refer to the case with equal dominance. It may be noted that for the convergence of the age–sex distributions, it is enough if the ratios for the male populations and for the female populations converge to separate to a limits. The two limits need not be equal as is the case under constant conditions.

5.5.1 Female dominance with no migration

Using the subscripts m and f to distinguish the male and the female populations respectively, and assuming $f_f(x, t)$ to be the age-specific birth rate (taking births of both sexes) for females and s_t to be the male proportion at birth for the year t, the projection matrix $L'(t)$ in the case with no migration can be written as follows:

$$
\begin{bmatrix}
0 & . & 0 & m_f(\alpha, t) & . & m_f(\beta, t) & 0 \\
S_f(0, t) & . & 0 & 0 & . & 0 & 0 \\
. & . & . & . & . & . & . \\
0 & . & 0 & 0 & . & 0 & 0 \\
0 & . & 0 & m'_f(\alpha, t) & . & m'_f(\beta, t) & 0 \\
0 & . & 0 & 0 & . & 0 & 0 \\
. & . & . & . & . & . & . \\
0 & . & 0 & 0 & . & 0 & 0
\end{bmatrix}
$$

where $m_f(x, t)$ and $m'_f(x, t)$ are similar to $m(x, t)$ in $L(t)$, but multiplied by $(1 - s_t)S_f(b, t)$ and by $s_t S_m(b, t)$ respectively, instead of by $S(b, t)$.

If the population vectors (V_t) and (W_t) are now formed in such a way that females by age are respectively in the first $(w + 1)$ places followed by the males by age in the other $(w + 1)$ places, we have a similar situation as in the one-sex model. In fact, it is not difficult to see that $L'(t)$ can be partitioned as follows:

$$\begin{bmatrix} L(t) & 0 \\ A'(t) & B'(t) \end{bmatrix}$$

where $L(t)$ is the same matrix as in the one-sex model. By matrix multiplication we can show that, in any product, the elements of the first row are not affected by the elements of the second row. Thus the growth of the female population is not affected by the changes in the male population. Further, in course of time, the male population at each age becomes a linear function of the female populations at ages below the highest age at which reproduction occurs and the coefficients of that function are determined entirely by the fertility and survival rates which are common to both the populations. Hence the convergence of the age–sex distributions takes place as the convergence of the female age distributions below the age β years happens. The duration of convergence is also the same as required for the convergence of the female age distribution, provided that duration is greater than $(w + 1)$ years which is the time needed for the male populations at all ages to become functions of the female populations at ages below β years. In fact, the sex ratios in the two populations become arbitrarily close when the male populations become functions of the female populations and as the convergence of the female age distributions occurs, automatically the male age distributions also converge.

$$\begin{bmatrix} 0 & 0 & 0 & . & 0 & 0 \\ 0 & 0 & 0 & . & 0 & 0 \\ . & . & . & . & . & . \\ \cdot(w-1,t) & 0 & 0 & . & 0 & 0 \\ 0 & 0 & 0 & . & 0 & 0 \\ 0 & 0 & S_m(0,t) & . & 0 & 0 \\ . & . & . & . & . & . \\ 0 & 0 & 0 & . & S_m(w-1,t) & 0 \end{bmatrix}$$

5.5.2 Female dominance with migration

When migration is included into the process of population change, the projection matrix can be obtained, as in the one-sex model, by adding the migration coefficients to each of the elements in the respective rows of the matrix $L'(t)$.

The new matrix $L'_M(t)$, thus obtained, is presented at the foot of this page, where

$$u_f(t) = \left[(1 - s_t)S_f(b, t) \sum_\alpha^\beta \tfrac{1}{2}a_f(x - 1, t)f_f(x, t) \right]$$
$$+ \tfrac{1}{4}((1 + S_f(0, t))(1 - s'_t)n_f(0, t)n(t)$$

s'_t being the male proportion among the net migrants;

$$u_m(t) = s_t S_m(b, t) \sum_\alpha^\beta \tfrac{1}{2}a_f(x - 1, t)f_f(x, t) + \tfrac{1}{4}(1 + S_m(0, t))s'_t n_m(0, t)n(t)$$

$$a_f(x, t) = \tfrac{1}{4}[(1 + S_f(x, t))n_f(x, t) + (1 + S_f(x + 1, t))n_f(x + 1, t)](1 - s'_t)n(t)$$

and

$$a_m(x, t) = \tfrac{1}{4}[(1 + S_m(x, t))n_m(x, t) + (1 + S_m(x + 1, t))n_m(x + 1, t)]s'_t n(t).$$

Examining the matrix $L'_M(t)$ we see that, when net immigration occurs at all ages for both males and females, the age–sex distributions converge and the duration will be less than that in the absence of migration. On the other hand, if there is emigration at all ages for both sexes, we have only one element per row, which is positive except in the first row and the

---

Matrix $L'_M(t) =$

$u_f(t)$	.	$u_f(t)$	$[m_f(\alpha, t)$ $+ u_f(t)]$	.	$[m_f(\beta, t)$ $+ u_f(t)]$	$u_f(t)$
$[S_f(0, t)$ $+ a_f(0, t)]$	.	$a_f(0, t)$	$a_f(0, t)$	.	$a_f(0, t)$	$a_f(0, t)$
.	.	.	.	.	.	.
$a_f(w - 1, t)$	.	$a_f(w - 1, t)$	$a_f(w - 1, t)$	.	$a_f(w - 1, t)$	$a_f(w - 1,$
$u_m(t)$	.	$u_m(t)$	$[m'_f(\alpha, t)$ $+ u_m(t)]$	.	$[m'_f(\beta, t)$ $+ u_m(t)]$	$u_m(t)$
$a_m(0, t)$	.	$a_m(0, t)$	$a_m(0, t)$	.	$a_m(0, t)$	$a_m(0, t)$
.	.	.	.	.	.	.
$a_m(w - 1, t)$	.	$a_m(w - 1, t)$	$a_m(w - 1, t)$	.	$a_m(w - 1, t)$	$a_m(w - 1,$

$(w + 2)$-th row in each of which there are at least two positive elements at fixed positions. As seen in the case of the one-sex model, convergence takes place but the duration needed will be greater than that in the case where there is no migration.

If migration affects only the males, then migration will have no effect on the female population because the matrix $L'_M(t)$ can be partitioned as the matrix $L'(t)$, and the changes in the male population will have no effect on the changes in the female population. But, as in the case with no migration, the male population at each age becomes, in course of time, a function of the female populations at ages below β years because we have assumed female dominance. The coefficients of these functions are determined entirely by the fertility, mortality and migration schedules which are common to the two populations. Thus as the female age distributions in the two populations come closer, the male age distributions also converge and therefore the age–sex distributions converge. The duration needed will depend on the time required for the male populations at all ages to become entirely functions of the female populations at ages below β years, and on the time needed for the age distributions for females to converge. It may be noted that $(w + 1)$ years will be necessary for the male populations at all ages to become functions of the female populations at ages below β years. Hence by $(w + 1)$ years the differences in the sex ratios in the two populations again vanish. The differences in the age distributions vanish as the female age distributions converge.

$$
\begin{bmatrix}
u_f(t) & u_f(t) & u_f(t) & \cdot & u_f(t) & u_f(t) \\[4pt]
{}_{\cdot}(0,t) & a_f(0,t) & a_f(0,t) & \cdot & a_f(0,t) & a_f(0,t) \\[6pt]
\vdots & \vdots & \vdots & \vdots & & \vdots \\[6pt]
(w-1,t) & a_f(w-1,t) & a_f(w-1,t) & & a_f(w-1,t) & a_f(w-1,t) \\
(w-1,t)] & & & & & \\[8pt]
u_m(t) & u_m(t) & u_m(t) & \cdot & u_m(t) & u_m(t) \\[6pt]
{}_{\cdot}(0,t) & a_m(0,t) & [S_m(0,t) & \cdot & a_m(0,t) & a_m(0,t) \\
& & + a_m(0,t)] & & & \\[8pt]
\vdots & \vdots & \vdots & \cdot & \vdots & \vdots \\[6pt]
w-1,t) & a_m(w-1,t) & a_m(w-1,t) & \cdot & [S_m(w-1,t) & a_m(w-1,t) \\
& & & & + a_m(w-1,t)] &
\end{bmatrix}
$$

Once migration affects the female population, the results would be as in the case of the one-sex model. Similarly, if age–sex-specific net migration rates are used, the results would depend entirely on the convergence of the female age distributions as in the absence of migration.

5.5.3 Equal dominance of the sexes

In this case, only the growth equations for the male and the female populations at age 0 years change, so that the projection matrix $L'(t)$ will remain the same except for the first row and the $(w + 2)$-th row which become now, as follows:

First row:

$$0 . 0 \; m_f(\alpha', t) . \; m_f(\beta', t) \; 0 . 0 \; 0 \quad 0 . 0 \; m_m(\alpha', t) . \; m_m(\beta', t) \; 0 . 0 \; 0$$

and the $(w + 2)$-th row:

$$0 . 0 \; m_f'(\alpha', t) . \; m_f'(\beta', t) \; 0 . 0 \; 0 \quad 0 . 0 \; m_m'(\alpha', t) . \; m_m'(\beta', t) \; 0 . 0 \; 0$$

where $m_f(x, t)$ and $m_f'(x, t)$ are half of the corresponding values in $L'(t)$,

$$m_m(x, t) = \tfrac{1}{2}(1 - s_t)S_f(b, t)[\tfrac{1}{2}\{f_m(x, t) + S_m(x, t)f_m(x + 1, t)\}]$$

and

$$m_m'(x, t) = \tfrac{1}{2}s_t S_m(b, t)[\tfrac{1}{2}\{f_m(x, t) + S_m(x, t)f_m(x + 1, t)\}].$$

Let this new matrix be denoted by $L''(t)$. Partitioning the matrix at the $(\beta' + 1)$-th, where β' is the oldest age at which reproduction occurs among females or among males, $(w + 1)$-th and $(w + 1 + \beta' + 1)$-th rows and columns, we can write the matrix $L''(t)$ as follows:

$$\begin{bmatrix} Q(t) & 0 & R(t) & 0 \\ A(t) & B(t) & 0 & 0 \\ Q_1(t) & 0 & R_1(t) & 0 \\ 0 & 0 & A_1(t) & B_1(t) \end{bmatrix}.$$

By multiplying $L''(t)$ in this form for various values of t, we find that the population change below age β' years is independent of the population change above that age at any time, for males and females. Hence we first consider the female and the male populations at ages up to β' years only. We can then write down the projection matrix as follows:

$$\begin{bmatrix} Q(t) & R(t) \\ Q_1(t) & R_1(t) \end{bmatrix}.$$

Since the fertility rate for males at age β' years can be assumed to be positive (because the oldest age of reproduction is generally higher in the case of males than in the case of females) for all t, we can now find a lumped matrix of positive elements, for some k, by multiplying the matrices of the form given above. Thus we conclude that the convergence of the truncated age–sex distributions occurs. Consequently, the convergence of the entire age–sex distributions also takes place because the populations at ages above β' years become, in course of time, the survivors of those below that age.

When migration is introduced into this process, the results obtained earlier hold good with the change that the duration will be affected by the migration of males or females, or both. For instance, the duration is shortened if there is immigration and is lengthened if there is emigration as compared to the case with no migration, whether migration affects only males or only females, or both.

5.6 Numerical illustrations

For numerical illustrations, the three populations, 1911 obs., 1911 stb. and 1966 obs., which were considered in the case of constant conditions, were projected under identical assumptions of varying schedules of fertility, mortality and migration. The survival rates of the life tables interpolated for each year from the life tables for Australia at the census dates between 1911–66, were assumed to operate during the first 56 years and the values for 1966 were assumed to remain constant thereafter (see Section 2.4). As regards fertility, the sequence of hypothetical fertility rates derived for the study (see Section 2.4), was assumed. On the other hand, different assumptions were used for net migration.

(i) *Effects of migration on the duration of convergence of age–sex distributions*

Figure 5.1 compares the process of convergence in three situations—when there was no migration, when migration was specified by overall net migration rates and age–sex compositions of net migrants, and when the same migration situation was specified by age–sex-specific net migration rates. The legend accompanying the graph reveals the actual assumptions. It is clear from the graph that in all the three cases the initial differences between the given age–sex distributions vanished in course of time, indicating that the weak ergodicity theorem holds good.

Regarding the duration of convergence, the graph indicates that the

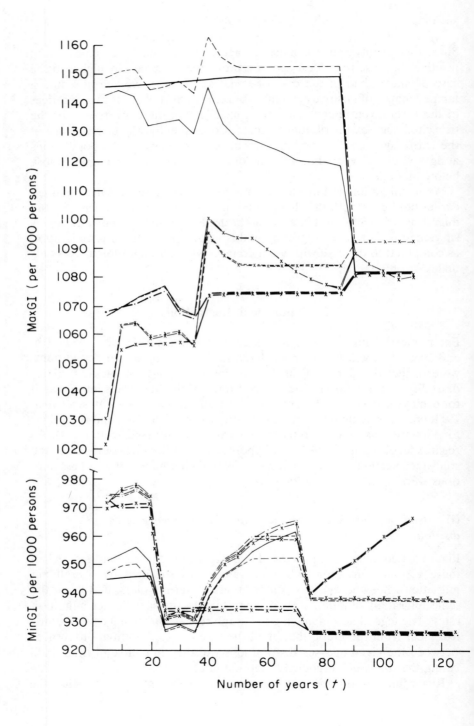

Table 5.1 Effect of migration on the duration of convergence of age–sex distributions under varying conditions of fertility, mortality and migration

	From actual projections Value of t in number of years		
Prevailing conditions	1911 obs. and 1911 stb.	1911 stb. and 1966 obs.	1966 obs. and 1911 obs.
1 Mortality: As observed in Australia during 1911–66 and the 1966 values remaining constant			
Fertility: Hypothetical fertility rates having the continuing trend similar to the one observed during 1911–61			
Migration: No migration	225	210	225
2 Mortality: Same as in 1			
Fertility: Same as in 1			
Migration: Net migration rates and the age–sex compositions of net migrants as observed in Australia during 1911–66 and the 1965–66 values remaining constant	150	150	165
3 Mortality: Same as in 1			
Fertility: Same as in 1			
Migration: Age–sex-specific net migration rates as observed in Australia during 1911–66 and the 1965–66 values remaining constant	225	220	225

FIG. 5.1. The process of convergence of age–sex distributions as seen from the convergence of MaxGI and MinGI for females under changing schedules of fertility, mortality and migration, when migration is specified in two different ways. Mortality: 1911–66 and 1966 constant. Fertility: Sequence of hypothetical rates. Migration: (i) No migration: – — — - 1911 obs. pop.; ⊷-×-×-×-×-×⊶ 1911 stb. pop.; ———— 1966 obs. pop. (ii) Net migration rates and age–sex composition of net migrants as observed in Australia, 1911–66 and 1966 values remaining constant: – — – 1911 obs. pop.; ×-×-×-×-×-× 1911 stb. pop.; ———— 1966 obs. pop. (iii) Age-specific migration rates as observed in Australia, 1911–66 and 1966 values remaining constant: ------ 1911 obs. pop.; ×-×--×-×-×-× 1911 stb. pop.; ------ 1966 obs. pop.

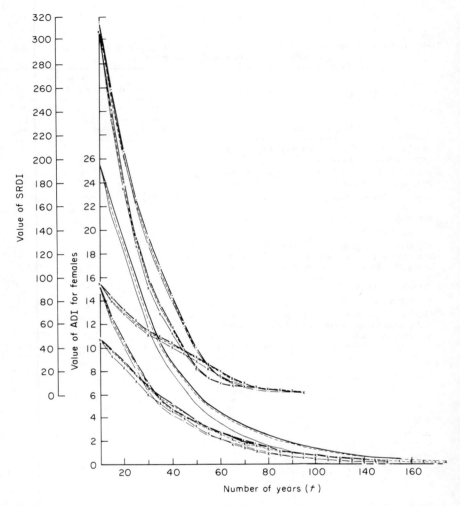

FIG. 5.2. Convergence of age–sex distributions as seen from the decrease in the values of ADI and SRDI under changing schedules of fertility, mortality and migration, when migration is specified in two different ways. Note: At larger values of t the values which could not be distinguished from those already plotted have been omitted, but the merging of the respective curves can easily be seen. Mortality: 1911–66 and 1966 constant. Fertility: Sequence of hypothetical rates. Migration: (i) No migration: —·——·— 1911 obs. and 1911 stb.; ·—·—·—·—·—·· 1911 stb. and 1966 obs.; ———— 1966 obs. and 1911 obs. (ii) Net migration rate and age–sex composition of net migrants as observed in Australia, 1911–66 and the 1965–66 values remaining constant: – – – –1911 obs. and 1911 stb.; ×—·—·—·—× 1911 stb. and 1966 obs.; ———— 1966 obs. and 1911 obs. (iii) Age-specific net migration rates as observed in Australia, 1911–66 and the 1965–66 values remaining constant: ––– –– 1911 obs. and 1911 stb.; ×—··—·I·—·×·· 1911 stb. and 1966 obs.; –––––––1966 obs. and 1911 obs.

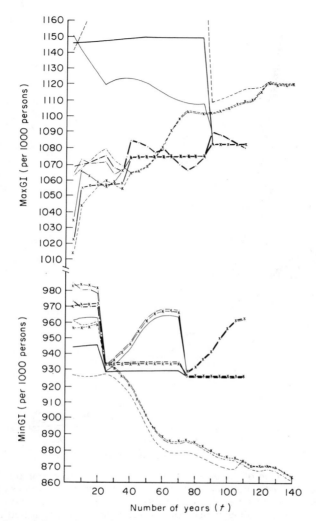

FIG. 5.3. Comparison of the effect of immigration and emigration on the process of convergence of age–sex distributions as seen from the convergence of MaxGI and MinGI for females, under changing schedules of fertility, mortality and migration. Mortality: 1911–66 and 1966 constant. Fertility: Sequence of hypothetical rates. Migration: (i) No migration: $-\cdot-\cdot-$ 1911 obs.; $\cdot-\cdot-\cdot-\cdot-\cdot$ 1911 stb.; ———— 1966 obs. (ii) Net immigration rate given by $[0.01 \{ABS (\cos 0.0628318(t-1))\}]$ and age–sex composition of migrants being the same as for the net migrants in Australia, 1962–66: $-\ -\ -$ 1911 obs.; $\cdot-\cdot-\cdot-\cdot-$ 1911 stb.; ———— 1966 obs. (iii) Net emigration rate given by $[-0.1 \{ABS (\cos 0.0628318(t-1))\}]$ and age–sex composition of migrants being the same as for the net migrants in Australia, 1962–66: $------$ 1911 obs.; $\cdot-\cdot-\cdot-\cdot-$ 1 1911 stb.; $------$ 1966 obs. Here ABS denotes the absolute value.

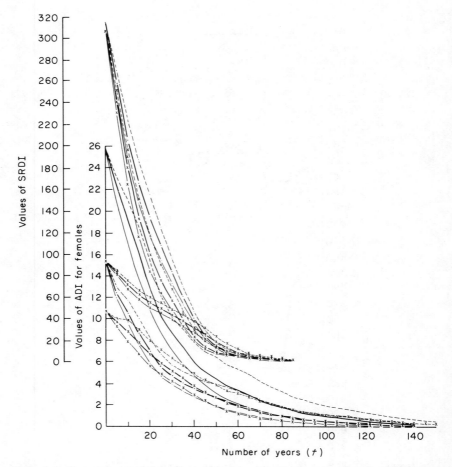

FIG. 5.4. Comparison of the effect of immigration and emigration on the convergence of age–sex distributions as seen from the decrease in the values of ADI and
SRDI under changing schedules of fertility, mortality and migration. Note: At
larger values of t the values which could not be clearly distinguished from those
already plotted have been omitted, but the merging of the respective curves
can easily be seen. Mortality: 1911–66 and 1966 constant. Fertility: Sequence
of hypothetical rates. Migration: (i) No migration: — · — · — 1911 obs. and 1911 stb.;
×—·—·—×—·—× 1911 stb. and 1966 obs.; ———— 1966 obs. and 1911 obs.
(ii) Net immigration rate given by $[0.01 \{ABS (\cos 0.0628318(t - 1))\}]$ and age–sex
composition of migrants being the same as for the net migrants in Australia,
1962–66: – – – 1911 obs. and 1911 stb.; ×—·—·—·—·× 1911 stb. and 1966 obs.;
———— 1966 obs. and 1911 stb. (iii) Net emigration rate given by $[-0.01$
$\{ABS (\cos 0.0628318(t - 1))\}]$ and age–sex composition of migrants being the same
as for the net migrants in Australia, 1962–66: · – · – · – 1911 obs. and 1911 stb.;
×—·—·—·—·× 1911 stb. and 1966 obs.; – – – – – – 1966 obs. and 1966 stb. Here ABS
denotes the absolute value.

duration was smaller when migration was specified by the overall net migration rates and age–sex compositions of net migrants, than when there was no migration or when migration was specified by the age–sex-specific net migration rates. But this is not very clear from the graph. Hence Table 5.1 and Fig. 5.2 were prepared. The values in the table and the decrease in the values of ADI and SRDI seen in the graph, depict very clearly the expected changes in the duration of convergence. Figure 5.2 also supports the conclusion that the differences in the sex ratios vanish as soon as the cohorts which were alive at the initial point of time, die out. This happens in all the three cases, as can be observed from the graph.

Table 5.2. Comparison of the effect of immigration and emigration on the duration of convergence of age–sex distributions under varying conditions of fertility, mortality and migration

Prevailing conditions	From actual projections Value of t in number of years		
Mortality: As observed in Australia during 1911–66 and the 1966 values remaining constant Fertility: Hypothetical fertility rates having the continuing trend similar to the one observed during 1911–61	1911 obs. and 1911 stb.	1911 stb. and 1966 obs.	1966 obs. and 1911 obs.
1 Age–sex composition of net migrants as observed in Australia during 1962–66			
(a) Net immigration for all years: Net rate given by 0.01 [ABS(cos 0.0628318(t − 1))]	155	155	165
(b) Net emigration for all years: Net rate given by −0.01 [ABS(cos 0.0628318(t − 1))]	275	275	275
(c) Net immigration and emigration alternating over time: Net rate given by 0.01 [cos 0.0628318(t − 1)]	225	210	245
2 Age–sex composition of net migrants as observed in Australia during 1962–66 but with no (female or male) migrants below the age 50 years			
(i) Net immigration for all years: Net rate given by 0.01 [ABS(cos 0.0628318(t − 1))]	195	185	200
(ii) Net emigration for all years: Net rate given by −0.01 [ABS(cos 0.0628318(t − 1))]	250	250	250

Note:—ABS denotes the absolute value.

(ii) *Effects of immigration and emigration on the duration of convergence*

As we have seen in Chapter 2, net migration in Australia during 1911–66 which was assumed in the previous examples, was not always of one type—net immigration or net emigration—though, generally, there was net immigration into the country. Hence, to examine the effects of immigration and emigration operating continuously, the age–sex composition of net migrants was kept constant and was taken to be as in Australia

Table 5.3 Duration of convergence of age–sex distributions under certain special conditions of migration

Prevailing conditions	From actual projections Value of t in number of years		
Mortality: As observed in Australia during 1911–66 and the 1966 values remaining constant Fertility: Hypothetical fertility rates having the continuing trend similar to the one observed during 1911–61	1911 obs. and 1911 stb.	1911 stb. and 1966 obs.	1966 obs. and 1911 obs.
1 Age–sex composition of net migrants as observed in Australia during 1962–66			
(a) Net immigration for all years: Net rate given by 0.05 [ABS(cos 0.0628318(t − 1))]	95	100	110
(b) Net rate given by 0.05 [ABS(cos 0.3141590(t − 1))]	105	105	105
(c) Net rate given by 0.05 [ABS(sin 0.0628318(t − 1))]	100	105	110
(d) Net rate given by 0.05 [ABS(sin 0.3141590(t − 1))]	105	105	105
(e) Net rate constant at 0.01 per year	140	140	155
2 Age–sex composition of net migrants as observed in Australia during 1962–66 with no migrants (females or males) at ages 50 years and above; and Net rate given by 0.01 [ABS(cos 0.0628318(t − 1))]	160	160	165
3 Age–sex composition of net migrants as observed in Australia during 1962–66 with no female migrants at any age; and Net rate given by 0.01 [ABS(cos 0.0628318(t − 1))]	225	210	225

Note:—ABS denotes the absolute value.

during 1962–66, and the net migration rate was obtained using a cosine curve. The age compositions of net migrants in 1962–66, had positive values at all ages for both sexes. These were purposely reduced to zero at all ages up to β years in the case of two of the experiments. The actual situations of fertility, mortality and migration conditions assumed, are indicated in Figs 5.3 and 5.4 as well as in Table 5.2, which summarizes the results of these experiments.

The results support the conclusion that in the presence of immigration, the duration becomes less than and in the presence of emigration more than that in the absence of migration. It must be mentioned here that the use of the cosine curve resulted in the occurrence of no migration for one year in each of the cycles and this perhaps, increased the observed duration to some extent in the case of immigration and decreased it in the case of emigration. Further, Table 5.2 shows that when net immigration and emigration alternated over time, the duration remained the same as in the absence of migration in two of the cases considered while in the third, it increased. Figure 5.4 again makes it clear that the differences in the sex ratios vanished in $(w + 1)$ years, i.e. in eighty-six years in our examples.

(iii) *Duration of convergence in a few special cases*

The main purpose in continuing with these exercises, was to see whether a change in the magnitude of the net migration rate or a change in the time path of net migration rate would have an effect on the duration of convergence. The age–sex composition of net migrants was kept unchanged in these experiments also. The details of the assumptions in these exercises are given in Table 5.3. The results indicate that the difference in the time path had very little effect on the duration provided the magnitude of the net migration rate reached similar levels during a period of the same length. For example, the use of the sine curve which gave the opposite trend in the net migration rate to that given by the cosine curve, showed no change in the duration of convergence. This seems to happen because the structures of the matrices in the product, remain unchanged. But the change in the net rate of migration to a higher level indicated a reduction in the duration of convergence.

When the net immigration rate was kept constant at 1 per cent, the duration was found to be less than that under the assumption of the cosine curve. At least a part of this decrease has come due to the fact that for none of the years under this assumption the net migration rate became zero.

The last two examples presented in Table 5.3 show that, when the female population was not affected by migration, the duration remained the same as in the absence of migration as we expected it to be, and when there were no migrants above the oldest age at which reproduction occurred, the duration decreased as compared to the case with no migration, but increased as compared with that in the case with immigration at all ages in at least two of the three cases and remained the same in the other.

5.7 Summary

Thus the investigations in this chapter reveal that, when migration is included into the process of population growth using an overall net migration rate and an age–sex distribution of net migrants, the weak ergodicity theorem holds good. The time required for the convergence of any two arbitrary age distributions becomes less if there is continuous net immigration and becomes more if there is continuous net emigration, than if there is no migration. The actual number of years decreased or increased depends on the age distributions of the net migrants and the magnitude of the net migration rates. If net immigration, net emigration and zero migration affect the population for different years, the property still holds good, but the duration of convergence may decrease, remain the same, or increase as compared to the case with no migration, depending on the number of years each of the situations prevails and the age range affected by immigration, emigration or no migration in each case. On the other hand, if age–sex-specific net migration rates are used in the process of population change, the duration of convergence remains the same as in the absence of migration.

6

METHOD OF FACTORIAL PROJECTIONS FOR ANALYSING POPULATION CHANGE DURING A GIVEN PERIOD

6.1 Introduction

In any actual population the fertility, mortality and migration conditions rarely remain constant. Hence the analysis of the characteristics of the equilibrium-state populations or of those resulting under a cyclical model is of theoretical interest and is useful mainly in examining the implications of certain observed or assumed conditions. When the fertility, mortality and migration schedules are changing over time, no definite age–sex distribution nor fixed growth rate is evolved. In fact, both are modified at each period of time owing to the changes in the fertility, mortality and migration schedules during the period. It is of interest, therefore, to examine the contributions of the observed changes in the components in changing the characteristics of a population during a given period. This question is taken up in this chapter.

Keyfitz (1968b) suggested that the effects of the changes in fertility and mortality, and those of the interactions of these changes, on the characteristics of a population could be separated by constructing stable populations under four different assumptions which could be considered to conform to a 2 × 2 factorial design of experiments. A similar procedure has already been used to decompose the changes in the characteristics of the equilibrium-state populations into the effects of the changes in the components (see Section 4.4(iv)). Such an analysis will not, however, give the decomposition of the observed change in an actual population during a given period.

Some authors have used other numerical population models to study the effects of the changes in the components on the population characteristics.

Schwartz (1968) examined the influence of natality and mortality on the age composition and on the population growth by constructing numerical population models under assumptions comparable to those of Keyfitz. Notestein (1960) tried to assess the contribution of the actual changes in fertility, mortality and migration to the population growth in the United States during 1930–55 through the construction of the population projection models.

Our attempt in this chapter is to present a method, similar to the one adopted by Notestein, to decompose the changes in the characteristics of a population during a certain period into the effects of changes in the components and those of the interactions of these changes. The method is applied to analyse the changes in the characteristics of the population of Australia which had experienced considerable changes due not only to changes in the vital rates, but also to those in migration. The analysis covers the period 1911–66.

The basic step in the method proposed here is to project the population as at the beginning of the period under study to the end of the period— from 30 June 1911 to 30 June 1966 in the case of the Australian population—under different assumptions which conform to a $2 \times 2 \times 2$ factorial design. The method is therefore called the factorial projections method. It must be mentioned, however, that the design is used here not for the purpose for which the designs of experiments are commonly used in the Statistical Designs of Experiments and to that extent the analysis adopted is also different from the usual one.

The decomposition of the changes in the population characteristics during a certain period, as suggested here, would help to give a better understanding of the effects of the changes in the components during that period.

6.2 The factorial projections method

In demographic analysis, the main interest is to assess separately the contribution of the main effects and the effects of the interactions of the changes in the components from a certain initial situation to the observed changes in the population characteristics. Hence the term interaction has the following meaning. Suppose we are considering a period during which both fertility and mortality declined and there was no migration. Owing to the decline in mortality, more women would be in the reproductive period than would have been if mortality had not declined. These extra women saved, would have given birth to more children if fertility had not declined than if it did. The resultant addition or subtraction due to the simultaneous decline of mortality and fertility is termed as the effect of the interaction of the decline in mortality and fertility. Similarly, we can define the effects of the interactions between the changes in the other components.

Let P_t be the total population of a country at time t. If we start with a population P_0 at time $t = 0$, it will change through the operation of fertility, mortality and migration. These components, in turn, may remain the same as at $t = 0$ or change during the period 0 to t. To analyse the effects of the changes in these three components on the population characteristics, we shall use a $2 \times 2 \times 2$ factorial design. Let the factors in the design be represented as follows:

A: 1—Mortality specified by age-specific survival rates, remains as at $t = 0$.

a—Mortality changes as observed in a country or as assumed.

B: 1—Fertility specified by age-specific fertility rates, remains as at $t = 0$.

b—Fertility changes as observed in the country or as assumed.

C: 1—No migration or as assumed.

c—Migration given by the net numbers of migrants by age and sex or as assumed.

Let $P_t(A, B, C)$ denote the total population as obtained by projecting the initial population P_0 to time t with the respective assumptions regarding A, B, C and a constant sex ratio at birth. We may also assume this sex ratio to change. But, as seen in Chapter 2, the change in this sex ratio is not generally significant. Thus $P_t(a, b, c)$ is the projection of P_0 to t with the observed changes in fertility, mortality and migration. Hence it must be equal to P_t, the observed population at time t, except for some observational errors in the components and in P_t itself, and a small variation in the sex ratio at birth.

The assumptions needed for constructing the population projection models from the initial population P_0 according to the $2 \times 2 \times 2$ factorial design, could be set out in the form of an effect matrix as given below:

Factor combinations	Representation by signs			Resultant projections
	A	B	C	
$A = 1, B = 1, C = 1$	−	−	−	$P_t(1, 1, 1) = 1$
$A = a, B = 1, C = 1$	+	−	−	$P_t(a, 1, 1) = a$
$A = 1, B = b, C = 1$	−	+	−	$P_t(1, b, 1) = b$
$A = a, B = b, C = 1$	+	+	−	$P_t(a, b, 1) = ab$
$A = 1, B = 1, C = c$	−	−	+	$P_t(1, 1, c) = c$
$A = a, B = 1, C = c$	+	−	+	$P_t(a, 1, c) = ac$
$A = 1, B = b, C = c$	−	+	+	$P_t(1, b, c) = bc$
$A = a, B = b, C = c$	+	+	+	$P_t(a, b, c) = abc$

Note: The signs − and + denote respectively the absence and occurrence of change in the component concerned.

The population projections are carried out by the usual component method of projections with female dominance. Of course, the method of equal dominance could also be used. The study would be more interesting if the fertility and mortality rates are available separately for migrants and the native population. But this raises an important question: When should the migrants be considered as one with the native population? This question by itself needs a detailed investigation. However, in the absence of such detailed information and in view of the analysis of the fertility and mortality experience of the native-born and the outside-born populations given in Section 1.8, we shall continue with the assumption that the migrants experience the same fertility and mortality rates as the general population.

Now, to decompose the observed change in the total population during the period 0 to t into the effects of the changes in the components during that period, we set up the following model:

$$TC = [E(1) + E(a) + E(b) + E(c) + E(ab) + E(ac) + E(bc) + E(abc)]$$

where TC denotes the total effect on the population size of the changes in all the components during the period. The terms on the right-hand side have the meaning given below and their values could be calculated using the equations given along with the explanations. The term $E(abc)$ is the residual after all the effects and the interaction effects are taken out from the total change.

(i) $E(1)$ is the effect on the total population size of the vital rates remaining constant at the initial value with no migration or with migration at the level described as $C = 1$. This could be estimated by the equation: $E(1) = 1 - P_0$.

(ii) $E(a)$ denotes the effect of the change in mortality only with no change in fertility and migration, and is given by: $E(a) = a - 1$.

(iii) $E(b)$ stands for the effect of the change in fertility only with no change in mortality and migration and is estimated by: $E(b) = b - 1$.

(iv) $E(c)$ represents the effect of migration (or change in it) with no changes in vital rates and is given by: $E(c) = c - 1$.

(v) $E(ab)$ is the effect of the interaction between the changes in mortality and in fertility with no change in migration. This is estimated by: $E(ab) = (ab - b) - (a - 1)$.

(vi) $E(ac)$ is the effect of the interaction between the changes in mortality and migration with no change in fertility and is computed from the equation: $E(ac) = (ac - c) - (a - 1)$.

(vii) $E(bc)$ is the effect of the interaction between the changes in fertility and migration with no change in mortality and this could be calculated by using the equation: $E(bc) = (bc - c) - (b - 1)$.

(viii) $E(abc)$ denotes, similarly, the effect of the interaction between the changes in all the components and is estimated by the equation: $E(abc) = [(abc - c) - (ac - c) - (bc - c)] - [E(ab)]$.

The sum of these effects is the total effect, TC, and hence it is equal to the change $(P_t(a, b, c) - P_0)$ which is approximately the actual observed change, $P_t - P_0$. The proportionate contribution of the changes in the components and their interactions are obtained by expressing the individual effects calculated above as the percentage of the total effect. However, the interpretation of the effects of the changes in the components will be clearer if the effects of the interactions are small.

It may be noted that the analysis detailed here has assumed P_0, the initial population, to be given and therefore the effects observed will be relevant only in connection with that initial size and age distribution of the population. If we wish to examine the effects of the changes in the initial population age distribution simultaneously with the changes in the components, then we will have to obtain population projections under different assumptions according to a $2 \times 2 \times 2 \times 2$ factorial design. However, for the analysis of the population dynamics in any country, it can be assumed that the initial population is given.

Although the total population has been used in the above discussion, the same procedure could be applied for analysing the change in any other population characteristics such as the mean age, proportion in the old age, the labour force, or the school age population, etc.

6.3 Limitations of the method

An advantage of this method over the one suggested by Keyfitz is that it could be used to study the changes during short periods as well as long periods. But the main drawback of the method is that it is based on the assumption that the variations in one component are independent of those in the others. It may be recalled that this assumption is basic for the whole of the present study, and does not appear to be a very serious assumption. Also, the method cannot reveal the many indirect effects of the changes in the components which are mainly socio-economic in nature, except those that are reflected in the variations of the measures used for representing the components. Further, the estimates of the effects of the changes and those of the interactions of the changes depend upon the magnitudes of the variations in the components themselves and also on the length of the period of analysis.

6.4 Analysis of the changes in the size and the age–sex distribution of the population of Australia during 1911–66

During the period 1911–66, there were significant changes in fertility and migration conditions in Australia. Mortality declined almost continuously during the period, but it was already at a comparatively low level by 1911. From the analysis of the changes observed in these components given in Chapter 2, we see that it would be interesting to study the contributions of the variations in the components to the changes in the characteristics of the population during the three periods: 1911–66, 1933–66 and 1947–66. The period 1911–66 experienced compensating variations in the components such as decline and increase in both fertility and migration, whereas the period 1933–66 had very little effect of migration over the first fourteen years, and had a continuous effect of immigration thereafter, with fertility increasing from a very low level throughout the period, except during the last few years since 1961. On the other hand, there was a significant immigration throughout the period 1947–66, with fertility also increasing from a considerably higher level than that in 1933, except during the last few years since 1961.

The consideration of these three periods would also show how the contributions of the variations in the components estimated by this method, are dependent on the magnitudes of the variations in the components during the period and on the length of the period under study.

It must be mentioned here that the populations projected from 1911 to 1933 and to 1947, under the assumption of the observed changes in fertility, mortality and migration, were used as the initial populations respectively in the analyses for the periods 1933–66 and 1947–66. Hence the population in 1966 obtained by projecting the three initial populations at 1911, 1933 and 1947, assuming the observed conditions of fertility, mortality and migration during the respective periods, was identical. However, the populations as at 30 June 1933 and 1947 obtained from the projections did not differ very much from the corresponding populations enumerated in the censuses (see Appendix C).

The method suggested in Section 6.2 is used to analyse the changes in the following population characteristics:

(a) Population growth: (i) the total sizes of the male and female populations, and (ii) the total number of births, deaths and natural increase;

(b) Changes in the age–sex distribution: (i) the mean ages of the male and female populations, (ii) the proportion of the population in the old age group (65+) for males and females, and (iii) the proportion of males in the total population; and

(c) Changes in the sizes of certain segments of the population: (i) population in the school going age group (6–14), (ii) population in the working age group (15–64), and (iii) population in the old age group (65+).

For all the analyses presented here, the actual change in any of the characteristics refers to the total change between the value at the initial time and the value obtained from the projected population under the assumption of the observed changes in mortality, fertility and migration.

6.4.1 Population growth

In analysing the growth of the population, it is necessary to consider the change in the size of the total population as well as the natural increase because, while the changes in fertility and their interactions with the changes in mortality and with migration affect the population growth through the natural increase, the changes in mortality or migration and their interactions affect the populations at all ages and thus cause the change in the total population. Hence we have chosen to analyse these two separately.

(i) *Changes in the size of the male and female populations*

The population of Australia consisted of 2334 thousand males and 2156 thousand females as at 30 June 1911. It increased to 5881 thousand males and 5738 thousand females by 30 June 1966. At 30 June 1933, the population had 3394 thousand males and 3280 thousand females while at 30 June 1947 its size was made up of 3848 thousand males and 3780 thousand females.

The analysis of the changes in the size from these initial values to that in 1966, is presented in Table 6.1. The table shows clearly that the changes during 1911–66 had compensating effects of increasing and decreasing the size while those during 1933–66 and during 1947–66 were all towards increasing the size. Consequently, about 66 per cent out of the total change of 3547 thousands in the case of males, and about 71 per cent of the total change of 3582 thousands in the case of females, would have occurred even if migration had not contributed to the population growth, but if fertility and mortality conditions as in 1911 had remained unchanged. On the other hand, the continuation of the low fertility level of 1933 and the corresponding mortality with no migration during that period, would have caused

Table 6.1 Analysis of the changes in the total sizes of male and female populations in Australia

Source of change	During 1911–66 Absolute value ('000)	Per cent to TC	During 1933–66 Absolute value ('000)	Per cent to TC	During 1947–66 Absolute value ('000)	Per cent to TC
			MALE			
Value in the initial year	2333.8		3393.9		3847.7	
$E(1)$	2359.2	66.51	599.0	24.09	780.5	38.39
	(4693.0)*	(79.80)[a]	(3993.0)*	(67.90)[a]	(4628.2)*	(78.70)[a]
$E(a)$	785.1	22.13	132.8	5.34	41.8	2.06
$E(b)$	−1049.0	−29.57	601.1	24.17	119.1	5.86
$E(c)$	1646.2	46.41	1029.5	41.40	1068.8	52.57
$E(ab)$	−180.4	−5.09	31.5	1.27	1.5	0.07
$E(ac)$	144.4	4.07	16.7	0.67	5.9	0.29
$E(bc)$	−136.0	−3.83	73.2	2.94	15.3	0.75
$E(abc)$	−22.4	−0.63	3.1	0.12	0.2	0.01
TC	3547.1	100.00	2486.9	100.00	2033.1	100.00
Value in 1966	5880.9	—	5880.9	—	5880.9	—
			FEMALE			
Value in the initial year	2155.8		3279.8		3780.0	
$E(1)$	2539.0	70.88	692.0	28.16	829.1	42.35
	(4694.8)*	(81.82)[a]	(3971.8)*	(69.22)[a]	(4609.1)*	(80.33)[a]
$E(a)$	804.7	22.46	210.5	8.56	87.3	4.46
$E(b)$	−1022.8	−28.55	580.1	23.60	114.5	5.85
$E(c)$	1447.1	40.40	856.8	34.86	903.2	46.13
$E(ab)$	−168.2	−4.70	27.1	1.10	1.0	0.05
$E(ac)$	135.6	3.79	18.5	0.75	8.0	0.41
$E(bc)$	−132.5	−3.70	70.6	2.87	14.7	0.75
$E(abc)$	−20.7	−0.58	2.5	0.10	0.1	0.01
TC	3582.2	100.00	2458.1	100.00	1957.9	100.01
Value in 1966	5738.0	—	5738.0	—	5738.0	—

Note: The symbols in the column "Source of Change" have the following explanations:

$E(1)$ —No change in mortality and fertility conditions and no migration;

$E(a)$ —Observed change in mortality conditions, no change in fertility conditions and no migration;

$E(b)$ —No change in mortality conditions, observed change in fertility conditions and no migration;

$E(c)$ —No change in mortality and fertility conditions, and observed migration;

$E(ab)$ —Observed change in mortality and fertility conditions and no migration;

$E(ac)$ —Observed change in mortality conditions, no change in fertility conditions and observed migration;

$E(bc)$ —No change in mortality conditions, observed change in fertility conditions and observed migration;

$E(abc)$ —Observed change in mortality and fertility conditions and observed migration;

* —This is the value of the characteristic when there is no change in mortality and fertility conditions and no migration;

[a] —Ratio (per cent) of the value * to the value in 1966.

only one-fourth of the actual change of 2487 thousands during 1933–66 in the case of males and about 28 per cent of the actual change of 2458 thousands in the case of females. During 1947–66, the population would have increased by about 780 thousands only as against the actual increase of 2033 thousands (i.e. about 38 per cent) in the case of males and by about 829 thousands instead of 1958 thousands (about 42 per cent) in the case of females, if the fertility and mortality as in 1947 had not changed and no migration had occurred.

After almost a continuous decline till about 1935, fertility recovered and its level remained less than that in 1911 for the whole of the period 1911–66. The result of this was that the whole effect of mortality decline which caused an increase in the sizes of the male and female populations was completely offset and even a part of the effect of migration was reduced. Thus most of the extra increase in the population size during 1911–66, which could be attributed to the changes in the components, came from immigration.

If we study the changes during 1933–66 and 1947–66, we observe that the increase due to the improvement in mortality became comparatively smaller, especially for males, and for the period 1947–66. This is in accord with the observation that the improvement in mortality slowed down during this period and even a slight retardation had occurred at some ages after 1961. Fertility improvements from the 1933 level contributed about one-fourth of the total change during 1933–66, whereas their contribution to the population growth during 1947–66 reduced to about one-twelfth. In fact, immigration played a major role in the growth of the male and female populations during 1947–66. It may be recalled that during this period there was a consistent inflow of migrants. The comparison of the magnitudes of the interaction effects indicates that the length of the period as well as the magnitudes of the changes in the components during the period have an effect on their value.

(ii) *Analysis of the total number of births, deaths and natural increase*

Variations in the mortality, fertility and migration schedules affect the total number of births and deaths, and thus the natural increase of the population during a period. Therefore, it is of interest to examine the part played by the changes in each of these components in changing the number of births and deaths, and natural increase. Such an analysis in respect of births and deaths is presented in Table 6.2 and that for the natural increase in Table 6.3.

It can be seen that the births contributed by immigrants and due to the improvement in mortality could not compensate the reduction due to

Table 6.2 Contribution of the changes in the components to the number of births and deaths in Australia

Source of change	During 1911–66		During 1933–66		During 1947–66	
	Absolute value ('000)	Per cent to TC	Absolute value ('000)	Per cent to TC	Absolute value ('000)	Per cent to TC
	Births					
$E(1)$	9583.6	109.79	4026.8	69.04	3296.2	82.28
$E(a)$	487.0	5.58	48.2	0.83	9.8	0.24
$E(b)$	−2417.9	−27.70	1258.0	21.57	242.5	6.05
$E(c)$	1485.6	17.02	322.5	5.53	425.2	10.61
$E(ab)$	−142.4	−1.63	20.6	0.35	−0.1	−0.00
$E(ac)$	61.1	0.70	3.0	0.05	1.3	0.03
$E(bc)$	−310.5	−3.56	152.2	2.61	31.1	0.78
$E(abc)$	−17.2	−0.20	1.1	0.02	0.0	0.00
TC	8729.3	100.00	5832.4	100.00	4006.0	100.00
	Deaths					
$E(1)$	4685.3	125.67	2735.7	107.06	1686.5	102.84
$E(a)$	−1102.8	−29.58	−295.2	−11.55	−119.2	−7.27
$E(b)$	−346.0	−9.28	76.8	3.01	9.0	0.55
$E(c)$	520.5	13.96	104.3	4.09	78.3	4.77
$E(ab)$	206.2	5.53	−38.0	−1.49	−2.7	−0.16
$E(ac)$	−218.9	−5.87	−32.0	−1.26	−12.7	−0.77
$E(bc)$	−42.0	−1.13	8.4	0.33	1.1	0.07
$E(abc)$	25.9	0.70	−4.6	−0.18	−0.3	−0.02
TC	3728.2	100.00	2555.3	100.00	1640.0	100.00

Note: See the note to Table 6.1 for exaplanations of the symbols in the column "Source of Change".

the decline in fertility from the level in 1911 so that during 1911–66 there would have been nearly 10 per cent more births than the actual number occurring even in the absence of migration, if fertility and mortality had remained at the same level as in 1911. But in that case, the number of deaths would have gone up by about 26 per cent as compared with the actual number observed so that the natural increase would have been less by about 2 per cent of that actually observed (see Table 6.3).

During 1933–66, the increase in the level of fertility from the low level in 1933 contributed more than one-fifth of the actual number of births, while during 1947–66 its contribution was around only 6–7 per cent. This was expected because by 1947 the level of fertility had become considerably higher than that in 1933 and the increase in the level of fertility slowed down in later years after 1951. The increase in the number of deaths due

Table 6.3 Contribution of the changes in the components to the natural increase of the population in Australia

	Natural increase = Births − Deaths					
	During 1911–66		During 1933–66		During 1947–66	
Source of change	Absolute value ('000)	Per cent to TC	Absolute value ('000)	Per cent to TC	Absolute value ('000)	Per cent to TC
$E(1)$	4898.3	97.94	1291.1	39.40	1609.6	68.03
$E(a)$	1589.8	31.79	343.4	10.48	129.1	5.46
$E(b)$	−2071.9	−41.43	1181.2	36.05	233.6	9.87
$E(c)$	965.1	19.30	218.2	6.66	347.0	14.67
$E(ab)$	−348.6	−6.97	58.6	1.79	2.6	0.11
$E(ac)$	280.0	5.60	35.1	1.07	13.9	0.59
$E(bc)$	−268.5	−5.37	143.8	4.39	29.9	1.26
$E(abc)$	−43.1	−0.86	5.6	0.17	0.3	0.01
TC	5001.1	100.00	3277.0	100.00	2366.0	100.00

Note: See the note to Table 6.1 for explanations of the symbols in the column "Source of Change".

to the increase in the number of births as a result of the changes in fertility was not very much—about 3 per cent during 1933–66 and about 0.5 per cent during 1947–66. It may also be observed that the effect of migration was more on the number of births than on the number of deaths during all the periods, especially during 1947–66. This was because the migrants were concentrated in the age group (15–44), except during the later years after 1961; and in this age range the change in mortality was very little. Again the interaction effects were significant only during the long period 1911–66.

From Table 6.3 it can be seen that the effect of the improvement in mortality and of net migration during all the three periods was to increase the natural growth of the population, while the change in fertility reduced it during 1911–66 but increased it during 1933–66 and 1947–66. These consequences could easily be expected from the study of the changes in these components during the respective periods. But a quantitative estimation of the actual effects of their operation could only be made by an analysis similar to the one presented here. It may be noted that the effect of the improvement in mortality which contributed a larger portion of the total natural increase than that by migration during 1911–66 and 1933–66, became considerably smaller during the period 1947–66, and its place was taken by the effect of migration. The total effect of the increase in fertility contributed over 40 per cent of the actual natural increase during 1933–66 while its contribution during 1947–66 was only about 11 per cent. As could be seen, the effects of the interactions of the changes in the components were prominent mainly in the period 1911–66.

6.4.2 changes in the age–sex distribution of the population

In order to examine the part played by the changes in each of the components in changing the age–sex distribution of the population of Australia, we shall examine the changes in the mean age and the proportion in the old age group (65+) separately for males and females; and the changes in the proportion of males in the total population. The proportion of males is preferred to the analysis of the ratio of males per females, as this proportion would have a finite bound in any population and the analysis would be comparable to that of the analysis of the proportion of population in a particular age group such as the old age group (65+).

Although it is difficult to find out which of the components is more powerful in changing the age distribution (or even any other characteristic of the population), since the nature of their operation is different (Coale, 1957a), the importance of the effect of the observed variations in any of the components during a certain period on the characteristics of the population could be assessed with the analysis suggested here. It may also be noted that mortality and migration are similar in nature in their effects on the age structure because they can affect all ages in each year, though with different intensity, whereas the effect of a change in fertility must pass age by age starting from the age zero. Thus it may be expected that the effect of the changes in fertility would be more prominent than that of mortality or migration. However, the relative effects depend on the magnitudes of the actual variations in the components during the period under consideration. With these preliminary remarks in mind we shall examine what has happened in the population of Australia.

(i) *Mean ages of the male and female populations*

Table 6.4 gives the analysis of the observed change in the mean ages for males and females during the three periods. An examination of the results reveals that the mean ages of both males and females increased during 1911–66 and 1933–66, but decreased during 1947–66. The increase was more for females whereas the reduction was more for males. The effect of the variation in mortality in all the three periods was to decrease the mean age for males and to increase it for females. This was due to the fact that the improvements in mortality were more for females and occurred in the old age groups.

Table . Analysis of the changes in the values of the mean ages of male and female populations in Australia

Source of change	During 1911–66		During 1933–66		During 1947–66	
	Absolute change	Per cent to TC	Absolute change	Per cent to TC	Absolute change	Per cent to TC
MALE						
Value in the initial year	27.67		30.10		32.30	
$E(1)$	1.49	43.70	5.30	540.82	0.20	16.39
	$(29.16)^*$	$(93.82)^{(a)}$	$(35.40)^*$	$(113.90)^{(a)}$	$(32.50)^*$	$(104.57)^{(a)}$
$E(a)$	−0.37	−10.85	−0.29	−29.59	−0.02	−1.64
$E(b)$	2.76	80.94	−3.29	−335.71	−0.64	−52.46
$E(c)$	−0.06	−1.76	−1.17	−119.39	−0.83	−68.03
$E(ab)$	−0.00	0.00	−0.02	−2.04	0.00	0.00
$E(ac)$	0.04	1.17	0.06	6.12	0.00	0.00
$E(bc)$	−0.52	−15.25	0.40	40.82	0.07	5.74
$E(abc)$	0.07	2.05	−0.01	−1.02	0.00	0.00
TC	3.41	100.00	0.98	100.01	−1.22	−100.00
Value in 1966	31.08	—	31.08	—	31.08	—
FEMALE						
Value in the initial year	26.64		30.43		33.22	
$E(1)$	3.58	61.83	6.01	300.50	0.54	68.35
	$(30.22)^*$	$(93.19)^{(a)}$	$(36.44)^*$	$(112.37)^{(a)}$	$(33.76)^*$	$(104.10)^{(a)}$
$E(a)$	0.14	2.42	0.36	18.00	0.35	44.30
$E(b)$	2.94	50.78	−3.34	−167.00	−0.64	−81.01
$E(c)$	−0.48	−8.29	−1.31	−65.50	−1.04	−131.65
$E(ab)$	0.10	1.73	−0.03	−1.50	−0.01	−1.27
$E(ac)$	0.03	0.52	−0.01	−0.50	−0.04	−5.06
$E(bc)$	−0.54	−9.33	0.33	16.50	0.05	6.33
$E(abc)$	0.02	0.34	−0.01	−0.50	0.00	0.00
TC	5.79	100.00	2.00	100.00	−0.79	−100.01
Value in 1966	32.43	—	32.43	—	32.43	—

Note: See the note to Table 6.1 for explanations of the symbols in the column "Source of Change".

Table 6.5 Analysis of the change in the proportion of the population in the old age group (65 years and over) in Australia

Source of change	During 1911–66		During 1933–66		During 1947–66	
	Absolute value (per 100)	Per cent to TC	Absolute value (per 100)	Per cent to TC	Absolute value (per 100)	Per cent to TC
	MALE					
Value in the initial year	4.34		5.95		7.09	
E(1)	2.13 (6.47)*	71.00 (88.15)[a]	4.42 (10.37)*	317.99 (141.28)[a]	1.78 (8.87)*	712.00 (120.84)[a]
E(a)	0.07	2.33	−0.35	−25.18	0.02	8.00
E(b)	1.87	62.33	−1.36	−97.84	−0.22	−88.00
E(c)	−0.65	−21.67	−1.76	−126.62	−1.37	−548.00
E(ab)	0.02	0.67	0.03	2.16	0.00	0.00
E(ac)	0.05	1.67	0.09	6.47	0.00	0.00
E(bc)	−0.53	−17.67	0.34	24.46	0.05	20.00
E(abc)	0.04	1.33	−0.02	−1.44	−0.01	−4.00
TC	3.00	100.00	1.39	100.00	0.25	100.00
Value in 1966	7.34	—	7.34	—	7.34	—
	FEMALE					
Value in the initial year	4.20		6.29		8.70	
E(1)	3.77 (7.97)*	63.68 (78.75)[a]	6.05 (12.34)*	157.96 (121.94)[a]	2.44 (11.14)*	171.83 (110.08)[a]
E(a)	0.88	14.86	0.76	19.84	0.60	42.25
E(b)	2.22	37.50	−1.58	−41.25	−0.27	−19.01
E(c)	−0.62	−10.47	−1.55	−40.47	−1.31	−92.25
E(ab)	0.22	3.72	−0.08	−2.09	−0.01	−0.70
E(ac)	−0.03	−0.51	−0.06	−1.57	−0.07	−4.93
E(bc)	−0.52	−8.78	0.29	7.57	0.04	2.82
E(abc)	0.00	0.00	0.00	0.00	0.00	0.00
TC	5.92	100.00	3.83	99.99	1.42	100.01
Value in 1966	10.12	—	10.12	—	10.12	—

Note: See the note to Table 6.1 for explanations of the symbols in the column "Source of Change"

During 1911–66, the reduction of fertility from the level in 1911 was the main cause for the increase in the mean ages, while during 1933–66 the increase in fertility from the low level in the beginning years of the period effected a big reduction in the increase of the mean age which would have occurred otherwise.

The total effect of migration was comparatively small during 1911–66, while during the other two periods it contributed considerably to decrease the mean ages. In fact, during 1947–66, the part played by migration in reducing the mean ages was more prominent than that of the variations in fertility.

(ii) *Proportion of the population in the age group (65+) years*

We have observed in the analysis of mortality that, except at the two youngest ages, the variation in mortality was more at the old ages. The male–female differences were also very significant at these ages. Hence it was considered worthwhile to analyse the proportion in this old age group. In all the three periods considered here, this proportion increased both for males and females (see Table 6.5). The increase was less for males than for females. Mortality decline was more prominent in increasing the proportion for females than for males. Migration played a very important role in reducing the proportion, and its effect was more on the proportion for males than on that for females. While the declines in fertility from that in 1911 caused an increase in the proportion during 1911–66, the increases in fertility from that in 1933 and in 1947 effected a decrease in the proportion during the respective periods both for males and females. The effect of the interaction of the variation in fertility and net migration was the only interaction effect which was prominent.

(iii) *Proportion of males in the total population*

Analysis of this proportion was taken up to examine the effects of the variations in the components on the sex distribution in the total population. Since we have assumed a constant sex ratio at birth, the variations in this proportion will be accounted for wholly by the variations in the components. It is to be expected from the nature of the changes that the effects of migration and the improvements in mortality would be in opposite directions—migration tending to increase the proportion and the variations in mortality tending to decrease it. This is supported by the results presented in Table 6.6. In fact, without the counteracting effect of migration, the proportion of males in 1966 would have been much less than it was. The effect of the variations in fertility was to decrease the proportion during 1911–66 and to increase it during the other two periods.

Table 6.6 Analysis of the change in the proportion of males in the population of Australia

Source of change	During 1911–66		During 1933–66		During 1947–66	
	Absolute value	Per cent to TC	Absolute value	Per cent to TC	Absolute value	Per cent to TC
Value in the initial year	51.98		50.86		50.44	
$E(1)$	−1.99	−146.32	−0.73	−304.17	−0.34	−212.50
	(49.99)*	(98.77)[a]	(50.13)*	(99.05)[a]	(50.10)*	(98.99)[a]
$E(a)$	−0.09	−6.62	−0.47	−195.83	−0.25	−156.25
$E(b)$	−0.18	−13.24	0.10	+41.67	0.02	+12.50
$E(c)$	0.80	+58.82	0.85	+354.17	0.72	+450.00
$E(ab)$	−0.07	−5.15	0.08	+33.33	0.01	+6.25
$E(ac)$	−0.05	−3.68	0.05	+20.83	0.02	+12.50
$E(bc)$	0.22	+16.18	−0.11	−45.83	−0.02	−12.50
$E(abc)$	0.00	0.00	−0.01	−4.17	0.00	0.00
TC	−1.36	−100.01	−0.24	−100.00	0.16	100.00
Value in 1966	50.61	—	50.61	—	50.61	—

Note: See the note to Table 6.1 for explanations of the symbols in the column "Source of Change".

6.4.3 Changes in the sizes of certain segments of the population

From the point of view of the study of population change in any actual situation, it is necessary to analyse the population change in certain important segments of the population. The choice of the segments depends on the purpose of the analysis. Since we are concerned here with the general analysis of the population change in Australia, three segments which are of general interest are selected for analysis.

(i) *The population in the school going age group (6–14 years)*

The age range 6–14 years is selected as the school age on the basis of the legislation for compulsory school attendance in the different states of Australia.‡ Though this has not always been uniform in all the states, the age range considered here more or less covers most of the ages specified in all the cases. Since the age group contains ages up to 15 years of age, the variations in the components during the fifteen years previous to the date at which the analysis is made, are of importance.

From Table 6.7, it may be observed that, during 1911–66, the total change in the school age population would have been about 28 per cent less in the case of males and about 26 per cent less in the case of females if fertility and mortality conditions had remained as in 1911 and no migration had occurred. Improvements in mortality compensated for this deficit, but the fertility rates during the 6–15 years previous to 1966 as compared to those in 1911 being lower, caused a larger deficit. Hence, if net migration had not contributed nearly four-ninths of the actual change, the size of the school going age population would have been smaller than what it actually was. The interaction effects were not insignificant but they operated in opposite directions so that the net effect was very little.

Because the fertility rates 6–15 years prior to 1966 were higher than in 1933, because there was a decline in mortality, and because considerable immigration occurred during that period, the size of the population in this segment would have been lower in 1966 than in 1933 both for males and females if the low rates of fertility in 1933 had continued, with mortality also remaining as in 1933 and with no migration (see Table 6.7). It is mainly because of the recovery of fertility rates since 1935 and because of immigration that this situation was averted and an increase of about 447 thousands in the case of males and about 421 thousands in the case of

‡ Commonwealth Bureau of Census and Statistics, *Year Book of the Commonwealth of Australia*, No. 51, 1965, p. 687. (Recently the upper age limit has been changed to 15 years.)

Table 6.7　Analysis of the change in the size of the school age population (6–14 years) in Australia

Source of change	During 1911–66		During 1933–66		During 1947–66	
	Absolute change ('000)	Per cent to TC	Absolute change ('000)	Per cent to TC	Absolute change ('000)	Per cent to TC
MALE						
Value in the initial year	400.9		572.9		509.4	
E(1)	446.6	72.18	−38.2	−8.55	255.1	49.99
	(847.5)*	(83.11)[a]	(534.7)*	(52.44)[a]	(764.6)*	(74.98)[a]
E(a)	174.1	28.14	30.2	6.76	10.6	2.08
E(b)	−224.4	−36.27	260.1	58.20	64.3	12.60
E(c)	273.2	44.15	144.9	32.42	170.9	33.49
E(ab)	−45.2	−7.31	13.5	3.02	1.2	0.24
E(ac)	32.4	5.23	3.0	0.67	1.8	0.35
E(bc)	−31.5	−5.09	31.6	7.07	6.8	1.33
E(abc)	−6.4	−1.04	1.8	0.40	−0.4	−0.08
TC	618.8	100.00	446.9	99.99	510.3	100.00
Value in 1966	1019.7	—	1019.7	—	1019.7	—
FEMALE						
Value in the initial year	392.6		554.3		491.0	
E(1)	431.8	74.16	−38.0	−9.03	244.1	50.43
	(824.4)*	(84.56)[a]	(516.3)*	(52.96)[a]	(735.2)*	(75.41)[a]
E(a)	155.6	26.72	25.3	6.02	8.8	1.82
E(b)	−218.5	−37.53	250.7	59.61	61.7	12.75
E(c)	261.5	44.90	136.0	32.33	161.2	33.31
E(ab)	−40.2	−6.91	11.9	2.83	0.4	0.08
E(ac)	28.3	4.87	3.1	0.74	0.6	0.12
E(bc)	−30.6	−5.26	30.7	7.30	6.1	1.26
E(abc)	−5.6	−0.96	0.9	0.21	1.1	0.23
TC	582.3	100.00	420.6	100.01	484.0	100.00
Value in 1966	974.9	—	974.9	—	974.9	—

Note: See the note to Table 6.1 for explanations of the symbols in the column "Source of Change".

females, was obtained. Mortality improvements contributed to only a small extent to increase the size of this group.

At 1947, the size of this group was small since it consisted of the cohorts born during the years when fertility was at its lowest levels during the period 1911–66 and when migration was considerably small. But, during 1947–66, fertility increased and immigration became a continuous force in

Table 6.8 Analysis of the change in the size of the population in the working age group (15–64 years) in Australia

Source of change	During 1911–66		During 1933–66		During 1947–66	
	Absolute change ('000)	Per cent to TC	Absolute change ('000)	Per cent to TC	Absolute change ('000)	Per cent to TC
	MALE					
Value in the initial year	1512.7		2247.6		2628.5	
E(1)	1400.1	63.36	448.7	30.42	318.4	29.11
	(2912.8)*	(78.25)[a]	(2696.3)*	(72.43)[a]	(2946.9)*	(79.17)[a]
E(a)	416.6	18.85	82.1	5.57	17.1	1.56
E(b)	−611.7	−27.68	156.2	10.59	2.4	0.22
E(c)	1096.1	49.60	768.6	52.12	753.5	68.88
E(ab)	−88.3	−4.00	6.4	0.43	0.0	0.00
E(ac)	74.8	3.39	9.9	0.67	2.6	0.24
E(bc)	−68.4	−3.09	2.8	0.19	−0.1	−0.01
E(abc)	−9.5	−0.43	0.1	0.01	0.0	0.00
TC	2209.7	100.00	1474.8	100.00	1093.9	100.00
Value in 1966	3722.4	—	3722.4	—	3722.4	—
	FEMALE					
Value in the initial year	1364.2		2160.9		2540.3	
E(1)	1522.4	71.09	470.0	34.95	334.3	34.63
	(2886.6)*	(82.34)[a]	(2630.9)*	(75.05)[a]	(2874.6)*	(82.00)[a]
E(a)	410.6	19.17	108.6	8.08	33.2	3.44
E(b)	−598.3	−27.94	151.1	11.24	2.3	0.24
E(c)	903.5	42.19	595.9	44.31	591.4	61.27
E(ab)	−85.5	−3.99	5.7	0.42	0.0	0.00
E(ac)	64.8	3.03	10.5	0.78	4.1	0.42
E(bc)	−66.7	−3.11	2.8	0.21	−0.1	−0.01
E(abc)	−9.4	−0.44	0.1	0.01	0.1	0.01
TC	2141.4	100.00	1344.7	100.00	965.3	100.00
Value in 1966	3505.6	—	3505.6	—	3505.6	—

Note: See the note to Table 6.1 for explanations of the symbols in the column "Source of Change".

the population growth. Hence the increase in this segment during this period was more than that in the period 1933–66 both for males and females. The improvements in mortality contributed very little. The proportion of the total change due to the variations in fertility also became considerably less during this period than during the other periods, so that immigration contributed as much as one-third of the total change for males and females. Thus, in the absence of migration since 1947, the sizes of this segment for males and females in 1966 would have been much smaller than they actually were.

(ii) Population in the working age group (15–64 years)

Analysis of this segment is of particular importance because it gives an indication of the contribution of the variations in the components to the labour force. Table 6.8 presents the relevant analysis for the three periods. A point which may be noticed from the table is that the effect of the changes in fertility on this group had become negligible during 1947–66. This is simply because the changes in fertility had just reached this age group.

During 1911–66, about 37 per cent of the total change of about 2210 thousands in the case of males and about 29 per cent of the total change of about 2141 thousands in the case of females, were contributed by the changes in fertility and mortality, and due to migration. In fact, migration was a major factor in increasing the size of this group. It accounted for as much as about 50 per cent of the total increase for males and about 42 per cent for females. The declines in mortality contributed a little less than one-fifth of the total change in the case of both males and females. But the declines in fertility brought down the increase by about one-third of the total change for both males and females.

Out of the total change of about 1475 thousands for males and of about 1345 thousands for females during 1933–66, nearly 70 per cent in the case of males and 65 per cent in the case of females were accounted for by the changes in fertility and mortality, and due to migration. The effect of the interactions of the changes became smaller and the contributions of the variations in fertility and mortality also reduced to a considerable extent, as compared to their values during 1911–66. Hence migration was again the major contributor to the increase in the size of the population in this segment.

During 1947–66, almost the whole of the extra growth in the working age population, which was the result of the changing conditions during the period, came from migration.

The policy pursued by the Australian Governments throughout the

Table 6.9   Analysis of the change in the size of the population in the old age group (65 years and over) in Australia

Source of change	During 1911–66		During 1933–66		During 1947–66	
	Absolute change ('000)	Per cent to TC	Absolute change ('000)	Per cent to TC	Absolute change ('000)	Per cent to TC
MALE						
Value in the initial year	101.3		201.9		272.9	
E(1)	202.4	61.26	212.2	92.34	137.8	86.78
	(303.7)*	(70.35)[a]	(414.1)*	(95.92)[a]	(410.7)*	(95.14)[a]
E(a)	54.6	16.53	−0.6	−0.26	4.5	2.83
E(b)	0.0	0.00	0.0	0.00	0.0	0.00
E(c)	65.4	19.79	18.3	7.96	16.5	10.39
E(ab)	0.0	0.00	0.0	0.00	0.0	0.00
E(ac)	8.0	2.42	−0.1	−0.04	0.0	0.00
E(bc)	0.0	0.00	0.0	0.00	0.0	0.00
E(abc)	0.0	0.00	0.0	0.00	0.0	0.00
TC	330.4	100.00	229.8	100.00	158.8	100.00
Value in 1966	431.7	—	431.7	—	431.7	—
FEMALE						
Value in the initial year	90.6		206.3		328.9	
E(1)	283.6	57.84	283.7	75.73	184.6	73.25
	(374.2)*	(64.42)[a]	(490.0)*	(84.35)[a]	(513.5)*	(88.40)[a]
E(a)	112.4	22.92	57.9	15.46	38.0	15.08
E(b)	0.0	0.00	0.0	0.00	0.0	0.00
E(c)	77.3	15.77	30.8	8.22	28.1	11.15
E(ab)	0.0	0.00	0.0	0.00	0.0	0.00
E(ac)	17.0	3.47	2.2	0.59	1.3	0.52
E(bc)	0.0	0.00	0.0	0.00	0.0	0.00
E(abc)	0.0	0.00	0.0	0.00	0.0	0.00
TC	490.3	100.00	374.6	100.00	252.0	100.00
Value in 1966	580.9	—	580.9	—	580.9	—

Note: See the note to Table 6.1 for explanations of the symbols in the column "Source of Change".

period 1911–66, except during the last few years, was responsible for the observed contribution of migration to the growth of the population in this segment. Comparing the results of Tables 6.7 and 6.8, we can observe that the proportionate contribution due to mortality declines was less on the population in the working age group than on the school age population in all the periods in the case of males, while in the case of females this was higher during the two periods 1933–66 and 1947–66. This was due to the smaller changes in the survival rates in the age group (15–64) than in the younger age group (6–14) in the case of males; actually there were small decreases in the survival rates at some of the ages 45 years and above in 1947 as well as in 1966 compared respectively with the values observed in 1933 and 1961. As far as females were concerned, there were comparatively larger improvements, especially in the age groups 35 years and above, and this explains the higher proportionate contribution of mortality change in the case of females, during the two periods.

(iii) *Population in the old age group (65 years and above)*

Table 6.9 shows the analysis of the change in the old age populations during the three periods. Since the effect of the changes in fertility had not reached this age group during any of these periods, all the terms involving fertility change have become zero. Hence, the whole of the change in this population due to the changes in the conditions, during the respective periods, came from the changes in mortality and migration.

During 1911–66, about 39 per cent of the total change of 330 thousands in the case of males was due to the change in mortality and due to migration. Out of this, migration contributed about 20 per cent the improvements in mortality about 17 per cent, and the remaining 2 per cent was accounted for by their interaction. In the case of females, out of nearly 42 per cent of the total change attributable to the changes occurring in the components, about 23 per cent came from the decline in mortality, about 16 per cent from migration, and the rest from their interaction.

The changes in the size of this population during the other two periods due to the changes in the mortality conditions and migration were comparatively small, and were contributed almost wholly by migration in the case of males. On the other hand, in the case of females these changes were quite considerable, though smaller than during 1911–66, and variations in mortality contributed a larger share than migration. Again, the consequences observed here are in accordance with the observed variations in the components.

6.5 Summary

Analysis of the population change in Australia during three selected periods using the method of factorial projections suggested here, provides a complete picture of the dynamics of population change during the three periods taken for study. It is observed that the effects and their interactions depend on the magnitudes of the changes in the components and the length of the period of analysis.

During the period 1911–66, the effects of fertility decline and those of mortality decline acted in opposite directions and almost cancelled their mutual effects so that migration formed the major determinant in the growth of the total population for males and females and in changing the sex distribution. The changes in fertility and their interactions with the changes in other components maintained their usual upper hand in changing the number of births and the age distributions. During 1911–66, migration contributed nearly 44 per cent to the school age population, 50 per cent to the population in the working age group, and 22 per cent to the old age group in the case of males, while in the case of females the corresponding percentages were about 44, 42 and 19.

During the other two periods, 1933–66 and 1947–66, improvements in mortality had a larger share in the changes in the female population than in those in the male population. The effect of fertility improvements was more prominent in the period 1933–66 and that of migration during 1947–66.

Owing to the decrease in the length of the period of analysis, the effect of the change in fertility on the population in the working ages decreased from one period to the other. Its effect on the old age population was zero in all the periods for the same reason.

It appears from this analysis of the changes in the population of Australia that the proposed decomposition of the observed changes in the characteristics of a population during a given period is useful in studying the relative impact on them of the variations in the components during that period.

APPENDIX A

ESTIMATION OF THE DISTRIBUTION OF THE MIGRANTS BY SINGLE YEARS OF AGE AND THE FERTILITY RATES BY SINGLE YEARS OF AGE OF FEMALES FOR THE PERIOD 1911–20

A.1 Introduction

Though most of the data needed for the study were available for Australia in published or unpublished form, the distributions by age of the number of arrivals and departures as well as the age-specific birth rates by single years of age of females were not available for the decade 1911–20. The survival rates were also not available for all the intercensal periods, but were interpolated from the official life tables and the life table presented in Appendix B. We shall discuss in this appendix the procedures adopted to obtain the migration data and the fertility rates for the period 1911–20.

A.2 Estimation of the age distributions of arrivals and departures

The total number of arrivals and departures for males and females were available for every year during this period. Hence it was necessary only to obtain the proportionate distribution by single years of age for arrivals and departures in the case of males and females.

To achieve this, two procedures were possible. One was to utilize the age distribution of the arrivals and departures during a period similar to the one under consideration; and the other was to make use of the information available in the census, i.e. the statistics on the duration of stay in Australia. Each procedure has some advantages and disadvantages, and involve certain assumptions which are sufficiently well known and need no further elucidation.

Whichever procedure we adopt, it is necessary that the net effect on the population must be such that the components put together should yield approximately the population enumerated in a subsequent census. In Australia, the estimates of the total population of males and of females were published for each year during 1911–20;† and the population by age as at 30 June 1921 was estimated by adopting the age distributions observed in the census of 1921, which was taken on 3 and 4 April 1921, to the published total population of males and females. Hence it was prescribed that the age distributions of arrivals and departures should be such that, when these data on migration were used along with the data on births and the interpolated survival rates, (a) the resultant total population must be tolerably close to the published value for each of the years 1911–20; and (b) the resultant populations in five year age groups as at 30 June 1921 must not differ very much from the corresponding populations estimated on the basis of the census of 1921.

Using these two criteria for testing the estimates, some trials were made adopting the age distributions observed during other periods for which the age data were available. The results obtained from these trials did not satisfy the above criteria. Hence it was decided to try and estimate the age distributions of arrivals from the statistics on the duration of stay in Australia, as reported at the census of 1921; and using them, to obtain the age distributions of the departures.

In the census of 1921, males and females born outside Australia were classified in five year age groups and in single years of duration of stay in Australia for the first five years and then in groups of five years of duration of stay.‡ These data were used, as described below, to obtain the age distributions of the male and female arrivals. The procedure adopted was the same in the case of males and females.

First, the populations with the duration of stay of (0–4) years, in five year age groups, were subtracted from the total populations in those age groups. Thus two populations—one including the immigrants and another excluding them—were obtained as at the census date. These were then reverse survived using the five year survival rates obtained by interpolation from the official life tables. In computing the survival rates for this purpose, the fact that the census was taken on 4 April 1921 was taken into account. By computing the simple averages of the respective populations at 1921 and the reverse survived ones, two populations—one including immigrants and another excluding them—were obtained at the mid-point of the period 1916–21. The population without the immigration component was then subtracted from the one with it and the percentage age distribution of immigrants at the mid-point of the period 1916–21 was obtained. The persons born outside Australia and enumerated in the census are referred

† Commonwealth Bureau of Census and Statistics, *Australian Demography*, Bulletin No. 41, 1923, pp. 12–13.

‡ Commonwealth Bureau of Census and Statistics, *Census of the Commonwealth of Australia*, 3 and 4 April 1921, Vol. 1, Part 4, pp. 270.

to here as immigrants to distinguish them from arrivals during the different years. Similarly emigrants and departures are distinguished.

A similar procedure was used to obtain the age distribution of immigrants at the mid-point of the period 1911–16, taking the total population excluding those with the duration of stay (0–4) years and the population excluding those with duration of stay (0–9) years at the census of 1921.

But it was observed that the percentages in the older age groups 75 years and over for males and females, obtained from the above procedure, were small compared to the age distributions of arrivals during the years for which data were available. To examine whether this had arisen due to the use of the duration of stay data which show only the survivors of the arrivals and also exclude the arrivals who returned before the census date, the populations with duration of stay of 0 years in the censuses of 1911 and 1921, were used. The populations in five year age groups, excluding the population with 0 years duration of stay, were distributed into single years of age by using the Karup–King interpolation formula for the age groups (5–9) to (70–74) years and by adopting the single years age distribution of the total population for the age groups (0–4) years, (75–79) and (80–84) years. The population with 0 years of duration of stay was negligible in the age group (85+) years.

The populations by single years of age enumerated in the censuses of 1911 and 1921 and the ones excluding the populations of 0 years duration of stay, obtained as above, were then reverse survived and the age distributions of the immigrants at the mid-point of the periods 1910–11 and 1920–21, were obtained. From these estimates also, it was observed that the percentages in the older age groups, 75 years and above, were small in the earlier estimates. Since the percentages in the age groups (75–79) and (80–84) years obtained in this case appeared more reasonable when compared with those of age distributions of arrivals in other years for which data were available and since the data for 0 years of duration represent a situation nearer to the dates of arrival of immigrants, it was decided to utilize these proportions for the age groups (75–79) and (80–84) years. But it was found that these proportions were sufficiently different for 1910–11 and 1920–21 in the case of females, while they were practically the same for males in the two years. Hence, for the females, the proportions in these age groups in the age distributions at the mid-points of the periods 1911–16 and 1916–21 were obtained by a linear interpolation of the respective proportions for 1910–11 and 1920–21. The percentages in the other age groups were proportionately adjusted to make the sum equal to 100. While this adjustment altered the percentages in the other age groups to a very small extent, it made the percentages in the age groups (75–79) and (80–84) years look reasonable as compared with the known age distributions of arrivals. Thus the age distributions in five year age groups of the immigrant males and females at the mid-point of the periods 1911–16 and 1916–21, were calculated.

Then the age distributions in five year age groups of the emigrants were computed separately for males and females by using the ratios of the percentages in the age distributions of the departures to those in the age distributions of the arrivals during the period 1925–29, the earliest period for which data on the age distribution of arrivals and departures were available and during which the effect of the economic depression was still not very great. The values of the percentages in five year age groups, thus obtained, were adjusted to make the sum equal to 100.

Finally the male and female arrivals and departures in five year age groups were obtained by adopting the estimated age distributions of immigrants and emigrants, at the mid-point of the period 1911–16, to the published number of arrivals and departures of males and females during each of the five calendar years 1911 to 1915. Similarly the age distributions at the mid-point of the period 1916–21 were used to distribute by five year age groups the total number of arrivals and departures of males and females during the five calendar years 1916 to 1920. These were then distributed into single years of age with the help of the estimated single years of age distributions of arrivals and departures during 1925–29.

These estimated arrivals and departures by single years of age were used along with the published data on births and the interpolated survival rates to project the population from 30 June 1911 to 30 June 1921. The resultant total populations for each of the calendar years were compared with the totals published by the Commonwealth Bureau of Census and Statistics, and were found to be quite satisfactory in the case of females. The comparison of the projected population as at 30 June 1921 with the one obtained by adopting the census age distribution also showed that the female population was obtained within reasonable limits (see Tables A.3 and A.4, Females).

In the case of males, though, the results were not satisfactory. This was expected because the effect of troop movements was greater on the male population than on the female population during the years 1914–19. In fact, as could be seen from Table A.1, the proportions of the troop movements among the total arrivals and departures were comparatively insignificant for females. Hence the arrivals and departures by single years of age, as estimated above, were kept for the females.

In the case of males some adjustment was needed to take account of the troop movements. If we had excluded the troop movements, it would have become necessary to adjust the total populations and the population at 30 June 1921 so as to make them comparable. Hence it was decided to try

Table A.1 Number of troop movements included in the migration statistics: Australia, 1914–19

Year	Arrivals		Departures	
	Males	Females	Males	Females
1914	—	—	34 355	186
			(37.17)	(0.69)
1915	8423	102	95 097	615
	(16.63)	(0.50)	(68.65)	(3.64)
1916	15 739	273	143 566	542
	(32.17)	(1.88)	(81.51)	(3.38)
1917	28 244	205	45 553	935
	(51.10)	(2.08)	(62.44)	(9.38)
1918	43 714[a]	437	23 124	381
	(62.87)	(4.65)	(50.51)	(4.91)
1919	162 498	1258	1336	44
	(82.18)	(4.98)	(3.24)	(0.28)

Note: The figures in parentheses are the ratios (per cent) of the troop movements to the total arrivals and departures.

[a] Corrected for misprint on the basis of the total figure published in *Quarterly Summary of Australian Statistics*, 1920, p. 8; and in the official *Year Book*, 1901–1919, p. 1101.

[Source: Commonwealth Bureau of Census and Statistics, *Australian Demography*, Bulletin No. 38, 1920, pp. 20–21.]

and make some adjustments in the age distributions for males. After some trial and error, the 5 year age distributions were adopted as shown below.

Male arrivals

(i) For each of the calendar years 1911 to 1915 the estimated age distribution of immigrants at the mid-point of the period 1911–16;
(ii) For each of the calendar years 1916 to 1918 the average of the estimated age distribution of immigrants at the mid-point of the period 1916–21 and that of the arrivals during 1925–29;
(iii) For the calendar year 1919 the estimated age distribution of immigrants at the mid-point of the period 1916–21;
(iv) For the calendar year 1920 the age distributions of arrivals during 1925–29.

Male departures

(i) For each of the calendar years 1911 to 1913 the estimated age distribution of emigrants at the mid-point of the period 1911–16;

Table A.2 Percentage age distributions of arrivals and departures: Australia, 1911–20

Age groups	Arrivals Males 1911–15	Arrivals Males 1916–18	Arrivals Males 1919	Arrivals Males 1920	Arrivals Females 1911–15	Arrivals Females 1916–20	Departures Males 1911–13	Departures Males 1914	Departures Males 1915–18	Departures Males 1919	Departures Males 1920	Departures Females 1911–15	Departures Females 1916–20
0–4	6.51	6.02	7.65	4.39	8.13	7.15	5.63	6.64	7.65	6.56	3.31	6.59	5.77
5–9	8.66	5.06	5.92	4.21	10.87	5.50	6.89	6.41	5.92	4.68	2.92	8.22	4.14
10–14	7.80	5.31	6.96	3.66	9.19	4.91	5.40	6.18	6.96	4.78	2.21	6.78	3.60
15–19	10.95	11.12	12.62	9.62	9.39	12.24	4.40	8.51	12.62	5.03	3.37	7.04	9.13
20–24	15.84	15.81	16.98	14.64	12.16	21.12	12.96	14.97	16.98	13.79	10.45	11.14	19.28
25–29	16.05	14.25	15.00	13.50	14.20	18.28	17.57	16.29	15.00	16.30	12.90	15.10	19.38
30–34	12.36	10.50	11.10	9.90	12.52	11.23	15.12	13.11	11.10	13.48	10.58	14.40	12.87
35–39	8.71	8.38	7.89	8.87	8.87	6.64	11.82	9.86	7.89	10.64	10.51	10.92	8.15
40–44	5.79	6.58	5.54	7.62	5.79	4.03	8.60	7.07	5.54	8.18	9.89	7.47	5.17
45–49	3.42	5.38	3.83	6.94	3.66	2.77	4.95	4.39	3.83	5.50	8.76	4.71	3.55
50–54	1.88	3.96	2.60	5.31	2.20	2.24	3.13	2.86	2.60	4.29	7.70	3.23	3.27
55–59	1.01	3.02	1.77	4.26	1.35	1.73	1.68	1.72	1.77	2.94	6.20	1.94	2.49
60–64	0.51	2.29	1.16	3.42	0.82	1.10	0.92	1.04	1.16	2.06	5.36	1.23	1.65
65–69	0.26	1.39	0.60	2.18	0.42	0.61	0.46	0.53	0.60	1.05	3.34	0.62	0.89
70–74	0.11	0.64	0.24	1.04	0.19	0.26	0.21	0.22	0.24	0.45	1.74	0.29	0.39
75–79	0.09	0.22	0.09	0.35	0.17	0.13	0.17	0.13	0.09	0.17	0.59	0.23	0.19
80–84	0.05	0.07	0.05	0.09	0.07	0.06	0.09	0.07	0.05	0.10	0.17	0.09	0.08
85+	0.00	0.00	0.00	0.00	0.00	0.00	0.00	0.00	0.00	0.00	0.00	0.00	0.00
Total	100.00	100.00	100.00	100.00	100.00	100.00	100.00	100.00	100.00	100.00	100.00	100.00	100.00

(ii) For the calendar year 1914 the average of the estimated age distribution of emigrants at the mid-point of the period 1911–16 and the estimated age distribution of immigrants at the mid-point of the period 1916–21;
(iii) For each of the calendar years 1915 to 1918 the estimated age distribution of immigrants at the mid-point of the period 1916–21;
(iv) For the calendar year 1919 the estimated age distribution of emigrants at the mid-point of the period 1916–21;
(v) For the calendar year 1920 the age distribution of departures during 1925–29.

The actual percentage age distributions in five year age groups adopted for the arrivals and departures during 1911–20 are shown in Table A.2. The distributions of the arrivals and departures of males by single years of age, were obtained by utilizing the estimated single years age distributions of arrivals and departures during 1925–29. Thus the complete set of arrivals and departures by single years of age of males and females was estimated for the period 1911–20. These data have been published in the Australian Economic Review of March 1976.

The projected populations at 30 June of the calendar years 1911–20, obtained from these estimated data on migration, the published data on births and the interpolated survival rates, are presented in Table A.3. It may be observed that the total populations for males, as well as for females,

Table A.3   Comparison of the total population of Australia at 30 June of each calendar year: published and projected, 1911–21

	MALE			FEMALE		
Year	Published (E) ('000)	Projected (P) ('000)	$\left(\dfrac{E-P}{E}\right)100$	Published (E) ('000)	Projected (P) ('000)	$\left(\dfrac{E-P}{E}\right)100$
1911	2333.8	—	—	2155.8	—	—
1912	2428.9	2425.2	+0.15	2224.8	2225.3	−0.02
1913	2517.3	2512.2	+0.20	2302.8	2298.7	+0.18
1914	2584.0	2562.5	+0.83	2365.0	2361.7	+0.14
1915	2565.0	2550.1	+0.58	2420.6	2412.8	+0.32
1916	2482.0	2481.7	+0.01	2461.2	2456.5	+0.19
1917	2438.2	2447.5	−0.38	2502.6	2497.0	+0.22
1918	2485.0	2486.5	−0.06	2544.4	2537.6	+0.27
1919	2610.9	2610.2	+0.02	2582.2	2581.3	+0.03
1920	2727.9	2732.8	−0.18	2632.6	2632.9	−0.01
1921	2771.9	2784.2	−0.44	2683.2	2687.2	−0.15

[Source: The published figures were taken from Commonwealth Bureau of Census and Statistics, *Australian Demography*, Bulletin No. 41, 1923.]

Table A.4 Comparison of the population of Australia in five year age groups as at 30 June 1921: enumerated and projected

Age groups	MALE			FEMALE		
	Enumerated (E) ('000)	Projected (P) ('000)	$\left(\dfrac{E-P}{E}\right)100$	Enumerated (E) ('000)	Projected (P) ('000)	$\left(\dfrac{E-P}{E}\right)100$
0–4	306.5	310.3	−1.22	295.8	295.3	+0.18
5–9	302.6	299.9	+0.88	295.3	299.7	−1.48
10–14	268.9	267.5	+0.52	262.0	265.5	−1.32
15–19	235.7	248.6	−5.49	230.2	239.4	−4.03
20–24	221.5	236.1	−6.62	234.2	225.1	+3.88
25–29	226.2	236.6	−4.61	237.9	234.1	+1.62
30–34	228.6	227.8	+0.33	222.4	225.5	−1.42
35–39	197.8	196.3	+0.77	190.7	193.2	−1.32
40–44	170.9	163.8	+4.14	161.8	160.5	+0.82
45–49	145.3	142.5	+1.91	136.2	137.6	−1.05
50–54	136.6	129.8	+4.95	120.4	119.4	+0.84
55–59	116.7	116.3	+0.35	99.9	101.1	−1.20
60–64	91.0	87.8	+3.52	79.0	74.5	+5.68
65–69	56.3	54.3	+3.56	49.1	48.5	+1.22
70–74	33.5	32.6	+2.69	31.9	31.7	+0.63
75–79	19.7	19.8	−0.51	20.5	20.8	−1.46
80–84	9.6	9.7	−1.04	10.4	10.6	−1.92
85+	4.7	4.4	+6.38	5.5	4.8	+12.73
Total	2771.9	2784.2	−0.44	2683.2	2687.2	−0.15

Note: The enumerated values were obtained by adopting the age distributions observed in the census of 1921, to the published total populations of males and females as at 30 June 1921.
[Source: Commonwealth Bureau of Census and Statistics, *Census of the Commonwealth of Australia, 3rd and 4th April 1921*, Vol. I; *Australian Demography*, Bulletin No. 41, 1923.]

were well within 1 per cent of the published values. The comparison of the populations in five year age groups from the projections and those obtained by adopting the census age distributions, presented in Table A.4, shows that the percentage difference was far below 5 per cent in each age group for each sex, except for the age groups (15–19), (20–24), (25–29), (50–54) and (85+) years in the case of males and for the age groups (60–64) and (85+) years in the case of females. The discrepancy could have arisen due to: (a) the arbitrary adjustments in the age distributions for arrivals and departures of males; (b) the influence of the epidemic of 1919 not being accounted for in obtaining the survival rates; (c) the errors of enumeration in the census data; and (d) the variations in the sex ratio at birth, however small. But the results appear to be satisfactory for practical purposes. Hence these data on migration were used in the study.

A.3 Estimation of the age-specific fertility rates for females 1911–20

The data on births by single years of age of females were published for all the calendar years 1911–20.‡ The mid-year population, i.e. the population as at 30 June of each year, was already obtained by projecting the population at 30 June 1911 for testing the consistency of the estimated age distributions of arrivals and departures. Hence the age-specific fertility rate at age x years was obtained by dividing the number of births of both sexes during each year to females aged x years by the total number of females at that age. The number of births to females whose ages were not known was allocated proportionately. The age-specific fertility rates thus obtained were negligible at ages below 15 years and above 49 years and were, therefore, assumed to be zero. For the calendar year 1912 the number of births registered was suspected to have been boosted up due to the maternity allowances granted during that year.‡. Therefore, the average number of births for the three years 1910–12 was used for the year 1911 and the average of those for 1911–13 was used for the year 1912. For the other years the number of births as published for each year was utilized. Thus the gap in the age-specific fertility rates by single years of age of females was filled in.

From the procedure of estimation of the fertility rates, it is clear that these fertility rates used in conjunction with the estimates of migration and the interpolated survival rates would approximately give the same results as presented in Tables A.3 and A.4.

‡ Commonwealth Bureau of Census and Statistics, *Commonwealth Demography*, Bulletin Nos. 29–38, 1911–20.

‡ Commonwealth Bureau of Census and Statistics, *Official Year Book of the Commonwealth of Australia, 1901–13*, No. 7, 1914, p. 146.

APPENDIX B

A COMPLETE LIFE TABLE FOR AUSTRALIA: 1965–67

B.1 Introduction

The official life table for Australia based on the 1966 census was not available at the time of this study. Hence, to obtain the survival rates required for the study, a life table with single years of age was constructed using the data on the deaths and the populations for the three years 1965–67. An account of the procedure used in the construction of the life table is given in this appendix.

B.2 The data used

The basic data used in the construction of the life table were the following.

The populations of males and females by single years of age were taken for 1966 from the census publication: Census of the Commonwealth of Australia, 30 June 1966, Census Bulletin No. 9.1, Summary of Population: Australia (p. 6), and for 1965 and 1967 from the estimates prepared by the Commonwealth Bureau of Census and Statistics. The data on deaths by single years of age, for the years 1965 and 1966 and on infant deaths, were published in Demography Bulletins 1965 and 1966; and the same for the year 1967, were supplied by the Commonwealth Bureau of Census and Statistics. They also made available the data on births registered in each calendar months and those on arrivals and departures at infant ages 0 and 1 years, in six monthly periods.

B.3 Method of calculation

In constructing a life table, as is well known, the primary step is the calculation of the probability of survival p_x or the probability of dying $q_x = 1 - p_x$. Then the other columns of the life table follow.

B.3.1 *Probability of survival at infant ages*

The method adopted in calculating these was essentially similar to the one used in the construction of the official life tables for Australia, 1960–62.‡ Since the deaths of infants under 1 year were available by months of age and the births were available by calendar months, a slight modification was made in the formulas given in the Australian life tables, 1960–62. These were as given below. The same procedures were applied separately for males and females.

For age 0 years

$$q_0 = \text{infant mortality rate or the probability of dying}$$
$$\text{before attaining the age of 1 year}$$
$$= q_0^0 + q_0^1 + q_0^2 + \ldots + q_0^{11}$$

where the indexes 0, 1, 2, . . . , 11 refer to the months of age at which death occurred.

q_0^0 was calculated as:

$$q_0^0 = \frac{\text{total deaths under 1 month of age during 1965, 1966 and 1967}}{P_{(0)}^0} \tag{B.1}$$

where

$$P_{(0)}^0 = [\tfrac{1}{4}B_{64}^{12} + B_{65}^{1-12} + B_{66}^{1-12} + B_{67}^{1-12} - \tfrac{1}{4}B_{67}^{12}]$$
$$+ \tfrac{1}{24}[\tfrac{1}{6}M_{64}^{(2)}(0) + (M_{65}^{(1)}(0) + M_{65}^{(2)}(0)) + (M_{66}^{(1)}(0) + M_{66}^{(2)}(0))$$
$$+ (M_{67}^{(1)}(0) + M_{67}^{(2)}(0)) - \tfrac{1}{6}M_{67}^{(1)}(0)]$$

in which the indexes for B_f—the births, refer to the calendar months and for $M_t(0)$—the net migrants at age 0, refer to the half years.

q_0^1 was calculated as:

$$q_0^1 = \frac{\text{total deaths aged 1 month during 1965, 1966 and 1967}}{P_{(0)}^1} \tag{B.2}$$

where

$$P_{(0)}^1 = [\tfrac{1}{2}B_{64}^{11} + B_{64}^{12} + B_{65}^{1-12} + B_{66}^{1-12} + B_{67}^{1-12} - B_{67}^{12} - \tfrac{1}{2}B_{67}^{11}]$$
$$+ \tfrac{1}{12}[\tfrac{1}{6}M_{64}^{(2)}(0) + (M_{65}^{(1)}(0) + M_{65}^{(2)}(0)) + (M_{66}^{(1)}(0) + M_{66}^{(2)}(0))$$
$$+ (M_{67}^{(1)}(0) + M_{67}^{(2)}(0)) - \tfrac{1}{6}M_{67}^{(1)}(0)] + \tfrac{1}{24}[\tfrac{1}{6}M_{64}^{(2)}(0) - \tfrac{1}{6}M_{67}^{(1)}(0)].$$

‡ See Commonwealth Bureau of Census and Statistics, *Australian Life Tables, 1960–62*, Commonwealth Government Printer, Canberra (Appendix G).

These formulas were derived on the assumption that the births were uniformly distributed over the month in which they were registered and the net number of migrants were evenly distributed over the year of age, as well as over the half year to which they refer. The formulas for q_0^2, etc. were similar to that for q_0^1 with suitable changes in the births and the net migration values. The formula for q_0^0 was made slightly different in order to take account of the higher risk of dying in the early weeks of life. The correction for the effect of migration did not make a significant difference to the q_0^i ($i = 0, 1, \ldots, 11$) values. After computing these q_0^i values, q_0 was obtained by adding them and the probability of survival p_0 was then computed by using the relation $p_0 = 1 - q_0$.

For age 1 year

To obtain the probability of dying between the age of 1 and 2 years the formula adopted in the construction of the Australian Life Table 1960–62 was used. Since the formula as given there did not present the adjustment for migration, the one used in the present study is given below:

$$q_1 = \frac{\text{total deaths aged 1 year during 1965, 1966 and 1967}}{P(1)} \qquad \text{(B.3)}$$

where

$$P(1) = [(\tfrac{1}{8}B_{63}^1 + \tfrac{3}{8}B_{63}^2 + \tfrac{5}{8}B_{63}^3 + \tfrac{7}{8}B_{63}^4) + (B_{64}^{1-4} + B_{65}^{1-4})$$

$$+ (\tfrac{7}{8}B_{66}^1 + \tfrac{5}{8}B_{66}^2 + \tfrac{3}{8}B_{66}^3 + \tfrac{1}{8}B_{66}^4)$$

$$- (\text{total deaths aged 0 years during 1964, 1965 and 1966})]$$

$$+ [\tfrac{1}{4}M_{64}^{(1)}(0) + \tfrac{3}{4}M_{64}^{(2)}(0) + \tfrac{1}{4}M_{64}^{(2)}(1) + \tfrac{1}{2}(M_{65}^{(1)-(2)}(0) + M_{66}^{(1)-(2)}(0)$$

$$+ M_{65}^{(1)-(2)}(1) + M_{66}^{(1)-(2)}(1)) + \tfrac{3}{4}M_{67}^{(1)}(0) + \tfrac{1}{4}M_{67}^{(2)}(0) + \tfrac{1}{2}M_{67}^{(1)}(1) + \tfrac{1}{4}M_{67}^{(2)}(1)]$$

in which the indexes for B—the births, indicate the quarters and those for M—net migration, refer to the half year.

The probability of survival was then obtained as $p_1 = 1 - q_1$.

B.3.2 *Age 2 years and above*

In the construction of the official life tables the ages (0–4) years were considered as infant ages and separate formulas were adopted. But the calculations in the present case showed that even at age 1 year the difference in the value of p_1 obtained by the elaborate method given above and the simple procedure given here, was small. Hence it was decided to adopt the same procedure from age 2 years onwards.

In the life tables of 1960–62, the populations enumerated in the census at the different ages were corrected for the effect of net migration by taking the figures of net movement in six monthly periods. As an alternative to this method, the averages of the populations in the three years 1965, 1966 and 1967 were used. Thus for all ages 2 years and above the procedure followed was as given below:

The age specific death rate at age x years was computed as:

$$m_x = \frac{\text{total deaths of persons aged } x \text{ years during 1965, 1966 and 1967}}{\text{total population aged } x \text{ years as at 30 June 1965, 1966 and 1967}} \qquad \text{(B.4)}$$

From the m_x values the probability of survival from age x to $(x + 1)$ years was then obtained from the following simple formula:

$$p_x = \frac{2.0 - m_x}{2.0 + m_x}, \qquad \text{for } x = 2, 3, \ldots, 84. \qquad \text{(B.5)}$$

An examination of the mortality rates, m_x values, showed that a pronounced peak occurred at ages 19–20 years in the case of males and a similar peak of lesser magnitude occurred around the same ages in the case of females. A similar feature was detected by the actuary in the 1960–62 mortality rates. To preserve this distinct feature of the mortality rates, no graduation was applied to the mortality rates for ages (5–30) years in the official life tables of 1960–62. However, the mortality rates for ages 31 years and above were graduated. Even then, considerable doubts were expressed regarding the values of m_x only at ages 89 or 90 years and above. Since the progression of the mortality rates from age to age in the present case was not too irregular even at ages 30 years and above except at very few ages, and since the effect of graduation would have caused only small changes in the probabilities of survival, it was decided to use the unsmoothed mortality rates in computing the probability of survival, p_x. Hence the p_x values as obtained from the above formula were used without any further graduation.

B.3.3 *Computation of the other life table values*

The other life table values were computed by the usual techniques employed in constructing life tables. The survivors at exact age x years were calculated by taking a radix $l_0 = 100\,000$ and using the relation: $l_{x+1} = l_x p_x$. From the l_x values the life table population or the number of years survived, L_x, was obtained from the following formulas:

$$L_0 = (1 - a)l_0 + al_1 \qquad \text{(B.6)}$$

where $a = 0.88186$ for males and $= 0.86692$ for females, is the proportion of deaths to persons born in the same year. The numerical values for males and females given here were the average values for the three years 1965–67.

$$L_x = \tfrac{1}{2}(l_x + l_{x+1}), \qquad \text{for } x = 1, 2, \ldots, 84 \qquad (B.7)$$

and

$$L_{85+} = l_{85} \log l_{85}. \qquad (B.8)$$

Then the survival rates were calculated from the relations:

$$S(b) = (L_0/l_0)$$

$$S(x) = (L_{x+1}/L_x), \qquad \text{for } x = 0, 1, 2, \ldots, 83 \qquad \left.\right\rbrace \qquad (B.9)$$

and $\quad S(84+) = [L_{85+}/(L_{84} + L_{85+})].$

Finally the expectation of life at age x years was computed as under:

$$\overset{\circ}{e}_x = \frac{1}{l_x}\left[\sum_{t=x}^{w} L_t\right]. \qquad (B.10)$$

B.4 The life tables for males and females

The complete life tables for males and females thus obtained are presented in Tables B.1 and B.2. A comparison of the mortality situation in 1965–67 as revealed by these life tables with those of the previous ones, is given in Chapter 2.

Table B.1 Australian life tables, 1965–67: males

Age x	Survivors l_x	Probability of survival p_x	Probability of dying $q_x = 1 - p_x$	No. of years lived L_x	Survival rates $S(x) = \dfrac{L_{x+1}}{L_x}$	Expectation of life at age x $\overset{\circ}{e}_x$
					$(0.98195)^a$	
0	100 000	0.97953	0.02047	98 195	0.99667	67.71
1	97 953	0.99825	0.00175	97 868	0.99863	68.12
2	97 782	0.99900	0.00100	97 733	0.99907	67.24
3	97 685	0.99915	0.00085	97 643	0.99928	66.30
4	97 602	0.99942	0.00058	97 573	0.99947	65.36
5	97 545	0.99953	0.00047	97 522	0.99952	64.40
6	97 499	0.99952	0.00048	97 476	0.99954	63.43
7	97 452	0.99955	0.00045	97 430	0.99957	62.46
8	97 408	0.99959	0.00041	97 388	0.99959	61.49
9	97 368	0.99960	0.00040	97 349	0.99960	60.51

Age x	Survivors l_x	Probability of survival p_x	Probability of dying $q_x = 1 - p_x$	No. of years lived L_x	Survival rates $S(x) = \dfrac{L_{x+1}}{L_x}$	Expectation of life at age x $\overset{\circ}{e}_x$
10	97 329	0.99960	0.00040	97 310	0.99962	59.54
11	97 290	0.99965	0.00035	97 273	0.99958	58.56
12	97 256	0.99952	0.00048	97 233	0.99952	57.58
13	97 210	0.99952	0.00048	97 186	0.99946	56.61
14	97 163	0.99940	0.00060	97 134	0.99935	55.63
15	97 105	0.99930	0.00070	97 071	0.99919	54.67
16	97 037	0.99909	0.00091	96 992	0.99885	53.70
17	96 948	0.99862	0.00138	96 881	0.99845	52.75
18	96 814	0.99828	0.00172	96 731	0.99817	51.83
19	96 648	0.99806	0.00194	96 554	0.99808	50.91
20	96 460	0.99810	0.00190	96 369	0.99817	50.01
21	96 277	0.99824	0.00176	96 192	0.99827	49.11
22	96 108	0.99831	0.00169	96 026	0.99846	48.19
23	95 945	0.99861	0.00139	95 878	0.99854	47.27
24	95 812	0.99848	0.00152	95 739	0.99850	46.34
25	95 666	0.99852	0.00148	95 595	0.99853	45.41
26	95 524	0.99854	0.00146	95 455	0.99859	44.47
27	95 385	0.99865	0.00135	95 321	0.99857	43.54
28	95 256	0.99850	0.00150	95 185	0.99846	42.60
29	95 113	0.99843	0.00157	95 039	0.99849	41.66
30	94 964	0.99855	0.00145	94 895	0.99854	40.72
31	94 826	0.99853	0.00147	94 756	0.99849	39.78
32	94 687	0.99845	0.00155	94 613	0.99834	38.84
33	94 540	0.99824	0.00176	94 457	0.99816	37.90
34	94 373	0.99808	0.00192	94 283	0.99797	36.97
35	94 192	0.99787	0.00213	94 092	0.99777	36.04
36	93 991	0.99767	0.00233	93 882	0.99770	35.11
37	93 772	0.99774	0.00226	93 666	0.99753	34.19
38	93 560	0.99731	0.00269	93 435	0.99729	33.27
39	93 309	0.99727	0.00273	93 181	0.99711	32.36
40	93 054	0.99696	0.00304	92 913	0.99681	31.44
41	92 771	0.99667	0.00333	92 617	0.99631	30.54
42	92 462	0.99595	0.00405	92 275	0.99587	29.64
43	92 088	0.99580	0.00420	91 894	0.99571	28.76
44	91 701	0.99562	0.00438	91 500	0.99533	27.88
45	91 299	0.99504	0.00496	91 073	0.99484	27.00
46	90 846	0.99465	0.00535	90 603	0.99438	26.13
47	90 360	0.99410	0.00590	90 094	0.99363	25.27
48	89 827	0.99316	0.00684	89 520	0.99275	24.41
49	89 213	0.99234	0.00766	88 871	0.99207	23.58

Table B.1—(continued).

Age x	Survivors l_x	Probability of survival p_x	Probability of dying $q_x = 1 - p_x$	No. of years lived L_x	Survival rates $S(x) = \dfrac{L_{x+1}}{L_x}$	Expectation of life at age x $\overset{\circ}{e}_x$
50	88 529	0.99180	0.00820	88 166	0.99148	22.76
51	87 803	0.99116	0.00884	87 415	0.99032	21.94
52	87 027	0.98947	0.01053	86 569	0.98885	21.13
53	86 111	0.98823	0.01177	85 604	0.98778	20.35
54	85 097	0.98732	0.01268	84 558	0.98703	19.59
55	84 018	0.98674	0.01326	83 461	0.98584	18.83
56	82 904	0.98493	0.01507	82 279	0.98402	18.08
57	81 654	0.98309	0.01691	80 964	0.98219	17.35
58	80 274	0.98127	0.01873	79 522	0.98032	16.64
59	78 770	0.97935	0.02065	77 957	0.97878	15.95
60	77 143	0.97820	0.02180	76 303	0.97699	15.27
61	75 462	0.97576	0.02424	74 547	0.97409	14.60
62	73 632	0.97237	0.02763	72 615	0.97090	13.95
63	71 598	0.96939	0.03061	70 502	0.96819	13.34
64	69 406	0.96695	0.03305	68 259	0.96455	12.74
65	67 112	0.96207	0.03793	65 840	0.96210	12.16
66	64 567	0.96214	0.03786	63 345	0.95915	11.62
67	62 122	0.95604	0.04396	60 757	0.95514	11.06
68	59 391	0.95419	0.04581	58 031	0.95234	10.54
69	56 671	0.95040	0.04960	55 265	0.94890	10.02
70	53 860	0.94733	0.05267	52 441	0.94499	9.52
71	51 023	0.94252	0.05748	49 557	0.93832	9.02
72	48 090	0.93386	0.06614	46 500	0.93098	8.54
73	44 910	0.92790	0.07210	43 291	0.92548	8.11
74	41 672	0.92288	0.07712	40 065	0.91974	7.70
75	38 458	0.91633	0.08367	36 849	0.91359	7.30
76	35 240	0.91059	0.08941	33 665	0.90911	6.93
77	32 089	0.90748	0.09252	30 605	0.90267	6.56
78	29 120	0.89737	0.10263	27 626	0.89261	6.17
79	26 132	0.88731	0.11269	24 659	0.88381	5.82
80	23 187	0.87986	0.12014	21 794	0.87888	5.50
81	20 401	0.87777	0.12223	19 154	0.86895	5.18
82	17 908	0.85891	0.14109	16 644	0.85415	4.83
83	15 381	0.84861	0.15139	14 217	0.84036	4.55
84	13 052	0.83064	0.16936	11 947	0.78549[b]	4.27
85+	10 842	—	—	43 748	—	4.04

[a] This is the value of $S(b) = (L_0/l_0)$.
[b] This is the value of $S(84+) = (L_{85+}/L_{84+})$.

Table B.2 Australian life tables, 1965–67: females

Age x	Survivors l_x	Probability of survival p_x	Probability of dying $q_x = 1 - p_x$	No. of years lived L_x	Survival rates $S(x) = \dfrac{L_{x+1}}{L_x}$	Expectation of life at age x $\overset{\circ}{e}_x$
					$(0.98603)^a$	
0	100 000	0.98389	0.01611	98 603	0.99711	74.11
1	98 389	0.99856	0.00144	98 319	0.99890	74.32
2	98 248	0.99924	0.00076	98 211	0.99932	73.43
3	98 173	0.99941	0.00059	98 144	0.99945	72.48
4	98 116	0.99950	0.00050	98 091	0.99953	71.52
5	98 066	0.99957	0.00043	98 045	0.99960	70.56
6	98 024	0.99964	0.00036	98 007	0.99967	69.59
7	97 989	0.99970	0.00030	97 974	0.99970	68.62
8	97 960	0.99970	0.00030	97 945	0.99969	67.64
9	97 930	0.99968	0.00032	97 914	0.99971	66.66
10	97 899	0.99975	0.00025	97 886	0.99976	65.68
11	97 874	0.99977	0.00023	97 863	0.99976	64.69
12	97 852	0.99975	0.00025	97 839	0.99974	63.71
13	97 827	0.99973	0.00027	97 814	0.99970	62.72
14	97 801	0.99968	0.00032	97 785	0.99965	61.74
15	97 769	0.99963	0.00037	97 751	0.99957	60.76
16	97 733	0.99950	0.00050	97 709	0.99947	59.78
17	97 684	0.99944	0.00056	97 657	0.99941	58.81
18	97 630	0.99938	0.00062	97 599	0.99937	57.85
19	97 569	0.99936	0.00064	97 538	0.99937	56.88
20	97 507	0.99938	0.00062	97 476	0.99936	55.92
21	97 446	0.99935	0.00065	97 414	0.99941	54.95
22	97 383	0.99947	0.00053	97 357	0.99938	53.99
23	97 331	0.99930	0.00070	97 297	0.99934	53.02
24	97 263	0.99939	0.00061	97 233	0.99937	52.05
25	97 204	0.99936	0.00064	97 172	0.99932	51.08
26	97 141	0.99928	0.00072	97 106	0.99929	50.12
27	97 071	0.99930	0.00070	97 037	0.99932	49.15
28	97 003	0.99934	0.00066	96 971	0.99923	48.19
29	96 939	0.99913	0.00087	96 897	0.99915	47.22
30	96 855	0.99917	0.00083	96 815	0.99916	46.26
31	96 774	0.99915	0.00085	96 733	0.99903	45.30
32	96 692	0.99891	0.00109	96 639	0.99890	44.33
33	96 587	0.99889	0.00111	96 533	0.99895	43.38
34	96 479	0.99902	0.00098	96 432	0.99888	42.43
35	96 385	0.99874	0.00126	96 324	0.99868	41.47
36	96 263	0.99863	0.00137	96 197	0.99860	40.52
37	96 131	0.99857	0.00143	96 063	0.99853	39.58
38	95 994	0.99849	0.00151	95 921	0.99823	38.63
39	95 849	0.99798	0.00202	95 752	0.99802	37.69

Table B.2—(continued).

Age x	Survivors l_x	Probability of survival p_x	Probability of dying $q_x = 1 - p_x$	No. of years lived L_x	Survival rates $S(x) = \dfrac{L_{x+1}}{L_x}$	Expectation of life at age x $\overset{\circ}{e}_x$
40	95 655	0.99806	0.00194	95 562	0.99802	36.77
41	95 470	0.99799	0.00201	95 374	0.99776	35.84
42	95 278	0.99753	0.00247	95 160	0.99754	34.91
43	95 042	0.99756	0.00244	94 926	0.99748	33.99
44	94 810	0.99741	0.00259	94 688	0.99716	33.08
45	94 565	0.99690	0.00310	94 418	0.99675	32.16
46	94 272	0.99660	0.00340	94 111	0.99638	31.26
47	93 951	0.99616	0.00384	93 771	0.99594	30.36
48	93 590	0.99572	0.00428	93 390	0.99552	29.48
49	93 190	0.99533	0.00467	92 972	0.99523	28.60
50	92 754	0.99513	0.00487	92 528	0.99503	27.74
51	92 303	0.99493	0.00507	92 069	0.99457	26.87
52	91 835	0.99421	0.00579	91 569	0.99399	26.00
53	91 303	0.99376	0.00624	91 018	0.99325	25.15
54	90 733	0.99274	0.00726	90 404	0.99293	24.31
55	90 074	0.99312	0.00688	89 764	0.99246	23.48
56	89 455	0.99179	0.00821	89 087	0.99159	22.64
57	88 720	0.99139	0.00861	88 338	0.99103	21.82
58	87 956	0.99067	0.00933	87 546	0.99019	21.01
59	87 136	0.98971	0.01029	86 687	0.98926	20.20
60	86 239	0.98881	0.01119	85 756	0.98861	19.41
61	85 274	0.98840	0.01160	84 779	0.98756	18.62
62	84 285	0.98672	0.01328	83 725	0.98596	17.83
63	83 165	0.98519	0.01481	82 549	0.98434	17.07
64	81 934	0.98347	0.01653	81 256	0.98234	16.31
65	80 579	0.98119	0.01881	79 821	0.98099	15.58
66	79 064	0.98079	0.01921	78 304	0.97993	14.87
67	77 545	0.97906	0.02094	76 733	0.97792	14.15
68	75 921	0.97675	0.02325	75 038	0.97524	13.44
69	74 156	0.97370	0.02630	73 180	0.97177	12.75
70	72 205	0.96978	0.03022	71 114	0.96944	12.08
71	70 023	0.96908	0.03092	68 941	0.96628	11.44
72	67 858	0.96339	0.03661	66 616	0.96080	10.79
73	65 374	0.95812	0.04188	64 005	0.95620	10.18
74	62 636	0.95420	0.04580	61 202	0.95189	9.61
75	59 767	0.94947	0.05053	58 257	0.94730	9.04
76	56 747	0.94502	0.05498	55 187	0.94383	8.50
77	53 627	0.94258	0.05742	52 088	0.93755	7.96
78	50 548	0.93222	0.06778	48 835	0.92777	7.42
79	47 122	0.92299	0.07701	45 307	0.91966	6.92

Table B.2—(continued).

Age x	Survivors l_x	Probability of survival p_x	Probability of dying $q_x = 1 - p_x$	No. of years lived L_x	Survival rates $S(x) = \dfrac{L_{x+1}}{L_x}$	Expectation of life at age x $\overset{\circ}{e}_x$
80	43 493	0.91606	0.08394	41 668	0.91377	6.46
81	39 842	0.91127	0.08873	38 075	0.90409	6.00
82	36 307	0.89622	0.10378	34 423	0.88912	5.54
83	32 539	0.88119	0.11881	30 606	0.87463	5.12
84	28 673	0.86719	0.13281	26 769	0.80326[b]	4.75
85+	24 865	—	—	109 296	—	4.40

[a] This is the value of $S(b) = (L_0/l_0)$.
[b] This is the value of $S(84+) = (L_{85+}/L_{84+})$.

APPENDIX C

CONSISTENCY OF THE DATA ON THE COMPONENTS OF POPULATION CHANGE: AUSTRALIA, 1911–66

C.1 Introduction

The data on the components—fertility, mortality and migration, viz. the fertility rates by single years of age of females, the survival rates by single years of age for males and females, and the numbers of arrivals and departures of males and females by single years of age—were taken for this study from different sources, published and unpublished, and were also estimated for some period. Hence it was felt necessary to check whether they would yield results consistent with those observed in the different censuses. It must, however, be noted that the consistency tests which are applied show only whether the sets of data—one on the components and the other on the population—are in agreement within a tolerable limit or not; but it would not mean that the two sets are accurate. In fact, there may be compensating errors. However, for practical purposes, such consistency checks do give some confidence in the numerical data used to represent the situation in the country. The other data used in the study were derived from these basic data. Hence there was no need to examine them separately.

With this purpose in mind, two tests were applied to check the consistency. One was to compare the total population obtained by projecting the population as at 30 June 1911 successively for each calendar year with the values published by the Commonwealth Bureau of Census and Statistics.‡ Another was to examine the differences between the projected populations in five year age groups and the corresponding populations enumerated in the censuses.

---

‡ In the Demography Bulletin published by the Bureau, the estimated total populations of males and females at the end of each quarter in each year are given. These estimates are revised after every census to make them consistent with the census enumerations.

C.2 Comparison of the total population for males and females

In Appendix A, the data on the components for the period 1911–20 were obtained to make the projected populations consistent with the published values. Hence the projected total populations from 1921 onwards were to be compared with the published values. However, for convenience of comparison, the values from 1911 to 1966 are presented in Table C.1 at five year intervals. The table shows that the populations were generally overestimated in the projections as compared with the published values. The differences for females were very small for all the years, almost negligible for many of the years. But in the case of males, the differences were considerable, especially after 1936. The deficiencies in the migration statistics during the war years 1939–45 and the exclusion of the troop movements in those statistics seem to have increased the differences as could be observed in 1946. However, in none of the years the overestimation in the projections was very high. In fact, the differences were only around 1 per cent of the published values. Hence it was concluded that the data on the components which were used in the study were consistent with the published values of the total population.

C.3 Consistency of populations in five year age groups

In the comparison of the total population, the age distributions were not taken into account. The only way of seeing how best the projected age distributions were, was to compare them with those observed in the respective censuses. This could be done by comparing the percentage age distributions or by comparing the populations in each of the age–sex groups. Since the second procedure would show how much difference there was in the populations in each age–sex group, irrespective of their relative magnitude in the total population, it was considered that this procedure would be better than the first one and was therefore utilized.

The differences between the enumerated and the projected populations in the respective age–sex groups as percentages of the enumerated populations in those age–sex groups are presented in Table C.2. A quick glance at the table shows that the values for females were considerably smaller than for males, suggesting that the projected values for females were more consistent with the census values than those for males. The total populations were obtained within reasonable limits for both sexes, though the differences for females were again smaller. The larger differences in the case of males may have arisen due to the following factors: the effects of migration and troop movements were significantly greater on the male population; arbitrary adjustments were made in obtaining the age distribution for the

Table C.1 Ratio (per cent) of the difference between the published (E) and the projected (P) total populations to the published population: Australia, 1911–66

Year	MALES			FEMALES		
	Published (E) ('000)	Projected (P) ('000)	$\left(\dfrac{E-P}{E}\right)100$	Published (E) ('000)	Projected (P) ('000)	$\left(\dfrac{E-P}{E}\right)100$
1911	2333.8	—	—	2155.8	—	—
1916	2482.0	2481.7	+0.01	2461.2	2456.5	+0.19
1921	2771.9	2784.2	−0.44	2683.2	2687.2	−0.15
1926	3091.5	3104.9	−0.43	2964.8	2969.4	−0.16
1931	3321.2	3342.3	−0.64	3205.3	3215.6	−0.32
1936	3433.8	3467.4	−0.98	3344.6	3366.5	−0.65
1941	3584.5	3621.5	−1.03	3525.4	3542.9	−0.50
1946	3739.5	3800.1	−1.62	3725.6	3734.6	−0.24
1951	4253.7	4307.4	−1.26	4168.0	4167.4	+0.01
1956	4776.0	4831.7	−1.17	4649.5	4651.2	−0.04
1961	5312.3	5359.8	−0.89	5195.9	5190.4	+0.11
1966	5816.4	5880.8	−1.11	5734.1	5737.9	−0.07

Note: For convenience of presentation, only values at five year intervals are shown here. The published values are from the Demography Bulletins.

[Source: Commonwealth Bureau of Census and Statistics, *Demography*, 1938, 1950, 1966.]

Table C.2 Comparison of the enumerated (E) and the projected (P) populations in five year age groups, Australia 1921–66: values of $[(E - P)/E]100$ at census dates

Age groups	MALE						FEMALE					
	1921	1933	1947	1954	1961	1966	1921	1933	1947	1954	1961	1966
0–4	−1.22	−5.88	+4.03	+0.46	+0.21	0.00	+0.18	−6.46	+3.83	+0.37	−0.11	−0.67
5–9	+0.88	−0.39	+1.95	+2.69	+1.11	+0.08	−1.48	−0.55	+2.00	+2.29	+0.81	+0.49
10–14	+0.52	+0.30	−0.10	+2.57	+3.00	+1.11	−1.32	+0.56	+0.15	+2.88	+2.66	+0.79
15–19	−5.49	−0.57	−4.41	+0.69	+2.50	+1.99	−4.03	+0.06	−3.93	+1.35	+2.59	+1.95
20–24	−6.62	+1.66	−3.36	−4.54	+1.65	+1.39	+3.88	+0.44	+0.73	−4.25	+1.75	+2.39
25–29	−4.61	−1.31	−4.56	−3.27	−2.18	+0.88	+1.62	+0.10	+1.53	−0.14	−1.44	+1.47
30–34	+0.33	−5.65	−2.93	−3.19	−4.02	−3.37	−1.42	+0.90	+0.26	+1.06	−1.97	−2.09
35–39	+0.77	−7.60	+0.65	−3.69	−2.56	−3.83	−1.32	+1.79	+1.36	+1.13	+1.57	−1.55
40–44	+4.14	−1.80	−3.23	+0.09	−4.54	−3.59	+0.82	−2.47	−1.71	−0.17	+1.23	+0.62
45–49	+1.91	+2.27	−4.34	−1.09	−0.88	−4.50	−1.05	−1.62	+2.53	−1.15	−0.45	+0.64
50–54	+4.95	+3.03	−7.76	−3.44	−0.32	−1.79	+0.84	−1.84	−1.25	+0.71	−0.58	−0.92
55–59	+0.35	−0.58	−5.28	−11.72	−5.25	−0.78	−1.20	−4.80	−4.52	−4.96	−5.25	−1.79
60–64	+3.52	+4.15	+0.77	−4.12	−6.25	−5.37	+5.68	+1.95	−3.12	−2.45	+1.18	−4.33
65–69	+3.56	+3.58	+2.56	−0.48	−8.43	−6.87	+1.22	+1.88	−1.65	−4.26	−2.97	+0.64
70–74	+2.69	+4.70	+1.03	+0.96	−0.63	−9.08	+0.63	+3.27	−2.25	−3.22	−4.19	−3.74
75–79	−0.51	+10.31	+5.87	+2.24	+1.39	+0.11	−1.46	+7.44	+0.37	−3.58	−5.21	−4.42
80–84	−1.04	+12.23	+4.35	+4.73	+0.34	+1.52	−1.92	+5.83	+0.31	+0.40	−1.12	−4.10
85+	+6.38	+16.67	+12.66	+9.71	+8.84	+9.28	+12.73	+15.97	+15.99	+12.07	+12.92	+14.92
Total	−0.44	−0.80	−1.32	−1.42	−0.89	−1.11	−0.15	−0.52	+0.05	−0.16	+0.11	−0.07

Note: A −ve sign shows that the enumerated population was less than that obtained in the projections and a +ve value shows that it was greater. The values for 1921 were adjusted to refer to 30 June 1921.

[Source: Commonwealth Bureau of Census and Statistics, Census of the Commonwealth of Australia 30 June, 1947 Vol. I, Part IX; 1961 Vol. VIII, Part I; and 1966 Bulletin No. 9.1.]

arrivals and departures of males during the period 1911–20; and a constant sex ratio at birth was used in the projections.

A striking feature in the table is the large differences in the age group (85+) years, both in the case of males and females. These were not given serious consideration because the numbers involved were comparatively small. Apart from this group, the values for the age groups (75–79) and (80–84) years were significantly high in 1933, especially in the case of males. This discrepancy is hard to explain except through the deficiencies in the data on the departures. It may be mentioned that this source of error was considered a major source and often corrections were effected accordingly.‡ Since only the projected populations were used in the present study, no adjustment was made in the data on departures.

Another point which can easily be noticed in the table is the large overestimation in 1933 and the considerable underestimation in 1947 of the population in the age group (0–4) years. When we recall that the female dominant method was used to obtain the projected populations and note that the differences for females were not large, it appears that these discrepancies could have arisen mainly due to the enumeration errors and the errors in the migration data.

It may also be observed that the overestimation in the age groups (15–29) years for males, which was the result of the arbitrary adjustments made in the age distributions of the arrivals and departures of males, was carried through the age range at the successive censuses. But the large value in the age group (55–59) years was probably the combined result of this error and the errors of age reporting in the census. This idea is somewhat confirmed when we look at the values for females in the same age group at the successive censuses.

The deficiencies in the migration data during the Second World War seem to have caused the observed overestimation in the age group (15–29) years for males at the census of 1947 and this again has passed into the older ages in the subsequent censuses.

C.4 Concluding remarks

In view of the long period of time under consideration, and considering the disturbances that occurred during this period, the differences on the whole were not too large to invalidate the assumption that the data on the components which were used in the study were consistent with the published estimates of the total populations for the calendar years 1911–66 and with the results of the census enumerations.

‡ See Commonwealth Bureau of Census and Statistics, *Census of the Commonwealth of Australia*, 30 June 1947, Vol. III, Statistician's Report, p. 29.

APPENDIX D

LIFE TABLE VALUES FOR AUSTRALIAN-BORN AND OUTSIDE-BORN POPULATIONS

Table D.1(a) Survivors (l_x) at exact age x in abridged life tables for Australian-born and outside-born males: 1911–66

Exact age x	Australian-born males					Outside-born males					Total males				
	1911	1921	1933	1961	1966	1911	1921	1933	1961	1966	1911	1921	1933	1961	1966
0	100 000	100 000	100 000	100 000	100 000	100 000	100 000	100 000	100 000	100 000	100 000	100 000	100 000	100 000	100 000
5	88 390	89 656	94 020	97 140	97 509	93 499	95 917	98 845	99 403	99 572	88 464	89 738	94 070	97 193	97 582
10	87 409	88 745	93 305	96 885	97 290	92 296	95 174	96 762	99 150	99 381	87 478	88 833	93 345	96 938	97 365
15	86 681	88 034	92 727	96 642	97 068	90 967	94 526	96 240	98 969	99 138	86 735	88 127	92 771	96 704	97 142
20	85 635	87 046	91 918	96 026	96 388	89 086	93 310	95 228	98 494	98 708	85 659	87 126	91 954	96 109	96 505
25	84 254	85 759	90 821	95 238	95 548	86 254	91 253	94 057	97 767	97 979	84 125	85 775	90 852	95 337	95 692
30	82 655	84 217	89 685	94 496	94 791	83 526	89 264	92 832	97 147	97 400	82 329	84 187	89 707	94 631	94 938
35	80 804	82 541	88 362	93 657	93 957	80 551	87 099	91 511	96 455	96 734	80 236	82 440	88 393	93 834	94 209
40	78 415	80 385	86 676	92 571	92 769	77 223	84 535	89 676	95 468	95 702	77 624	80 219	86 689	92 781	93 072
45	75 495	77 741	84 462	90 819	90 894	73 214	81 437	87 278	93 952	94 226	74 393	77 498	84 451	91 092	91 320
50	71 741	74 148	81 305	88 064	87 995	68 415	77 147	83 652	91 520	91 922	70 245	73 773	81 211	88 420	88 579
55	67 098	69 708	76 826	83 664	83 452	62 681	71 694	78 813	87 398	87 502	65 094	69 103	76 674	84 114	84 080
60	60 936	63 776	70 334	76 907	76 422	55 839	64 588	72 268	80 761	81 134	58 460	62 846	70 229	77 426	77 252
65	52 866	55 863	61 935	67 349	66 103	47 486	55 141	62 500	70 976	72 086	50 025	54 421	61 527	67 861	67 306
70	42 828	45 279	50 931	54 615	52 713	37 106	44 247	50 451	57 573	59 342	39 452	43 852	50 286	55 034	54 093
75	29 905	33 223	37 695	39 695	37 987	26 032	31 680	36 609	42 009	41 120	27 662	31 639	36 923	40 036	38 638
80	16 331	19 825	23 594	24 584	23 082	14 584	18 223	21 236	25 947	24 279	15 468	18 381	22 318	24 777	23 314
85	8 279	8 928	10 496	11 862	10 888	5 634	7 584	9 042	11 729	11 073	6 059	7 733	9 660	11 735	10 894

Table D.1(b) Survivors (l_x) at exact age x in abridged life tables for Australian-born and outside-born females: 1911–66

Exact age x	Australian-born females					Outside-born females					Total females				
	1911	1921	1933	1961	1966	1911	1921	1933	1961	1966	1911	1921	1933	1961	1966
0	100 000	100 000	100 000	100 000	100 000	100 000	100 000	100 000	100 000	100 000	100 000	100 000	100 000	100 000	100 000
5	90 115	91 741	95 127	97 723	98 058	92 441	96 843	98 832	99 604	99 722	90 438	91 809	95 150	97 767	98 116
10	89 528	90 904	94 558	97 539	97 892	90 446	96 071	98 372	99 395	99 552	89 524	90 975	94 583	97 581	97 951
15	88 819	90 331	94 131	97 395	97 762	89 897	95 468	97 947	99 260	99 440	88 819	90 403	94 158	97 438	97 822
20	87 845	89 468	93 481	97 100	97 483	88 911	94 791	97 211	99 080	99 283	87 842	89 557	93 505	97 195	97 563
25	86 317	88 207	92 488	96 833	97 151	87 343	93 640	96 253	98 873	99 075	86 314	88 310	92 518	96 905	97 257
30	84 484	86 641	91 282	96 461	96 758	85 522	91 882	95 030	98 650	98 862	84 486	86 733	91 316	96 564	96 910
35	82 511	84 880	89 933	95 978	96 214	83 608	90 099	93 764	98 296	98 596	82 524	84 979	89 985	96 107	96 436
40	80 130	82 760	88 256	95 239	95 458	81 029	88 010	92 015	97 720	97 953	80 112	82 884	88 306	95 405	95 709
45	77 696	80 488	86 337	94 126	94 285	78 123	85 715	90 230	96 820	97 109	77 588	80 631	86 418	94 335	94 616
50	74 740	77 774	83 746	92 357	92 358	74 908	82 906	87 623	95 359	95 804	74 571	77 928	83 841	92 621	92 817
55	70 880	74 300	80 216	89 768	89 628	70 610	78 926	83 990	93 158	93 370	70 580	74 386	80 321	90 115	90 144
60	65 973	69 871	75 571	86 110	85 641	65 607	73 474	79 747	89 637	90 193	65 638	69 953	75 814	86 496	86 333
65	59 528	63 685	69 183	80 538	80 009	58 769	66 390	72 352	84 180	84 494	58 951	63 394	69 271	80 965	80 702
70	50 649	54 354	59 873	72 049	71 663	48 588	56 904	62 071	75 622	76 233	49 157	54 221	59 819	72 486	72 397
75	37 794	42 382	47 733	59 857	59 360	36 777	44 061	47 947	62 762	63 191	37 126	42 094	47 253	60 209	59 981
80	24 441	28 271	32 637	43 534	43 622	22 510	27 867	31 935	45 614	45 048	22 837	27 065	31 990	43 783	43 826
85	13 427	13 724	17 427	25 203	25 391	10 039	13 425	16 189	26 294	25 509	10 320	13 052	16 586	25 321	25 354

Table D.2(a) Five year age group ($5^Lx + 5/5^Lx$) survival rates from abridged life tables for Australian-born and outside-born males 1911–66

Age group	Australian-born males					Outside-born males					Total males				
	1911	1921	1933	1961	1966	1911	1921	1933	1961	1966	1911	1921	1933	1961	1966
S_b	0.93793	0.95103	0.96412	0.98284	0.98505	0.96100	0.97550	0.99307	0.99642	0.99743	0.93078	0.93843	0.96442	0.98316	0.98549
0–4	0.94481	0.97148	0.97148	0.98706	0.98877	0.96668	0.97945	0.98486	0.99633	0.99733	0.94513	0.95144	0.97165	0.98728	0.98909
5–9	0.99028	0.99091	0.99310	0.99743	0.99774	0.98637	0.99272	0.98668	0.99782	0.99782	0.99017	0.99098	0.99307	0.99748	0.99774
10–14	0.98981	0.99039	0.99255	0.99556	0.99536	0.98248	0.99018	0.99205	0.99669	0.99661	0.98955	0.99036	0.99253	0.99572	0.99558
15–19	0.98592	0.98701	0.98968	0.99271	0.99214	0.97383	0.98258	0.98860	0.99391	0.99414	0.98486	0.98658	0.98961	0.99291	0.99251
20–24	0.98246	0.98363	0.98778	0.99200	0.99168	0.96829	0.97808	0.98734	0.99314	0.99335	0.98039	0.98300	0.98771	0.99228	0.99211
25–29	0.97933	0.98107	0.98638	0.99167	0.99164	0.96641	0.97699	0.98638	0.99327	0.99363	0.97664	0.98038	0.98638	0.99209	0.99222
30–34	0.97406	0.97702	0.98310	0.98977	0.98929	0.96158	0.97319	0.98288	0.99133	0.99125	0.97106	0.97618	0.98305	0.99019	0.98987
35–39	0.96665	0.97054	0.97772	0.98476	0.98360	0.95350	0.96701	0.97664	0.98696	0.98697	0.96299	0.96962	0.97748	0.98531	0.98458
40–44	0.95663	0.96056	0.96861	0.97542	0.97400	0.94145	0.95549	0.96596	0.97916	0.98010	0.95146	0.95913	0.96799	0.97628	0.97563
45–49	0.94297	0.94711	0.95394	0.96000	0.95840	0.92563	0.93856	0.95047	0.96466	0.96388	0.93571	0.94450	0.95305	0.96113	0.95975
50–54	0.92217	0.92790	0.93062	0.93503	0.93250	0.90407	0.91562	0.92993	0.93987	0.93987	0.91293	0.92350	0.93045	0.93628	0.93440
55–59	0.88885	0.89628	0.89881	0.89830	0.89149	0.87179	0.87854	0.89202	0.90234	0.90858	0.87804	0.88873	0.89689	0.89939	0.89603
60–64	0.84088	0.80540	0.85330	0.84547	0.83365	0.81869	0.83011	0.83812	0.84718	0.85777	0.82478	0.83803	0.84864	0.84587	0.83979
65–69	0.76005	0.77616	0.78523	0.77326	0.76337	0.74638	0.76394	0.77078	0.77466	0.76438	0.75007	0.76817	0.77996	0.77359	0.76385
70–74	0.63570	0.67575	0.69155	0.68156	0.67331	0.64328	0.65725	0.66442	0.68241	0.65098	0.64263	0.66259	0.67930	0.68174	0.66809
75–79	0.53228	0.54202	0.55622	0.56701	0.55625	0.49778	0.51716	0.52342	0.55442	0.54056	0.49911	0.52207	0.53979	0.56334	0.55218
80+	0.34522	0.32817	0.33120	0.34659	0.34105	0.29482	0.31323	0.32092	0.33631	0.33630	0.29865	0.31534	0.32502	0.34347	0.33963
e_0^0	57.55	59.32	63.88	67.88	67.40	56.76	61.73	65.48	69.92	70.03	56.50	58.84	63.67	67.87	67.71

Note: $S_b = (5^L0)/(5^l0)$, and for 80+ $= (T_{85})/(T_{80})$.

Table D.2(b) Five year age group survival ratios ($5^{L}x + 5/5^{L}x$) from abridged life tables for Australian-born and outside-born females: 1911–66

Age group	Australian-born females					Outside-born females					Total females				
	1911	1921	1933	1961	1966	1911	1921	1933	1961	1966	1911	1921	1933	1961	1966
S_b	0.94249	0.95045	0.97076	0.98634	0.98835	0.95465	0.98106	0.99299	0.99762	0.99833	0.94263	0.95086	0.97090	0.98660	0.98870
0–4	0.95462	0.96084	0.97699	0.98983	0.99130	0.95788	0.98319	0.99298	0.99736	0.99803	0.95458	0.96116	0.97710	0.99000	0.99154
5–9	0.99113	0.99228	0.99475	0.99832	0.99849	0.98609	0.99287	0.99551	0.99827	0.99858	0.99101	0.99231	0.99477	0.99832	0.99850
10–14	0.99056	0.99208	0.99429	0.99797	0.99791	0.99149	0.99332	0.99408	0.99842	0.99865	0.99057	0.99218	0.99429	0.99802	0.99802
15–19	0.98584	0.98819	0.99124	0.99711	0.99687	0.98572	0.99040	0.99132	0.99805	0.99816	0.98582	0.98837	0.99127	0.99726	0.99711
20–24	0.98071	0.98409	0.98818	0.99649	0.99627	0.98077	0.98456	0.98872	0.99783	0.99788	0.98073	0.98412	0.98823	0.99675	0.99665
25–29	0.97772	0.98097	0.98610	0.99557	0.99516	0.97839	0.98091	0.98699	0.99708	0.99758	0.97781	0.98097	0.98622	0.99577	0.99577
30–34	0.97393	0.97737	0.98330	0.99365	0.99327	0.97344	0.97872	0.98403	0.99528	0.99540	0.97381	0.97759	0.98340	0.99399	0.99379
35–39	0.97040	0.97380	0.97982	0.99032	0.98994	0.96668	0.97539	0.98098	0.99247	0.99244	0.96965	0.97410	0.97999	0.99075	0.99053
40–44	0.96585	0.96946	0.97417	0.98478	0.98366	0.96154	0.97062	0.97590	0.98787	0.98898	0.96487	0.96969	0.97445	0.98533	0.98481
45–49	0.95528	0.96090	0.96401	0.97663	0.97505	0.95091	0.95974	0.96492	0.98095	0.98062	0.95394	0.96061	0.96410	0.97743	0.97614
50–54	0.83979	0.94803	0.95014	0.96570	0.96309	0.93608	0.94172	0.95410	0.96965	0.97034	0.93846	0.94633	0.95110	0.96648	0.96456
55–59	0.91705	0.92637	0.92918	0.94752	0.94512	0.91307	0.91774	0.92892	0.95088	0.95165	0.91463	0.92374	0.92923	0.94819	0.94650
60–64	0.87790	0.88382	0.89156	0.91562	0.91562	0.86316	0.88153	0.88379	0.91937	0.92008	0.86772	0.88334	0.88976	0.91634	0.91657
65–69	0.80274	0.81953	0.83380	0.86447	0.86390	0.79515	0.81890	0.81845	0.86598	0.86746	0.79812	0.81890	0.82943	0.86474	0.86465
70–74	0.70368	0.73037	0.74669	0.78382	0.78599	0.69452	0.71241	0.72608	0.78316	0.77633	0.69496	0.71806	0.74008	0.78369	0.78417
75–79	0.60846	0.59438	0.62291	0.66482	0.67011	0.54900	0.57407	0.60244	0.66350	0.65186	0.55296	0.58007	0.61300	0.66451	0.66643
80+	0.36927	0.35101	0.37128	0.39229	0.39328	0.33052	0.34930	0.36159	0.39264	0.38923	0.33320	0.34879	0.36562	0.39225	0.39233
e_0^0	60.93	63.17	67.38	73.86	73.91	60.37	66.53	69.85	76.02	76.16	60.45	63.08	67.30	74.04	74.17

Note: $S_b = ({}_5L_0)/({}_5l_0)$, and for $80+ = (T_{85}/T_{80})$.

SELECTED BIBLIOGRAPHY

A. Books and Articles

Basavarajappa, K. G. (1963). Effect of declines in mortality on the birth rate and related measures. *Population Studies* **16** (3), 237–256.

Basavarajappa, K. G. (1964). "Trends in Fertility in Australia, 1911–61". Ph.D. Thesis, Australian National University, Canberra.

Basavarajappa, K. G. (1968a). The significance of differences in patterns of mortality for projections of population. *Demography* **5** (1), 185–191.

Basavarajappa, K. G. (1968b). Pre-marital pregnancies and ex-nuptial births in Australia, 1911–66. *Australian and New Zealand Journal of Sociology* **4** (2), 126–145.

Bernard, W. S. (1950). "American Immigration Policy—A Reappraisal". Harper and Brothers, New York.

Bernardelli, H. (1941). Population waves. *Journal of Burma Research Society* **31** (I), 1–18.

Borrie, W. D. (1948). "Population Trends and Policies". Australian Publ. Co., Sydney.

Borrie, W. D. (1949). "Immigration". Angus and Robertson, Sydney and London.

Borrie, W. D. (1959). The growth of the Australian population with particular reference to the period since 1947. *Population Studies* **13** (1), 4–18.

Borrie, W. D. (1967). Pills and populations. *Current Affairs Bulletin* **40** (1), 3–16.

Borrie, W. D. (1969). Recent trends and patterns in fertility in Australia. *Journal of the Biosocial Science* **1** (1), 57–70.

Borrie, W. D. and Spencer, G. (1965). "Australia's Population Structure and Growth". Committee for Economic Development of Australia, Melbourne.

Brauer, A. (1961). On the characteristic roots of power positive matrices. *Duke Mathematical Journal* **28**, 439–445.

Burnside, W. S. and Panton, A. W. (1960). "The Theory of Equations", Vol. 1. Dover Publications, New York.

Chaddock, R. E. (1956). Age and sex in population analysis. In "Demographic Analysis" (Eds J. J. Spengler and O. D. Duncan), 443–451. The Free Press, Glencoe, Ill.

Coale, A. J. (1956a). The effect of declines in mortality on age distributions, in "Trends and Differentials in Mortality", 125–132. Milbank Memorial Fund, New York.

Coale, A. J. (1956b). The effects of changes in mortality and fertility on age composition. *Milbank Memorial Fund Quarterly* **34** (1), 79–114.

215

Coale, A. J. (1957a). How the age distribution of a human population is determined. *Cold Spring Harbor Symposia on Quantitative Biology* **22**, 83–89.

Coale, A. J. (1957b). Age distributions as affected by changes in fertility and mortality—a further note. *Milbank Memorial Fund Quarterly* **35** (3), 302–307.

Coale, A. J. (1957c). A new method for calculating Lotka's r—the intrinsic rate of growth in a stable population. *Population Studies* **11**, 92–94.

Coale, A. J. (1963). Estimates of various demographic measures through the quasi-stable age distribution. "Emerging Techniques in Population Research", 175–193. Milbank Memorial Fund, New York.

Coale, A. J. (1968). Convergence of a human population to a stable form. *Journal of the American Statistical Association* **63** (322), 395–435.

Coale, A. J. and Demeny, P. (1966). "Regional Model Life Tables and Stable Populations". Princeton University Press, Princeton, N.J.

Coale, A. J. and Hoover, E. M. (1958). "Population Growth and Economic Development in Low Income Countries". Princeton University Press, Princeton, N.J.

Coale, A. J. and Tye, C. Y. (1961). The significance of age-patterns of fertility in high fertility populations. *Milbank Memorial Fund Quarterly* **39** (4), 631–646.

Daw, R. H. (1961). The comparison of male and female mortality rates. *Journal of the Royal Statistical Society* Series A, **124** (1), 20–43.

Demeny, P. (1965). Estimation of vital rates for populations in the process of destabilization. *Demography* **2**, 516–530.

Downer, A. R. (1962). Our story is one of continuing success. "Digest of the Australian Citizenship Convention, Canberra", 12–14.

Durand, J. D. (1953). Population structure as a factor in manpower and dependency problems of underdeveloped countries. *Population Bulletin of the United Nations* No. 3, October, 1–16.

El-Badry, M. A. (1955). Some demographic measurements for Egypt based on the stability of census age distributions. *Milbank Memorial Fund Quarterly* **33** (3), 268–305.

Feller, W. (1941). On the integral equation of renewal theory. *Annals of Mathematical Statistics* **12**, 243–267.

Gantmacher, F. R. (1959). "The Theory of Matrices" (Trans. K. A. Hirsch), Vol. 2. Chelsea Publ. Co., London.

Geyl, W. F., Sr. (1963). A brief history of Australian immigration. *International Migration* **1** (3), 157–166.

Glass, D. V. (1967). "Population Policies and Movements in Europe", Reprint. Frank Cass, London.

Goodman, L. A. (1953). Population growth of the sexes. *Biometrics* **9**, 212–225.

Goodman, L. A. (1967a). On the reconciliation of mathematical theories of population growth. *Journal of the Royal Statistical Society* Series A, **130**, 541–553.

Goodman, L. A. (1967b). On the age–sex composition of the population that would result from given fertility and mortality conditions. *Demography* **4** (2), 423–441.

Goodman, L. A. (1968). An elementary approach to the population projection matrix, to the reproductive value, and to related topics in the mathematical theory of population growth. *Demography* **5** (1), 382–409.

Hamilton, C. H. (1965). Practical and mathematical considerations in the formulation and selection of migration rates. *Demography* **2**, 429–443.

Hermalin, A. I. (1966). The effect of changes in mortality rates on population growth and age distribution in the United States. *Milbank Memorial Fund Quarterly* **44** (4), 451–469.

Hyrenius, H. (1966). Population growth and replacement. In "The Study of Population (An Inventory and Appraisal)" (Eds P. M. Hauser and O. D. Duncan), Fifth Impression, 472–485. University of Chicago Press, Chicago.

International Labour Organization (1959). "International Migration, 1945–1957". Studies and Reports, New Series No. 54. ILO, Geneva.

Joshi, D. D. (1965). "Stochastic Models Utilized in Demography". United Nations World Population Conference, Belgrade.

Jupp, K. "Factors Affecting the Structure of the Australian Population with Special Reference to the Period 1921–33". MA Thesis, Australian National University, Canberra.

Karmel, P. H. (1947). The relations between male and female reproduction rates. *Population Studies* **1**, 249–274.

Kendall, D. G. (1949). Stochastic processes and population growth. *Journal of the Royal Statistical Society* Series B, **11** (2), 230–264.

Keyfitz, N. (1965). On the interaction of populations. *Demography* **2**, 276–288.

Keyfitz, N. (1967). Reconciliation of population models: matrix, integral equation and partial fraction. *Journal of the Royal Statistical Society* Series A, **130**, 61–83.

Keyfitz, N. (1968a). "Introduction to the Mathematics of Population". Addison–Wesley, Reading, Mass.

Keyfitz, N. (1968b). Changing vital rates and age distributions. *Population Studies* **22** (2), 235–251.

Keyfitz, N. (1968c). Une table de survie Europeenne et sa version stochastique [A European life table and its stochastic version]. *Population* **23** (1), 29–34.

Keyfitz, N. (1969). Mathematical demography. Paper presented at the International Union for the Scientific Study of Population Conference, London.

Keyfitz, N. and Flieger, W. (1968). "World Population—An Analysis of Vital Data". University of Chicago Press, Chicago.

Keyfitz, N. and Murphy, E. M. (1964). "Comparative Demographic Computations". Population Research and Training Centre, University of Chicago, Chicago.

Lee, Everett S. (1966). A Theory of Migration. *Demography* **3**, 47–57.

Leslie, P. H. (1945). On the use of matrices in certain population mathematics. *Biometrika* **33**, 183–212.

Leslie, P. H. and Gower, J. C. (1958). The properties of a stochastic model for two competing species. *Biometrika* **45**, 316–330.

Lewis, E. G. (1942). On the generation and growth of a population. *Sankhya* **6**, 93–96.

Lopez, A. (1961). "Problems in Stable Population Theory". Office of Population Research, Princeton University, Princeton, N.J.

Lopez, A. (1967). Asymptotic properties of a human age distribution under a continuous net maternity function. *Demography* **4** (2), 680–687.

Lorimer, F. (1951). Dynamics of age structure in a population with initially high fertility and mortality. *United Nations Population Bulletin* No. 1, 31–41.

Lorimer, F. and Osborn, F. (1934). "Dynamics of Population". Macmillan, New York.

Lotka, A. J. (1922). The stability of the normal age distribution. *Proceedings of the National Academy of Sciences* **8**, 339–345.

Lotka, A. J. (1931). The structure of a growing population. *Human Biology* **3** (4), 459–493.

McArthur, N. (1967). Australia's birth rate in perspective. *Economic Record* **43** (101), 57–64.

McDonald, P. F. (1969). Trends in major causes of deaths in Australia, 1950–67. A paper presented at Departmental Seminar, Department of Demography, Australian National University, Canberra.

McFarland, D. D. (1969). On the theory of stable populations: a new and elementary proof of the theorems under weaker assumptions. *Demography* **6** (3), 301–322.

Martin, L. V. (1967). The recent trend of mortality in Great Britain. *Journal of the Institute of Actuaries* **93**, 439–443.

Murphy, Edmund, M. (1965). "A Generalization of Stable Population Techniques", Unpublished Ph.D. dissertation, Dept. of Sociology, University of Chicago.

Namboodiri, N. K. (1969a). On the cyclical model of population change and its applications. A paper presented to the IUSSP Conference held in London.

Namboodiri, N. K. (1969b). On the dependence of age structures on a sequence of mortality and fertility schedules: an exposition of a cyclical model of population change. *Demography* **6** (3), 287–299.

Notestein, F. W. (1960). Mortality, fertility, the sex–age distribution and the growth rate. In "Demographic and Economic Change in Developed Countries". Report of the National Bureau of Economic Research, Princeton University Press, Princeton, N.J.

Pollard, A. H. (1948). The measurement of reproductivity. *Journal of the Institute of Actuaries* **74**, 288–305.

Pollard, G. N. (1969). Factors influencing the sex ratio at birth in Australia, 1902–65. *Journal of the Biosocial Science* **1** (2), 125–144.

Pollard, J. H. (1966). On the use of the direct matrix product in analysing certain population models. *Biometrika* **53** (3 and 4), 397–415.

Pollard, J. H. (1969). A discrete-time two-sex age-specific stochastic population programme incorporating marriage. *Demography* **6** (2), 185–221.

Price, C. A. (1959). Effects of the post-war immigration on the growth of population, ethnic composition and religious structure of Australia, 1945–56. *REMP Bulletin* (Research Group for European Migration Problems) **7** (2), 48–56.

Price, C. A. (1962). Overseas migration to and from Australia, 1947–61. *Australian Outlook* **16** (2), 160–174.

Rogers, A. (1968). "Matrix Analysis of Inter-regional Population Growth and Distribution". University of California Press, Berkeley.

Ryder, N. B. (1967). The emergence of a modern fertility pattern: United States, 1917–66. "Fertility and Family Planning: A World View". University of Michigan, Michigan.

Sheps, M. C. and Perrin, E. B. (1963). Changes in birth rates as a function of contraceptive effectiveness: some applications of a stochastic model. *American Journal of Public Health* **53** (7), 1031–1046.

Sheps, M. C., Menken, J. A. and Radick, A. P. (1969). Probability models for family building: an analytical review. *Demography* **6** (2), 161–183.

Schwarz, K. (1968). Influence de la natalite et de la mortalite sur la composition par age de la population et sur l'evolution demographique [Influence of natality and mortality on age composition of the population and on the demographic evolution]. *Population* **23** (1), 61–92.

Sivamurthy, M. (1970). Trends in first marriages in Australia: 1933–66. *Economic Record* Sept., 402–410.

Sivamurthy, M. (1971). The effects of variations in the components of change on the size and structure of the Australian population: 1911–66. *Australian Journal of Statistics* **13** (1), 7–18.

Sivamurthy, M. (1976). Estimation of the distribution of arrivals and departures in Australia by single years of age, 1911–20. *Australian Economic History Review* **16** (1), 50–66.

Sivamurthy, M. (1975). Contribution of migration to population change in Australia: 1911–66, in *Australian Immigration*, No. 3, A84–A112. Department of Demography, the Australian National University, Canberra.

Sivamurthy, M. (1979). Convergence of human age–sex distributions to an equilibrium state age–sex distribution. *Theoretical Population Biology* **16**, 233–252.

Spengler, J. N. (1962). Aging of populations: mechanics, historical emergence, impact. *Law and Contemporary Problems* (Problems of Aging) **27** (1), 2–21.

Spiegelman, M. (1968). Mortality in the United States: a review and evaluation of special reports of the National Centre for Health Statistics. *Demography* **5** (1), 525–533.

Stolnitz, G. J. (1956). Mortality declines and age distribution. *Milbank Memorial Fund Quarterly* **34** (2), 178–215.

Stone, L. O. (1967). External migration and the age structure of the Canadian population, 1851–1961. "Contributed Papers", 775–785. International Union for the Scientific Study of Population (IUSSP), Sydney Conference.

Stone, L. O. (1968). Stable migration rates from the multi-regional growth matrix operator. *Demography* **5** (1), 439–442.

Sykes, Z. M. (1969). Some stochastic versions of the matrix model for population dynamics. *Journal of the American Statistical Association* **64** (325), 111–130.

Tabah, L. (1960). "Poblaciones Modelos Estables, Cuasi-estables y en Trancision Demographica [Population Models: Stable, Quasi-stable and in Demographic Transition]". Centro Latinoamericano de Demografia, Santiago, Chile.

Tabah, L. (1965). Relationships between age structure, fertility, mortality and migration: population replacement and renewal. Background Paper B.7/15/E/476. United Nations World Population Conference, Belgrade.

Tabah, L. and Cataldi, A. (1963). Effets d'une immigration dans quelques population modeles [The effects of immigration in a few model populations]. *Population* **18**, 683–696.

Thomas, V. J. (1969). A stochastic population model related to human populations. *Journal of the Royal Statistical Society* Series A, **132** (1), 89–104.

United Nations (1951). Some quantitative aspects of the ageing of Western populations. *Population Bulletin of the United Nations* No. 1, 42–57.

United Nations (1953). "The Determinants and Consequences of Population Trends". ST/SOA/Series A/17. United Nations, New York.

United Nations (1954). The cause of the aging of populations: declining mortality or declining fertility? *Population Bulletin of the United Nations* No. 4, 30–38.

United Nations (1955). "Age and Sex Patterns of Mortality". ST/SOA/Series A, Population Studies No. 22. United Nations, New York.

United Nations (1956). "The Aging of Populations and its Economic and Social Implications". ST/SOA/Series A, Population Studies No. 26. United Nations, New York.

United Nations (1958). "The Future Growth of World Population". ST/SOA/Series A, Population Studies No. 28. United Nations, New York.

United Nations (1965). "Population Bulletin of the United Nations" (with special reference to conditions and trends of fertility in the world), No. 7, 1963, ST/SOA/Series N/7. United Nations, New York.

United Nations (1967). "Manual IV: Methods of Estimating Basic Demographic Measures from Incomplete Data". ST/SOA/Series A, Population Studies No. 42. United Nations, New York.

United Nations (1968). "The Concept of a Stable Population—Application to the Study of Populations of Countries with Incomplete Demographic Statistics". ST/SOA/Series A/39. United Nations, New York.

Wilhelm Winkler, H. C. (1961). Types and Models in Demography. "Proceedings of the International Population Conference". Vol. 1, 358–367. New York.

Whelpton, P. K. (1954). "Cohort Fertility". Princeton University Press, Princeton, N.J.

Yntema, L. (1952). "Mathematical Models of Demographic Analysis". Groen and Zoon, Leiden.

Zubrzycki, J. (1960). "Immigration in Australia, A Demographic Survey Based on the 1954 Census". Melbourne University Press, Melbourne.

B. Statistical sources

Brown, H. P. (Department of Economics, The Australian National University, Canberra). *Demographic Data Bank for Australia* (for the years 1921 onwards).

Commonwealth Bureau of Census and Statistics. *Census of the Commonwealth of Australia*, 1911 to 1961, Census Volumes.

Commonwealth Bureau of Census and Statistics. *Census of the Commonwealth of Australia*, 1966, Census Bulletins.

Commonwealth Bureau of Census and Statistics. *Demography Bulletins* [Called as: Population and Vital Statistics (Commonwealth Demography) for 1911–21; Australian Demography for 1922–37; and Demography for 1938 onwards].

Commonwealth Bureau of Census and Statistics. *Quarterly Summary of Australian Statistics*, Bulletin No. 79, 1920.

Commonwealth Bureau of Census and Statistics. *Year Book of the Commonwealth of Australia*, No. 13, 1901–1919 and No. 51, 1965.

Author Index

Subject Index

223

STUDIES IN POPULATION

Under the Editorship of: H. H. WINSBOROUGH

Department of Sociology
University of Wisconsin
Madison, Wisconsin

Samuel H. Preston, Nathan Keyfitz, and Robert Schoen. Causes of Death: *Life Tables for National Populations.*

Otis Dudley Duncan, David L. Featherman, and Beverly Duncan. Socioeconomic Background and Achievement.

James A. Sweet. Women in the Labor Force.

Tertius Chandler and Gerald Fox. 3000 Years of Urban Growth.

William H. Sewell and Robert M. Hauser. Education, Occupation, and Earnings: Achievement in the Early Career.

Otis Dudley Duncan. Introduction to Structural Equation Models.

William H. Sewell, Robert M. Hauser, and David L. Featherman (Eds.). Schooling and Achievement in American Society.

Henry Shryock, Jacob S. Siegel, and Associates. The Methods and Materials of Demography. *Condensed Edition by Edward Stockwell.*

Samuel H. Preston. Mortality Patterns in National Populations: *With Special Reference to Recorded Causes of Death.*

Robert M. Hauser and David L. Featherman. The Process of Stratification: *Trends and Analyses.*

Ronald R. Rindfuss and James A. Sweet. Postwar Fertility Trends and Differentials in the United States.

David L. Featherman and Robert M. Hauser. Opportunity and Change.

Karl E. Taeuber, Larry L. Bumpass, and James A. Sweet (Eds.). Social Demography.

Thomas J. Espenshade and William J. Serow (Eds.). The Economic Consequences of Slowing Population Growth.

Frank D. Bean and W. Parker Frisbie (Eds.). The Demography of Racial and Ethnic Groups.

Joseph A. McFalls, Jr. Psychopathology and Subfecundity.

Franklin D. Wilson. Residential Consumption, Economic Opportunity, and Race.

Maris A. Vinovskis (Ed.). Studies in American Historical Demography.

Clifford C. Clogg. Measuring Underemployment: Demographic Indicators for the United States.

Doreen S. Goyer. International Population Census Bibliography: *Revision and Update, 1945-1977.*

David L. Brown and John M. Wardwell (Eds.). New Directions in Urban–Rural Migration: *The Population Turnaround in Rural America.*

A. J. Jaffe, Ruth M. Cullen, and Thomas D. Boswell. The Changing Demography of Spanish Americans.

Robert Alan Johnson. Religious Assortative Marriage in the United States.

Hilary J. Page and Ron Lesthaeghe. Child–Spacing in Tropical Africa.

Dennis P. Hogan. Transitions and Social Change: *The Early Lives of American Men.*

F. Thomas Juster and Kenneth C. Land (Eds.) Social Accounting Systems: *Essays on the State of the Art.*

M. Sivamurthy. Growth and Structure of Human Population in the Presence of Migration.

In preparation

Robert M. Hauser, David Mechanic, Archibale O. Haller, and Taissa O. Hauser (Eds.) Social Structure and Personality: *Papers in Honor of William Hamilton Sewell.*

Valerie Kincade Oppenheimer. Work and the Family: *A Study in Social Demography.*